DR RICHARD BRIGHT
(1789–1858)

Dr Richard Bright
(1789–1858)

PAMELA BRIGHT

THE BODLEY HEAD
LONDON   SYDNEY
TORONTO

The author gratefully acknowledges the generosity of The Royal Literary Fund and of The Phoenix Trust in providing research grants for this book.

British Library Cataloguing
in Publication Data
Bright, Pamela
Dr Richard Bright (1789–1858)
1. Bright, Richard   2. Medicine, Biography
I. Title
610'.92'4   R489.B/
ISBN 0–370–30474–8

© Pamela Bright 1983
Printed in Great Britain for
The Bodley Head Ltd
9 Bow Street, London WC2E 7AL
by Redwood Burn Ltd, Trowbridge
set in Linotron 202 Baskerville
by Wyvern Typesetting Ltd, Bristol
First published 1983

CONTENTS

LIST OF PLATES

Author's Foreword

Richard Bright grew up in an age of expanding scientific horizons, and he was a child of his time. His interests spread out in all directions and he grew up to be tremendously gifted. He was an artist, a writer and no mean linguist. He was a philosopher, mathematician and an able botanist. He was cultivated by travel, an authority on gypsy dialects and he was broadened by a growing knowledge of geology. These subjects alone would have given him a rightful place in history, but it was medicine that finally captured him.

In this rapidly changing world, medicine was standing still. There was a ditty being sung in the streets which echoed the popular view of it and summed up the only therapeutic remedies then available. It described a Dr Lettsom, a popular physician of the time, who says,

'When any sick to me apply
I physicks, bleeds and sweats 'em.
If after that they choose to die
What's that to me? – I lets 'em.'

This intensive treatment had succeeded the earlier witchcraft incantations and philtres and medicines obtained from animal offal.

Looking back over the history of medicine one cannot help but be amazed at the amount of knowledge there was on the one hand and baffled by the seeming lack of curiosity on the other. The progress of medicine pursued no steady onward and upward course. The ground gained by one generation seems often to have been lost by the next. The sophisticated healing arts of Greece and China regressed to the simple Egyptian notions whereby the ears were believed to be the organs of respiration. In the time of Christ disease was defined in terms of possession by an evil spirit, while later in medieval Europe it was held to be a disturbance of the four cardinal humours – phlegm, blood, choler and melancholy. The power of the Church, sorcery, astronomy, alchemy all played a part, as did the world of metaphysics and philosophy and the vitalists too, who thought that life was due to a vital principle as distinct from a physical or chemical force.

7

Such medical advances as were made were often the results of a series of laborious steps undertaken by diligent workers. William Harvey studied the functions of the body and acquired such a knowledge of anatomy that he was able to make his far-reaching discovery about the circulation of the blood. Boerhaave of Leyden placed the patient firmly in the centre of the picture, favouring observation rather than argument. The brilliant anatomists John and William Hunter, and Morgagni of Padua demonstrated the importance of morbid anatomy, while Bichat introduced pathology when he described the tissues of the body.

Though Bright never told us of the feelings he entertained towards these great men of bygone years we know that he must have owed much to them. He was influenced also by such men as Jenner, learning from him the procedure of inoculation. From Auenbrugger he learnt about percussion. Laënnec led him to the stethoscope and showed him how the diseases of the lung could be foretold by careful clinical study in life. Through the Delft draper Leeuwenhoek he got to know the microscope and saw the new and disquieting world of the 'animalculae'.

Come the early nineteenth century, though, little progress had been made in unravelling the mysteries of disease. The body processes were imperfectly understood: the causes, the symptoms and progress of an illness were an unknown study. Moreover the current books on Physick were still crammed with folk tales and herbal cures and claims such as that decoctions of toads were a certain cure for the ravages of cancer. It was the business of Bright's generation to substitute careful and accurate observations for the vague descriptions, the false surmises and wild traditional treatments of earlier doctors. And so it was at Guy's Hospital in London that Bright, Addison and Hodgkin laid the foundation of modern clinical medicine. They were the first to study disease at the bedside, correlating the signs and symptoms with what they later observed at autopsy. But of the three of them it was Bright who became a physician of rare excellence, achieved immortality at the age of thirty-eight, and has come down to us with a reputation attributable only in part to the study of the disease named after him.

For seven years he studied disease and set himself the task of exact diagnosis in a way that no man had ever quite envisaged before. He was not only an acute observer but possessed that much rarer faculty of synthesis which makes an observer a discoverer. There were many clinical observations made by him which never got the acclaim awarded for his work on the kidneys. Indeed Bright himself attached no more importance to the diseases of the kidney than he did to the pathology of fever or to those of the liver, intestines or brain which he also described.

In 1827 he published his most memorable work, *Reports of Medical Cases*, selected with a view to illustrating the symptoms and cure of disease by reference to morbid anatomy. The publication filled the world with astonishment at the wealth of his knowledge and at the accuracy and truth of his observations. The book crystallizes and preserves for us the very stages by which each plane of truth was slowly arrived at. It shows us by what steps medicine felt its way in the later years of the nineteenth century.

With Richard Bright the observational study of disease finally came of age.

P.B.

Doctor Richard Bright of Guy's
Had several patients large in size.
Their legs were swollen as could be;
Their eyes so puffed they could not see.
To this oedema Bright objected,
And so he had them venesected.
He took a teaspoon by the handle
Held it above a tallow candle
And boiled some urine o'er the flame
(As you or I might do the same).
To his surprise, we find it stated
The urine was coagulated.
Alas, his dropsied patients died.
The thoughtful doctor looked inside
He found their kidneys large and white
The capsules were adherent quite.
So that is why the name of Bright is
Associated with nephritis.

*Anon. Quoted in the St Bartholomew's
Hospital Journal*

I

Richard Bright of Ham Green

Richard Bright, MD, was born nearly 200 years ago in Bristol – then the capital of the west of England, a major port, a banking centre and a core of world trade. Surrounded by hills, with the River Avon curving into its very heart, the city was dominated by all those ships which had so surprised Alexander Pope: 'hundreds of ships, their masts as thick as they can stand by one another, which is the oddest and most surprising sight imaginable.'[1]

At high tide the waters of the river slapped at the Brights' back garden and a sailor aloft in the foretops of a ship would have been on a level with the attic windows. The bustling quay was in strange contrast to the elegant gravity of the front of the home. No houses were more respected than the desirable residences of Queen Square. At No. 19 lived Joseph Smith the Mormon, and here Edmund Burke came to stay; next to the Mansion House was the neat home of the first American consul, and at No. 15 David Hume, the philosopher and historian, had once worked as a clerk. No. 29 – where a succession of Brights were bred – was a double-fronted house built in the days of Queen Anne, and though it looks shabby now and the fine wrought-iron gates are gone, it retains still its classical simplicity, with its canopies of stone, small rounded pillars and dog-toothed eaves.

When his grandfather, Henry Bright, of Worcestershire yeoman stock, settled in this house, he was already a merchant and shipowner of some reputation. At the age of sixteen he had been apprenticed to Richard Meyler; he was trained in the West Indian trade and became a man of some standing in Kingston. On his return to Bristol he married Sarah, the only daughter and heiress of Richard Meyler. Highly respected and trusted, Henry became a Whig Member of Parliament, sheriff and later mayor of the city:[2] he established one of the first banks in Bristol, founded the Theatre Royal, and devoted himself to the welfare and education of the poor. In 1747 Sarah had a still-born son, but seven years afterwards Richard Bright was born, amidst great rejoicing.

Richard Bright, Bright's father, was sent to Warrington Academy, one of the four Dissenting schools, where an unusual number of subjects were taught by a remarkable collection of dedicated tutors. From Richard Bright's great-grandson, Henry Arthur Bright of Liverpool, there is much to learn about the intellectual life of this unique school. Descended as he was from one of its earliest pupils, he felt that he owed many of his own 'high-thinking' views to their teaching.[3] Under Dr John Aikin[4] he developed his own ideas on education and religious liberty, and from Joseph Priestley he acquired a deep and lasting interest in chemistry. In Dr Turner's classes it was Priestley who gave the practical demonstrations that made anatomy live and chemistry explode. Science was his love; the behaviour of the tides and currents; light, shadow or colour; the life of a barnacle on a barge; trailing phosphorescence on the sea – all excited him. He had such a power of attraction that the Academy became a sort of meeting place for men of progressive interests. Benjamin Franklin embroiled the pupils in ideas about ventilation, asbestos teapots and machines for removing dust on summer roads. George Watts came to discuss animal behaviour and whether or not dogs could be trained to wipe their paws on mats. The spoilt and acclaimed young Joseph Banks told them of tropical skies and brilliant birds and the strange flora seen on Captain Cook's voyage. The philanthropist Howard appeared and Roscoe the botanist, Pennant the naturalist, Erasmus Darwin and even Currier the biographer.[5]

It was no wonder that all this remained with Richard Bright throughout his life – and that the fascination with all things scientific was to be passed on to his doctor son.

Among his fellow students at the Academy were Malthus, Percival Estlin, Martineau, the Gaskells, the Aikins, the Wedgwoods and the Vaughans of America. His particular intimate was Samuel Heywood and he spent many holidays in Manchester, at Claremont, the handsome and hospitable house of the lovable banker Benjamin Heywood. From Henry Bright's letters one gains an impression of how grateful he was that his only son was thus brought into contact with family life. Every visit Richard's admiration for Sarah, the second daughter, increased, but it was to be a long time before he realized his interest in her was more than just a brotherly affection.

After leaving Warrington, Richard turned reluctantly from science to the family business which his father, preoccupied with city politics, had left much in the hands of his nephew Lowbridge Bright. It was Lowbridge who nursed his young cousin through all the intricacies of banking, and the problems and snares of trade, and though business occupied a large part of Richard's time and energy, Lowbridge sympathized with his interest in scientific matters, and gave him the freedom to visit the many places where science flourished. In Birmingham, he went to the moonlit meetings of the Lunar Society and to the house of Joseph Priestley, now a minister in Leeds, and involved in discovering oxygen and proving that a mouse enclosed in a glass could survive longer with a plant beside it. In London he went to the Chapter Coffee House and joined the discussions of the Philosophical Society,[6] an exclusive club set up by his schoolfriend Benjamin Vaughan in 1780. Amongst others, there were the Hunter brothers, the two great anatomists; Dr Price of rabies fame; Whitehurst, the philosopher; Aubert, the astronomer; Horsefall, the calculator; Kirwan, the chemist; Blackhall the surgeon, and the patron, the Earl of Shelburne, who had once employed Priestley as his librarian. He went to the Tycho-Brake Heed showrooms where he lovingly examined the finest instruments in the world; being something of an inventor himself, barometers, chromoscopes, clocks, telescopes, mechanical pumps and queer contraptions intended to aid chimney-sweeps all caught his imagination. He went to Ireland, and travelled to Paris to see Lavoisier, Lafayette and Franklin.

In November 1777, when Richard Bright was twenty-three, his father died – eight years after his wife, Sarah. Richard's inheritance included several properties in Worcestershire, the Meyler estates of Haverford West, Hampshire and Somerset, the Rope Walk and other districts in Bristol. Then, there were the 'Old' bank in Small Street; trading connections in Jamaica and North Carolina, and the shipowning interests. At the time of his father's death, his property was worth £30,000, while his personal estate amounted to £40,000.

From now on Richard Bright was to impress almost everyone he met. There is much written about his kindliness and delicacy of feeling, his devotion to Bristol and its traditions. His vivacious mind responded to every kind of stimulus and he had an astonishing knowledge of diverse subjects. The arts, most especially music, and politics interested him intensely. He does not seem to have cared for society, but this might have had something to do with Sarah Heywood, for throughout this period he was keeping a tenuous hold on her, going to Manchester and sometimes seeing her in London.

The Heywoods always had a London season. Several letters show that his love for her filled his heart so completely as to render all other ties unimportant to him. But he was shy and diffident – traits which irritated Sam Heywood, whose sharp eye had long divined Richard's feeling for his sister. He had to keep urging him on to press his claims: 'Your intimacy with the family offers you all the advantages you could wish.' Besides, there were other suitors: a young lawyer was chasing her and 'a curate was making a good offer, and it is impossible to insure you against all this'. As Benjamin Heywood also encouraged the courtship, Richard's confidence slowly grew. On 24 March 1782 he and Sarah were married. Sarah declared herself to be the 'happiest of women', and according to Benjamin Heywood 'her beautiful eyes gave weight to that testimony'. She was a gay and lovable companion and pious with 'all the virtues which can endear life and constitute a perfect gentlewoman'.[7]

It was not long before their first son, Henry, was born. The event was recorded by Richard in the large family Bible, in the pages of the Apocrypha: 'On the 18th day of January, 1784, at nearly forty-five minutes after two o'clock in the morning my firstborn son was born.' Sarah did not believe in wet nurses and encouraged by her husband followed the new ideas of Rousseau, who maintained that it was not injurious for a mother to feed her baby. No sooner had the excitement subsided than a baby girl, Phoebe, arrived and was tucked into the basket cot beside the fire in Sarah's bedroom. With the appearance of a third child in 1787, Henry was put into breeches and old Benjamin Heywood came for the christening to hear his name being given to the second son. On 28 September 1789 a third son was born and named after his father. (For purposes of clarity the older Richard Bright will be referred to as Richard Bright throughout this book, while his son Richard will be referred to simply as Bright.)

*

Some time in 1790 Richard Bright decided to move his young family to Ham Green, the house which he had inherited from his mother, Sarah Meyler, and known intimately most of his youth. The baby Bright was thus taken away from the tumult and clamour of the quayside to the green fields of Somerset. In this quiet world he grew up.

For children Ham Green had everything to offer. The property ran in folds of pasture and woods from the small village of Abbot's Leigh on the north side down to Pill, centre of pilots for the Avon river. Here the few whitewashed cottages were tucked into an inlet on the muddy edge of the river. The lodge gates opened on the Portishead and Bristol drovers' highway, and an arched avenue of fine Spanish chestnuts – of which only a few now remain – led through the fields and orchards of the home farm to the beautifully proportioned Queen Anne house. In early summer it was swathed in roses, which formed a canopy over the bow window of the Georgian addition. It is a hospital now, its magic long since gone, but the lawns and a few of the fine old cedars still suggest the style of those times. The fish-ponds, ornamental walks and shrubberies have disappeared, so has the cut path lined with meadow grass which used to lead to the lake. But mossy paths still run down to the river, and to the round gazebo, once a favourite lookout spot where the children watched the ships glide by. They got to know all the different ships, as a child today will spot trains or aeroplanes. They could tell a converted warship, trading smack, sloop or ketch; they knew the cargo boats from the coast, the brigantines from Wales and the Humber keels, and every pilot cutter. They watched their father's ships swing to the Avon tides and the big horses on the tow path straining to pull the trows along. They knew every place on that curve of river. Then, there was the large vegetable patch with its rows of glass-frames and hothouses; there were the rosebeds imprisoned behind high box hedges and a fruit garden with peaches and nectarines ripening on the wall, and plums too heavy for the nets to catch them. There were stables, orchards, cowsheds and meadows, and a paddock for the ewes at lambing time. There was the field where the maypole stood, and where on the first of May the Brights and the children from Pill danced and clutched at the coloured ribbons.

The Bright children loved all this. They collected butterflies, bowled their hoops, threw their balls, lay in the woods with their books. They roamed on horseback, fished and scoured the hedges for fungi, the banks for clay, the cliffs for granite, the Gorge for spiked speedwell, the rare scarlet lichen, fossils and bones. There were family picnics on hot summer days and excursions with the cousins from Manchester or the Bushes from Bristol. There were games in the bracken with the Gibbses or the Eltons, the Tyndalls and the Schimmelpennincks. And few days were more enjoyable than those spent in the cottages at Pill, talking to the old sailors, or rejoicing in the stormy stories of old 'Pill Warner', whose job it was to ride daily into Bristol and there give tidings to the merchants of their ships' arrival at King Road in the Severn estuary.

Richard Bright was a good manager with a mania for improvising strategies that would help to keep his expenses down. He was an able farmer with progressive views, who influenced others in agriculture. He kept his hedges and spinneys trimmed, his woods clear and his tasselled copses pruned. He won prizes for his fruit and flowers, and for the fleece from his flocks, and admiration for the quality of his milk. He gained respect and love from all those who worked for him, whose lot he was always anxious to improve. Indeed, he often allowed his tenants to be years behind in their payments and, too trusting, failed to spot the agent who exploited him. He was an inspired horticulturist, collecting seeds and plants from all over the world. He grew olive trees and white mulberries, introducing them into his West Indian estates in the hope that they would be useful in a country that only produced sugar. He experimented with pomegranates, camphor, pepper, nutmeg and cloves; and being deeply interested in botany investigated both the culinary and medicinal value of herbs and spices.

No visitor was allowed to leave Ham Green without a full basket – and he was quite as generous with his increasing knowledge. He took in students and one of them, a Mr Ballard from Portbury – a round tub of a man fondly protrayed in family sketches strutting through the Portuguese laurels in tail-coat and tall hat – was eventually put in charge of the new Botanical Gardens in Calcutta. He claimed that all the knowledge which had fitted him for this undertaking had its foundation in the plant studies done at Ham Green.

Ham Green was a hospitable house to visit. Richard Bright opened his library to his friends and to those of his children as they grew up. He had the room enlarged to run the whole length of the west side of the house, in order to accommodate his large collection of books. Here, many of the latest publications were to be found, some written and given by his friends – a pamphlet by Edmund Burke, Dr Darwin's poems, Priestley's *Anthologie Hibernica* and Dr Price's wordy book on optics. Here, he also kept his many maps, blueprints of Bristol's Blind Asylum and other architectural dreams, his growing collection of minerals, fossils and geological specimens, and the newspapers of the day which, being considered essential but extravagant, were given away as soon as read, finding their way from house to house. On his writing bureau were piled his account and letter books, and notebooks into which went all his own scientific observations – like the halo seen around the sun; the circles of Sargons and Avebury, studied in detail; and Walshe's experiments on the torpedo with his own comments about it. All his creative ideas were put into notebooks, too, like the steam engine he designed to do the work of crushing and lifting sugar cane. But he rarely published his inventions and those which were recorded in the transactions of the learned societies of the day were all written anonymously; only the mathematical letters about improving the Bristol docks, which are in the library of the Royal Society, bear his signature.[8]

The children were encouraged to take an enquiring interest in everything they did. The flowers they picked had to be dissected, the fruits of trees identified, birds' habitat investigated. This was probably the source of Bright's meticulous accuracy when observing and recording data of any sort. They were included also in social events. Irrespective of age they were led into the drawing-room to meet the exceptional men and women whom Richard Bright gathered around him. Modest always of his own attainments, he was more often a silent listener, leaving his intelligent wife to act as hostess.

The charming Sarah Bright, with her never-failing interest in the affairs of others, seems to have been a competent housekeeper. The two large kitchens, the cavernous dairy, the laundry, the pantries and the garden room from which she filled the house with flowers were all her exclusive preserve. The drawing room had a rounded wall with wide curving windows and, like the dining room, it still retains today the feel of the ritual and exquisite manners of the eighteenth century. Then there was a family room with windows looking south over the park of grazing sheep. This was the place where mending, drawing, painting and lessons were done, while the attic rooms reflected the personality of each child, each with their own interests and their own chosen collections. But it was their mother's room, the 'middle parlour', which became the meeting ground for the children and their friends. Here, she heard all their confidences; here, working quickly, she covered chairs and stools with tapestry, embroidered petticoats with daisies, adorned her husband's waistcoats with sprays of roses and leaves.[9] Here, too, she wrote her family letters.

As parents they both took an active part in the lives of their children, and from infancy the greatest intimacy seems to have prevailed between them all. Busy as he was, Richard Bright found it increasingly difficult to resist the roomful of babies, and as they grew up each one of his eight children was studied, their every interest promoted from an early age. And though servant girls headed the children up the stairs, it was always one or other of the parents who read aloud to them, heard their prayers and tucked them into their beds. Religion was part of life at Ham Green. The Bible was read and discussed daily and the psalms learned.

*

For the first three years of his life Bright was the baby of the household. It was a privileged position of few memories. In a letter he wrote to his daughter some forty years later, he mentions that he could remember the birth of his sister, in March 1792, when he was two and a half, and 'liking her more than his toys', but he was probably not aware of the sorrow surrounding her death a few months later. He also recalled the bustle of parties held in his grandfather Benjamin Heywood's honour when he paid them a visit. Two events that took place in the world outside Ham Green in the year 1793 impressed him greatly. One was the lighting of beacons on the declaration of war with France, and the other was his father's sorrow centred around Joseph Priestley. Bright was too young to understand what was actually being said and the part his father was playing in getting the scientist to America, but he remembered vividly the description of the ransacked house and how his carefully set up experiments were smashed and how his reputation as an unorthodox preacher advocating freedom of religion was blown up to such an extent that he had to leave the country. Bright's first feeling of terror did not come from the gruesome tales told by maids, but from his mother talking about 'unruly mobs'.[10]

When he was five another sister, with the same name of Sarah, arrived to occupy the old cot. It was his turn once again to watch the swaddling, nursing, dressing, training and gurgling that surrounded a new baby. In the terrible drought of 1794, it is from one of Phoebe's letters that we get a picture of all the children being taken to the shade of the cedars and to the river's edge to catch a breeze, where the mud patterned with fissures looked 'like a huge jigsaw of flaking shapes.' None of them ever forgot either the intense cold of the following winter when small birds froze to the trees, and sheep were lost in snowdrifts, and men were too weak with hunger to dig them out. If it brought the Bright children the new thrill of learning to skate on the frozen lake, it meant also being taught by their father to do something practical to help the poor on the estate, for whom they provided much needed food and fuel. This must have been Bright's first conscious introduction to the miseries of the poor and his first realization of his father's philanthropic activities.

2
School
1795–1804

With September 1795 came the shock of school, when Bright joined his two elder brothers at Dr Estlin's establishment. According to Robert Southey it was 'esteemed as the best in Bristol' and run on the same kind of liberal and scientific lines as Warrington,[1] since the head was Dr John Prior Estlin, an old schoolfellow and friend. Richard Bright had been instrumental in procuring for him the ministry of Lewins Mead, and we are told that he was more than content to think that his sons would be in the care of such 'a wise, temperate and attractive man'. Dr Estlin not only had exceptional intellectual and classical gifts and a great fund of general knowledge, but he was also well travelled and a good linguist. At just the time when England was cut off by war from the Continent he opened up for his pupils a whole new field of contemporary French literature and German scientific thought.

The school was housed in the Estlins' large mansion, which was on the wide terraced street of St Michael's Hill. In one direction lay the green fields high on Kingsdown – where an old Civil War fort stood and where grazing sheep crowded out the ball games. In the other direction were the narrow streets of the mediaeval city.

Bristol then was small enough for everybody to know or have heard of everybody else. Incidents like the poet Chatterton dying of starvation in a garret, the beautiful Perdita Robinson captivating the Prince of Wales, and Hogarth refusing to paint new shop signs, saying he could not improve on the primitive masterpieces already hanging, were common knowledge. Everybody saw Samuel Coleridge and Robert Southey, in revolutionary dress and hatless, with flowing ringlets, rushing to the library to change their books more than twice a day. Everybody talked about the Fricker girls, and most people's bets were high on their taking the 'poets to the altar'; everybody knew the kind Mr Cottle and his bookshop in Wine Street. Hazlitt, Charles Lamb and Wordsworth all came to Bristol at various times, and when Brigadier-General Stradius Kosciuszko appeared there was a rustle of excitement throughout the city. Bright's father was one who wished to show his respects. He had first met the Pole when he visited Bristol on his way to fight for the American colonists under George Washington. Now, in 1797, he was returning to America as a defeated hero who had led his country against a mighty Russia. A pike-severed sciatic nerve had greatly altered his appearance. Bright, aged eight at the time must have seen his father's concern and heard about his attempts to get his friends at the Infirmary to find means of relieving the man's pain. We know that he accompanied his brother Henry to the banks of the river Avon to watch Kosciuszko's eventual departure. As the great ship slowly passed the gazebo, he was astonished to see Henry being rowed out to meet it, then disappearing carrying with him as a gift the biggest pineapple that the glass-houses of Ham Green could produce. 'Dickie thought I had gone for ever, you should have seen his face when he saw me again,' Henry told an Heywood aunt in a birthday letter, in which he described the incident.

There is nothing in the family correspondence to tell us how much the young Bright was aware of what was going on in the city around him. What must have mattered most to him in those early days at school was his own ability to keep up – the daily fight for the ewers and basins, groggy with dreams; the hunting for lost stockings in icy draughts; the fears, taunts, pulled ears, twigged hair and other mean acts; the fight for the frugal fare and the ability to cope with the long hours in the classroom. That he was greatly helped in the first year by the presence of his older brothers – Henry, aged eleven, and Benjamin, aged nine – is clear from the letters regularly received by Sarah Bright. We learn also from these letters of the happy atmosphere, in spite of the floggings. We learn of their schoolfellows – mostly from Dissenting families, many the sons of their father's friends. There were the young Vaughans, the two Estlins, John Cam Hobhouse (later to become Lord Broughton), and Joseph Priestley's son Henry, a bright and intelligent youth, who was 'much liked'.[2] We learn of the small formal classes, the boys addressing each other as 'mister'; they were taught science and maths, botany and geography; and as Dr Estlin was a dedicated classicist much stress apparently was put on ancient history, Greek and Latin. We learn of the long winter evenings when books were closed and long passages from the classics memorized, French comedies acted, German philosophers discussed. All had to take a turn in reading aloud fables and legends,

23

tales of chivalry and travel. The book *Strange and Dangerous Voyages* was familiar to every Bristolian, for all knew of the pious old Captain Thomas James. And there was nothing the pupils could not tell of the mermaids Columbus saw or the merman known to the surgeon, Thomas Glover. We learn how Dr Estlin encouraged hobbies and insisted on out-of-doors activities, from kite-flying to peg-tops; he himself was often seen cheering a whole field to action 'waving his hat at the hounds chasing the paper of the hare'. It seems that few places were out of bounds. His scholars were well spoken of in the town and according to Southey rarely 'did any of them disgrace the Rev. Doctor by their appearance or manner'.[3]

As had been the practice at Warrington Academy, Dr Estlin opened his home to the intellectuals of the day. On a Sunday evening the older pupils attended these open discussions or 'sizings' as they were called.[4] Over a modest supper, served by Mrs Estlin, new ideas about religious freedom and political reforms were aired. Coleridge was frequently to be found there, discoursing on 'Pantisocracy', his theory regarding communal life which he was envisaging for himself and his friends in America. The fine voice of Robert Lowell was often heard reading his own poems, and once Letitia Aikin, now Mrs Barbauld, called 'Bare-Bald' by Southey, came to defend her goody-goody stories which Southey complained were now taking hold of nurseries that had once thrilled to 'Tom Flickerthrift' and 'Jack and the Beanstalk'.

School Sundays were devoted to worship at Lewins Mead. Here, the relatives and friends of the pupils all gathered at the morning service, so timed that they did not conflict with those of the parish churches. It is John Cam Hobhouse who tells us that 'the chapel at which Dr Estlin preached was attended by the most influential merchants of the city, such as the Brights and the Castles and others of equal respectability'.[5] Lewins Mead was one of the more important of the eighty-six Dissenter places of worship in Bristol. It still stands today in the old thoroughfare of St James's Back, an elegant and lofty building. In those days it was filled by a congregation of every denomination, anxious to hear the distinguished and controversial Dr Estlin. From the aisles his pupils viewed a different headmaster; Henry told his mother that they were more afraid of him on Sunday than on any other day of the week. Looking more severe than usual in the black dress of the Puritan, he shouted and thumped and exulted.

Saturdays were given over to visiting the homes of their father's friends. Bright wrote once: 'We dined at the Golds on Saturday and we are going to dine at Mr Hilhouse next Saturday.' The Golds also had a son at the Fort school; they belonged to a musical set in the city and Dr Gold, who was an apothecary, had a fine voice and loved to sing the 'glees' at the Catch Club. Mr Hilhouse was a shipbuilder, and it is Bright himself who tells us how much he taught them to appreciate the work going on in the yards. He had built a great many frigates for the Royal Navy and his reputation as the owner of a privateer was nationwide. It was he who had procured the oak from the Forest of Dean to build *The Pilgrim* and *The Ocean* for the Brights.

Lowbridge Bright was another who welcomed them, and the three boys responded eagerly to his hospitality. He had built himself a large house at the top of Great George Street, with a view of the harbour and seven hills. Inside there was a specially designed gallery to hold his evergrowing collection of pictures, which he procured by haunting the sale-rooms of impoverished aristocrats from France. Lowbridge would feed them with ginger and sugar plums beside the fire, or trudge with them amongst the stalls of Redcliffe Street in search of a schoolbook. Sometimes, he took them to the Tolzey, where they watched the merchants 'pay on the nail' and listened to the simian chatter going on around them:

'The ox hides are selling better than the cows.'

'Olive oil is quiet.'

'The price of gold-leaf is too high.'

'The "Ruby" is overdue . . . thou heardst that the "Brises" tricked them?'[6]

Considering the number of letters – for any news was cherished by the old aunts and uncles, and the children's exploits were fondly repeated throughout the family – it is surprising how few allude to their school life. What distinctions, if any, Henry and Benjamin won at school go unrecorded, and nobody tells us how Bright did at his lessons. But we can envisage him during these early years as a gentle, kindly, dreamy youth, who never quarrelled and whose droll sense of humour helped to keep things in proportion. He possessed none of the good looks of his elder brothers, and the expression on his rather ugly face was, according to his brother Henry, 'more melancholy than dour'. He was affectionate, as his own childish letters show, for he was always sending his love, always including everybody – 'Please give my love to the cusses, aunts and grandmama, little Mama and Papa and all' – and always begging the recipient to take much of it too. He seems solitary and diffident, often mooning about by himself in a state of abstraction. He read a great deal and was engrossed in his hobby, collecting for his museum. The only day he shone amongst the rest of the boys was when one of his father's friends (perhaps it was Banks, who visited Iceland about this time) presented him with a stuffed eider duck. This was the envy of many a small collector, and in a letter he proudly instructed Phoebe how best to exhibit it. 'You must not forget the eggs either . . . the nest must be made of loose grass with a handful of eiderdown lying lightly on it . . . put it on the bottom shelf of the cupboard.' Within his own museum at Ham Green, his specimens were kept dusted, his birds' eggs were correctly labelled, his bottles shone and his beetles were neatly arranged; and his collection of flies came in for enormous care and attention. He had fifty special ones which were never taken off the shelf, and another fifty which he had with him at school and willingly exchanged. His sisters helped him to collect; he wrote once, admonishing Sarah: 'Dear Sal, the flies were a good deal worse for their journey for two or three of them were broken to bits but I had none of them before. Alfred Estlin is making a collection and he has given me one, which although I know to be killed I cannot help taking.'

The nine-year-old Bright was at an impressionable age. At the height of invasion fears, he must have shared with his classmates the excitement and increasing tension. In 1798 there were rumours that Napoleon was about to invade Britain, and with it came the realization that the Government was ill prepared for such an eventuality. It was largely left to the conscientious, worried landowners to plan their own defences and equip their men. Richard Bright, on the Committee of the 'Bristol Fencibles', was one of the first to organize a district, fitting out the pilots of Pill and the men in the Portbury area for combat and supplying them 'with drums and fife and uniforms from the best cloth'. We are told by Sarah that it was typical of him to refuse a commission in the Army, feeling that he had not the necessary experience for an officer. He was voted in to the Volunteers as an ordinary soldier, but not long afterwards he was made a Sergeant in the 9th Volunteers and became responsible for training others. He had to leave his home often, marching all over the West Country, and even getting as far as Cornwall. It is Sarah who tells us how anxious Bright was over his father's disappearances. She alludes also to the day when the city bells clanged at an unaccustomed hour, striking fear into every Bristolian's heart. It was a false alarm but all were convinced, she said, that the sound of the French drums could be heard in the Gorge.

Another time she mentions hearing of more than one small boy at the Fort School sleeping fitfully, while the kindly Mrs Estlin told them over and over again that there was no 'bad Boney' hiding under the beds. During the day, apparently, their fears were strictly controlled by Dr Estlin's discipline in the classroom and extra hours were spent composing verses in Latin about the Battle of the Pyramids and Nelson at Aboukir.

That year there was another disastrous harvest and the young Bright played a modest part in helping his father to find some substitute for flour in the farinaceous matter of the potato. Bright did some of the practical work and scribbled down, at his father's dictation, meticulous details of a chemical formula and substance that could replace wheat – a thesis which was to become Transaction No. 10 in the city archives. Having noted the sharpness and precision of his son's power of observation, he set Bright to help him in another project. His friend James Watt had designed an air pump and he wanted Richard Bright to add his own ideas and to try and make it more efficient. It was an affair which had to produce and administer by inhalation the therapeutic gases which their mutual friend Dr Beddoes was hoping to use in his new chest clinic.

Thomas Beddoes was active in improving the lot of the large consumptive population of Bristol and a pioneer in its treatment. He was frightening and touchy, but a kind physician. The young Coleridge was a patient of his and never forgot the comfort he received from him ('His death took more hope out of my life than any former event'[7]). Beddoes was often to be seen on St Michael's Hill visiting the apothecary's shop where Humphry Davy was working; while to the pupils of Estlin's school he was a figure of fun. Perched high in his carriage, his huge and unwieldy body overflowing, the boys would hover 'just to see the phaeton spring up as he descended'.

When in March 1799 Beddoes opened his clinic – the Pneumatic Institution – in Dowry Square, he put Humphry Davy in charge of the laboratory. Here the young chemist attacked the problems set him, and was soon to become the talk of the town. Society thrilled to his charm; every tavern and coffee house gawped at his exploits and to every schoolboy he became a hero. They adored his courage and listened eagerly to tales of his experiments with gases. They heard how he was blowing into a bag, risking his life, burning his mouth and throat, extracting his own teeth, suffocating himself and falling into unconsciousness; they heard how though a teetotaller he drank quantities of wine just to test his reaction; they heard of his willingness to throw himself over the high rocks of St Vincent to measure the time it took to fall to the gorge below; they saw Mr Tobin, Mr Clayfield, Mr Wordsworth and Robert Southey, dancing and fighting up Clifton Hill, jumping over the dogs that got in their way and laughing hysterically – all the result of inhaling his purified nitrous oxide.

It is said that Richard Bright first met Davy in a swinging basket going down a mine shaft in Cornwall. They were both quick to appreciate the lively mind of the other and so they kept in touch. As soon as Davy appeared in Bristol he was invited to Ham Green and there he became universal favourite. He spent many hours teaching the children to fish, 'using such devices as none of us had any idea of'. Later on in life he was to become a good friend of Bright's, when there sprang up between them a special understanding, in spite of the disparity in their years, and in spite of Davy's weakness for prestige that was to mar his professional career and sour many of his friendships.

Richard Bright managed to attend the lectures on chemistry which Davy gave at the clinic, and this re-awakened all the old enthusiasm he had once experienced under Priestley – so much so that he had a laboratory built in the grounds of Ham Green. It was in this neat, stuccoed edifice that, as Sarah said, 'her lads spent so much time'; Bright particularly was gripped by chemistry. Under his father's careful scrutiny he learned how to look at things, and how to analyse and describe what he saw. To the bench came also geological specimens, minerals and fossils; and in 1800, on the announcement of Volta's discoveries, he formed his own galvanic pile, using dollars as conductors.[8] But whether his sons experienced the electric shocks their father created is nowhere recorded.

At this particular period, 1800–1803, it was Bright of all the sons who was most in his father's company. Richard Bright was an ardent devotee of the Hotwells Spa, and much of Bright's future interest in the curative powers of hot and cold baths and drinking mineral waters may be traced to what he witnessed there by his father's side. 'I took Dick to Hotwells to see my machine yesterday,' Richard Bright wrote in an undated letter to Henry, at Glasgow University.

Bright himself had vivid memories of these occasional visits, recalled long afterwards in a letter he wrote to his son Franck. 'It was', he said, 'with the pumping apparatus of your grandfather's wheezing away like an animal in distress somewhere in the background', that he had to listen to subjects he could not understand. He found it tedious, being led through the colonnade of rooms, through bathroom, rest room, and card room to the pump room where the pumper got the water to give to the hopeful drinkers. Here, his father studied the register before seeking out his sick and infirm friends. Bright's reaction to the challenge of such a place was summed up in one sentence: 'It gave me the most valuable instruction I remember, in the feelings of pity.' The fact that he experienced such a sense of relief on departure, and always looked forward to the return journey to Ham Green with such delight, is some indication of the impact that particular district of Bristol had upon him. It could not have been easy to forget the sight of the consumptives crowding the entrance to the Pneumatic Institution, the comings and goings at the Dispensary situated also in Dowry Square, or the afternoon promenade at the Spa – the pale faces at carriage windows, the slow progress of sedan chairs along the terraces, the sad procession of parents and the moving mass of pillows and shawls as trusted servants carried the sick up Hill Road to Clifton. There is no doubt that what he saw at the Hotwells Spa; what he heard of Beddoes' work – the contrivances he conjured up to administer chemicals, the methods he tried in order to relieve breathlessness; and what he heard of Priestley's experiments with oxygen, were all to be of considerable educational value to him, and to have a lasting effect on his development as a doctor.

Life for the Bright children was punctuated by the yearly visits to Worcestershire to pick the fritillaries at Eastertime or the 'famous pears' in the orchards of Welland; the occasional stays of a few weeks with the cousins in Manchester, and the odd season taken in London by the older Brights. Then there had been the arrival of new babies, always anticipated with pleasure, when 'furniture was changed around and newly pressed petticoats and fine linen put into drawers'. By 1802, when Bright was thirteen, Robert was already seven, Mary four, and Sam three. The first gaps had long occurred in the family circle. Henry had already left Glasgow and was studying law under Serjeant Sam Heywood's guidance at the Inner Temple, and Benjamin had been sent to Edinburgh to study under the renowned Professor Dugald Stewart. Meanwhile Phoebe had taken over the housekeeping keys, was helping in the hothouses, learning how to nurse the 'sickly Mary' and taking 'all imaginable care of Sam'.

Richard Bright himself had achieved a position of great eminence. Widely known as a man of vision and ideas, wise and helpful, he was invited on to Boards dealing with the docks, the canals, the new boys' college of Clifton, the Observatory, the Infirmary and the Blind Asylum; he was continually being asked by his fellow Merchant Venturers to represent them in conferences and projects.[9] On several occasions he refused the position of mayor, and though he would have liked nothing better than to accept the offer of becoming the Lord Lieutenant of the County of Somerset, his honesty prevented him from taking the necessary sacramental vows of the Church of England.

It was at this high point of success that Richard Bright suddenly dropped out of public affairs and cut 'his working days from six down to two'. There were reasons for this change. He found himself able to spend less and less time with Sarah; she, more frail after every confinement, was getting less inclined to accompany him into the drawing rooms of Bristol society. Both preferred to spend more time with the children, while the loss of their little girl, Mary, shook and saddened them into extra vigilance. He was always drawn by the excitements of the laboratory and loved working in his hot-houses. It was at this particular time that celestine was discovered under the pastures of Ham Green, and it was this that finally turned him completely away from city politics and more into the path of a scientist and family man.

Whether the celestine was found through his own amateur endeavours, or by his friend William Smith, the geologist, who was in the vicinity at the time, or by Mr Tobin, as Sowerby suggests,[10] there is nothing in the letters to tell us. They only convey the excitement the discovery engendered. And the sight of the way the crystalline mass of blue, when subjected to heat, turned the flame into 'an undescribable scarlet', was to remain with the Brights for ever. Indeed, it was to become the inspiration for Henry and Benjamin's 'collecting excursions' and the basis of Bright's introduction into mineralogy and palaeontology. For a long time Bright had no particular friends at school. He tells us himself that he missed his elder brothers not being around, and it seemed to him a long time before he could look down on the long line of boys below him with condescending interest. As soon as Henry Holland, son of the much beloved Dr Peter Holland of

Knutsford in Cheshire, appeared at the school Dr Estlin made him head boy, a place just then vacated by John Cam Hobhouse. His impact was immediate. Even at the age of fifteen, no social art was beyond this boy's accomplishments. He was elegant, slight of figure, agile and neat, with fair skin and piercing blue eyes. His intellectual awareness, and his absorption in life and people, were acute, almost smug: indeed there was an element of the snob in him which he was never to lose. Bright was at once intensely aware of him; a strong affinity grew up between them, and it was not long before Bright found it possible to talk to him as he could to no one else.

Bright, a year younger, felt at first a child beside him, conscious of his own lack of charm and spotty plainness. He was too open-hearted to see in Holland's tendency to fight other boys, his polished exhibitions, his bluster and zest, childish traits which Bright himself had already long since shed. Charmed with his friendship, Bright still expected Holland to disappear into a life where he would not be asked to follow, and so was all the more surprised and pleased to find with what readiness Holland did respond to his particular humour and similar tastes, and how quickly their relationship developed into something close and constant. It was a friendship encouraged by Richard Bright, and in the holidays there was always a bed made ready for him at Ham Green. He was happy to give a helping hand to this aspiring young man, related as he was to Josiah Wedgwood and whose holiday guardian at Stoke Newington was Dr Aikin, his old schoolfellow and friend. Besides, he had always admired the prolific Hollands of Cheshire, who as Dissenters had the same Whig sympathies as he did. And through the Gaskells he knew Holland's father, who had passed on to his son the admirable manners and charm which endeared him to all.

In the classroom the two boys studied hard; both possessing the same sense of comedy and moods of optimism, they ignored the arctic temperatures of that winter, as arguments and wide-ranging discussions exercised their brains. It was during the spring that they discovered together the pleasures that lay outside the high railings of the school. On half-holidays and Saturdays the two were to be seen rambling about the city, with Bright acting as guide to the enthusiastic Holland, who was quickly smitten by the harbours and the Gorge. Encouraged by Dr Estlin, educated in Bristol's history by his cousin Lowbridge, schooled in its streets and wharfs by his father, Bright was able to impress the older boy with his knowledge; and the more they explored, the more interested they became in natural phenomena and the more involved in each other's quests. Holland helped Bright to add to his collection of flies and fill his schoolcap with the treasures of the earth. They hung over walls as new roads and canals revealed new grits, silicas and marls. They walked on the rain-washed soil of Kingsweston and in the quarries at Sea Mills; often, hungry for the smell of the sea, they went further afield to explore the rocks at Portishead for gypsum, calcite and jet, or the potholes of Clevedon for iron and lead. They climbed the crags of the Gorge, and stumbled along the alluvial flats of the Hung Road moorings. It was here that Bright helped Holland to fill his notebooks on his particular hobby, for it was rivers that had caught the boy's imagination. He read every book about them, pored over every map, studied every source, every stretch, every reach, every estuary. He was held by every tide, current and significant idiosyncrasy. He sought every aqueduct, iron bridge, mill, torrent and bore, and at Dr Estlin's Sunday sizings it was he that insisted upon the long discussions of Mungo Park's peregrinations on the River Niger, which were filling the newspapers at the time. To the very end of his long life he was to travel the great rivers of the world. Holland's passionate love for rivers was fired still further in Bristol. While the young Bright showed him the muddy Frome, the lovely reaches of the Severn to Aust and Gloucester and the eel-infested waters that meandered to Bath and Bradford-on-Avon, he was also fascinated by Bright's father's marvellous knowledge of the Bristol Avon.

For three long sessions (terms), this friendship dominated Bright's school life. It was hard having to return in the autumn of 1803 without Holland, now sitting reluctantly on an office stool in a mercantile house in Liverpool. Even though as head boy Bright was drawn much into the company of the other boys, he found their presence irksome. And instead of being stimulated by the responsibilities of his position, he was wearied by them.

There are letters from Dr Estlin telling Richard Bright of his concern as he watched at a distance Bright's long silences and tried to 'think of things to distract him'. Mrs Estlin kept saying he was sickening for something, that there was more to account for his mental torpor and lethargy than Holland's absence. Throughout that term no books stirred his interest, no half-holidays gave him pleasure. Being naturally unselfish and aware of his responsibilities Bright, it seems, did all that was necessary and expected of him: 'the younger boys look at him with respect but the spirit has gone out of him.'

When Christmas came, his health broke down so badly that his parents called for the family doctor, Dr Lovell. He could find little to account for his pallor, lethargy and lack of interest. He took little notice of the fever, recommending a change of air and scene and maintaining that horse-riding would benefit his headaches and malaise. Devon was suggested, and finally it was decided that Bright would lodge and learn in the home of the Revd Dr Lant Carpenter. ('Mr Gibbs cannot believe his name is Lant.' Letter from Bright to his sister Phoebe, 2 September 1806.) Richard Bright was confident that this kindly, gentle man would appreciate his son and, being frail himself, would surely understand his lack of strength and spirits.

3
Exeter
1805–1808

Bright had expressed a desire not to journey by water, and it was Lowbridge – his father being away at the time – who saw him off on the post-coach to Exeter. Other than being told by his cousin 'to use his jackboots should any fellow traveller molest him', there is little information about his departure. No date is given us other than the year 1805, so we have to content ourselves with an excerpt from a letter written by Phoebe from Bath to her mother: 'Richard will have fine weather for his journey. Bid him to be sure and not get up at two to-morrow morning but make him go to bed early . . .'

It is safe to assume, however, that he set off with apprehension and, feeling unwell, the distance between Ham Green and this unknown destination must have seemed very great. And when he did arrive, depressed as he was, Exeter was scarcely the place to raise his spirits. Improvements were later to alter the character of the little town, but now there were still gutters running down the middle of every street and every lane; there were mean backyards full of refuse, with dripping pumps and open ovens for the public; the shops were for the most part unglazed; the houses were old and crooked.

Bright's sense of forlornness must have taken a long time to leave him, for the puritanical rigour of Dr Carpenter's household can hardly have been uplifting. The young Mrs Carpenter, having spent the whole of her honeymoon preparing the parsonage to accommodate her husband's few pupils, was, by the time of Bright's arrival, resenting the fact that these boys were to share their lives. Sitting straight at the breakfast table, 'becapped and frowning, behind a large coffee pot', she looked a formidable figure. Neat, punctual and strict, of cultivated mind and polished manners, she was frightening and managerial.[1] She meant to be kind, but being totally and passionately absorbed in her newly wedded husband – preoccupied with the running of the penniless household, worrying about his health and his privacy, protecting him from noisy boys, guarding his study door from intruders, fighting for the quiet he needed for his work – she had little time to spare for the feelings of homesick boys. 'She is busy but means to be kind,' Bright wrote to his mother.

It was Dr Lant Carpenter himself (1780–1840) whose personality filled the house. Known and praised by Henry Bright at Glasgow University, he was, at the age of twenty-five, a tall, toppling man with long limbs and a transparency of skin which gave his saintly face a look of delicacy. Henry told his father that he was a man indifferent to food, sleep and rest, and yet being of a nervous disposition he was much in need of them. He was a whirlpool of emotions, persistently oppressed by his sense of responsibility. He had to save souls; he had to be needed in the parish; he wanted to care for, guide and teach his scholars. As soon as he had graduated, he took the living at St George's, Exeter, and it was not long before the sleepy town was jerked into wakefulness by his enthusiasm and passion. Drawn by his melodious voice and his simple sermons, people abandoned their pews in the cathedral for the meeting house. Even some influential members of the Established Church were seen sidling into the chapel to hear his views on theology and education. He also started a public library and established the first savings bank in Exeter.

The first month seemed an age to Bright. Accustomed to Mrs Estlin's cheerful regime, it was hard to adapt to the Carpenters' more rigid standards and ceaseless reprimands. He was still far from well – with a malaise easily suggestive of today's glandular fever. At first, he was permitted unlimited licence, as Dr Lovell had recommended 'horse exercise and as much foot exercise on the intervening days as is consistent with his avocations'. He was therefore fully able to enjoy, unwatched and almost always alone, the scenes around Exeter. He walked over the marshes to the coast, along the river and the Trew canal, amongst the maze of shrouds and ratlines, always conscious of the lack of a companion. His pony took him further west where the wild daffodils grew, and inland to Dartmoor. Little escaped his quick and observant eye, but where before he would have leapt down to pick and examine a wild flower, coax and follow a reluctant beetle or identify a rock, the forlornness that he felt so profoundly left him now disinterested. But he valued these excursions, coming as they did between him and Dr Carpenter's exacting demands of study. The discovery of that beautiful region had a lasting effect on him. Long after he was married he was to write, 'Indeed except for the lake scenery of England, I think Devonshire contains more variety of beauty than any other individual county.'

Although Sarah Bright informs us that Bright wrote regularly that first year, only a few letters survive. There is a brief mention of the pattern of every day. He describes 'a decorum of the dining room . . . we kneel for prayers and have to shake hands as we wish each other a "good morning".' Breakfast with the curate, the Revd Manning, at the table, momentarily altered the pitch of their thoughts, as he read clearly the political news from the papers of the day. 'Bells summon us every hour', marking the end of every strictly measured lesson; every afternoon was set aside for study and the early evening for essays. Sometimes before supper there was a sermon – 'easier to follow than Dr Estlin's ever were' – and after a Bible reading and hymns the small boys 'had to be got into their night shirts'. It was not until after the book at bedtime – Bishop Law's *Consideration on the Character of Christ* – that Bright had any time to himself.

Another time he wrote that Dr Carpenter had invested him with the office of teacher. The heights that Holland had once enjoyed at Estlin's school and which 'I thought unattainable for myself, have at last been reached . . . I have six small boys set before me to whom I have to teach French and the New Testament . . . when I try to make them comprehend Latin I am surprised to find how much easier it is to remember from what I teach them than it is listening to a master's words which are easily forgotten.' But it is mostly from his father's letters to Dr Carpenter that we learn of his progress. 'He promises to avail himself fully of the advantages offered him,' wrote his father.

. . . he is fond of Hartley's dictums, Joyce's dialogues and the Greek Testament. He would be mortified at having to give up the Dialogues on chemistry and anatomy, pursuits which he confesses are useful and entertaining . . . and he is grateful to you for the trouble you are taking with the experiments in Science. As for history and geography he must attain all the knowledge which time permits . . . and whatever is to be his ultimate vocation, a neat hand will be found a valuable qualification. Your calling his attention to it from time to time will oblige me.

It is from this same letter that one gains the impression that Dr Carpenter was a forceful teacher and hard task-master and that under his certain spell Bright found himself trying to excel 'in order to please him'.

Otherwise the rest of the year 1805 passes under a blanket of silence; one can only assume that Bright continued to take an interest in his studies. According to the reports he took back with him to his father that Christmas he had responded well to the Carpenter treatment.

I have with much pleasure looked over the proofs my son has brought with him of his diligence and improvement, during the last half year, which coupled with the testimony you gave me of his progress in Greek and Latin are highly satisfactory to me. I doubt not anything you say of the increasing powers of his mind and I flatter myself that although he may never show great brilliancy or genius, yet he will make a respectable figure in any profession.

From a house where a brief burst of laughter from a couple who laughed little was almost startling, to return to Ham Green, a house bright with it, must have been an immeasurable pleasure. Restored to his home, to his own room, to the unvarying indulgence of the household, Bright seems to have taken little part in the preparations. His father said it was to be a quiet Christmas, because of the continuing war, but there had never been such activity. The house was full of extra lights, wood was piled upon fires, Sam and the youngest housemaid roamed the grounds for holly and evergreens. Phoebe surveyed the pantry and brought out all the glittering trimmings; Sal 'put the alms boxes' on the hall table in readiness for St Stephen's Day; Robert helped to polish the fruit for the dessert, while the rotund Mr Ballard transformed the rooms with bright red and white plants from the hot-houses.

The youthful Bright, disinclined to make any effort, turned with relief to the fireside of the 'middle parlour', watching his mother's embroidery grow on her lap, or stayed in the children's room to make a friend of his baby sister, Elizabeth, now aged one year. His vitality struggled unavailingly against the sense of negation he felt. 'He even seems to have forgotten the intense pleasure he received from his collection,' Sarah Bright complained to her brother, Serjeant Sam Heywood, always avid for news of the family. So, once more in the family circle, Bright remained in the shadow, taking silent refuge in all he loved best.

There must have been great bursts of chatter and excitement at every arrival. Lowbridge appeared, then Canon Randolph and his wife. (D. F. Randolph was Canon of Bristol Cathedral and Rector of Banwell. It is worth reading about his life in the *Dictionary of National Biography*. He figures much in Phoebe's letters, and seems rather to have 'sponged' on the Brights.) Sal tells us that Henry arrived from London 'in one of the tightest coats' that was ever made by the family tailor. Benjamin was wearing a gold chain, his hair plastered with bear's grease, and aglow over the cultural life he was experiencing in Edinburgh. This was exactly the sort of gathering Richard Bright enjoyed most; and even as host he could steal away to the laboratory with his sons, or occupy himself with 'the pleasures of the library', if he wanted. One day musical friends came to an evening supper, and the parish clerk and the choir of charity children sang carols around the hearth. On another day came the artist Nicholas Pocock, whose 'jolly red face' diffused such warmth that all he encountered were imbued with the same cheerful spirit. He was well pleased with the success of the Water Colour Society he had just formed. He brought with him a picture. One of the Brights had once complained to him that all his marine scapes showed a rough sea; could not 'his skilful brush be enlisted to paint' for once a calm sea?[2] And now their highest expectations were more than fulfilled at the sight of 'this delightful gift'. Then Dr Estlin came too with his son John, who had just graduated as a member of the College of Surgeons and was considering further experience at Edinburgh University.

At some point during these holidays Richard Bright must have asked Bright what his intentions were regarding his future, for in a letter to Dr Carpenter he says: 'I have taken pains since Richard's return to us, to discover whether he wishes to pursue a profession rather than a trade, and if a profession which one. . .' It is impossible to tell at what point it became clear to Bright that what he wanted most was to become a doctor. From that unidentified moment, however, it was the sole end to which he struggled. When his father understood his inclinations, he was shaken. He thought him quite unsuitable for such a profession and said so. He felt that his scholarly tastes, his sweet nature and quiet, private character made him a much more suitable candidate for the Church. Having hinted at his opinions, the subject was dropped. He was too wise a father to interfere, especially at a time when his son seemed so subdued and self-absorbed. When writing to Dr Carpenter he simply asked him, therefore, to give his son the encouragement necessary to support him 'in the arduous task he seems to wish to undertake'. Yet, he added,

If in his future progress you should observe anything that may change your opinion, or ought to influence my conduct in that respect, you will I hope freely communicate to me your sentiments. Your means of knowing the extent of his faculties, and their capability of improvement are so much greater than mine can be, that I must depend greatly on your opinion, in forming my own judgement . . .

Still feeling frail, but certain that 'the new medicine Dr Lovell had given' him was doing good, Bright returned to Exeter. The Carpenters were delighted to have him back and delighted also with the basket of fruit and other fare from Ham Green. The discussion between him and his parents as to what would be most appreciated had almost made him miss the coach; his father's generosity always involved these endless heart-searchings. Richard Bright was aware of the Carpenters' straitened circumstances, and along with the half-yearly fees of £6. 10s. he tucked into the envelope a generous gift of money – 'an addition you have allowed me to make'.

Time progressed towards Easter. As more Greek studies were added to his curriculum Bright's rambles into the countryside became shorter and more rare. Only on the occasional Saturday was it now possible for him to follow the towpath to Topsham to visit his father's friends. In Shapland Street there lived Captain William Gibbs, the brother of his father's business partner, but as he was away at sea much of the time it was his wife and daughters who welcomed 'the awkward youth'. Nearby, in an old rambling house of smugglers' passages and twisting stairs, lived the large family of Folletts. Here, we have to presume that Bright was a remote participant in their cheerful life. He tells us himself that Mr Follett, a timber merchant of wide interests, was a rewarding companion, and that he felt 'oddly at ease with him'; but of Elizabeth, the youngest daughter, who was to play such a significant part in his later life, we learn nothing.

His wish to become a doctor grew more pronounced during that summer. The exchange of letters between the schoolmaster and Richard Bright on the subject shows that Dr Carpenter was sympathetic. He saw quickly that his pupil was irretrievably committed, while it took Richard Bright some time to realize how deeply rooted his son's ambition really was. He had a poor opinion of the medical profession and was reluctant to see a son of his become part of it. As an anxious father he saw the pitfalls that surrounded it – 'the odium, the envy, the narrowmindedness'. He did not think that the young Bright had character or calibre enough to reform it: 'his bodily exertions are not enough, his social manners are of little grace, and though he has moral courage and honesty, I do not think he has the push to succeed in such a competitive field.'

Bright ignored the doubts and worked hard. He had at last a career in mind. This sense of purpose was consolation for every difficult day. It helped him to cope with his own general malaise and with the increasing tension of the household. The feeling of uneasiness which Mrs Carpenter's presence always produced in the boys grew as her own anxieties over her husband's frailties increased. The more effort she had to make to conserve his peace of mind, the sharper became her eye, and her tongue. Overburdened with a terrible conscience, Dr Carpenter found himself involved in a variety of parish duties which kept interrupting the clockwork regularity of the classroom; and, wholly committed to teaching as he was, this upset him. Henry tells the story of the occasion when Bright and Carpenter were sitting in the little green summerhouse, with a pot of tea and the Greek *Chronicles* of Xenophon between them, when Dr Carpenter suddenly plunged into the physical features of Palestine. So absorbed did they become that neither of them heard the hourly bell or the chimes of the cathedral clock. Not until the servant girl 'came to tell us that the letter woman was at the front door, awaiting his mail' did he realize that it was long past the hour when he had promised to be with a sick parishioner. He was horrified by his thoughtlessness, and according to Mrs Carpenter this incident precipitated his illness. Writing to Sarah Bright at a later date to thank her for some gift, she tells of Bright's sympathetic nature: 'he has an extraordinary understanding of the stresses that my husband has in trying to keep up with his successive labours.' His shy, uncertain attempts to relieve the doctor of some of his burdens and the way he tried to control the racket of the small boys endeared him to her; and though she remained severe, Bright tells us that she never again included him in her reprimands.

There were many anxieties that summer to upset the finely adjusted balance of Dr Carpenter's nervous temperament. It soon became evident that he was prone to imaginary fears. For the loss of his voice he blamed the acoustics of St George's Meeting House: the ceiling would have to be lowered and the position of the altar changed. His increasing exhaustion was due, he was convinced, to tuberculosis. So overwrought did he become that in July 1806, he was sent by the school doctor to rest at Teignmouth, while his pupils were dispersed for a premature summer holiday.[3]

When Bright returned home he found his father very ill with fever and gout and his family with little heart for the things they were doing. His mother was constantly at the bedside. Bright tried to concentrate on his books but he was always, it seems, on the alert for Dr Lovell, it being his duty to escort him up the stairs. Though his heart was in a turmoil, he was too shy to ask questions about his father; Dr Lovell instead kept 'asking me how I was keeping'. Through every room in the house he wandered, carrying a pile of books, but the smaller children would often follow him. Eleven-year-old Sal wanted a book explained to her, while Robert kept running away to the home farm. Sometimes, to shake off his mental fatigue, Bright followed him and together they walked in the sun-baked paddock and scented orchard and filled their arms 'with buttercups and ox-eyed daisies and love-in-a-mist to take to Mama'. Meanwhile, five-year-old Sam relieved his unrecognized grief by refusing to eat his meals, and at night he put on his own stockings, slippers and dressing gown and hurried down the attic stairs to his parents' room; he was invariably caught, though once he gained the garden door, and Bright found him 'trying to turn the handle'.

But, at last, their father got better. Phoebe returned to her good works in the neighbourhood and Bright was more often in his father's room. It is from Richard Bright's letters to Henry that we learn how Bright waited upon him when he was not asleep, giving him his medicines and trying to find ways to keep him cool. And when the sick man got stronger, and more irritable and resentful of his immobility, Bright read aloud to him and looked up references for him. He was asked many questions about what he had seen in the hot-houses and in the gardens. 'Father was surprised to hear,' he wrote to Henry, 'how late in flower was the Ghent Azalea . . . in one single blossom I found no less than six flies: two were alive but the Azalea had already nearly drained their life away, and held them so tightly with its viscid hairs that I could hardly release them from its grasp.' Another time, it was 'the green Rose from Baltimore' he was anxious about.

Then the day arrived when Bright received a letter from Dr Carpenter. He had gained 'some bodily strength', he said, though his voice was not fully restored he wished to 're-establish the school'.

Richard Bright's interest in his son never flagged even when he was ill himself. Although his hand 'was so weak as to make his writing indecipherable', although his body was so 'feeble that he had not yet been out of the house nor yet able to use his crutches and was still under the necessity of being carried up and down the stairs', he felt impelled to write and tell Dr Carpenter all over again 'his doubts and apprehensions' over his son's wish to become a doctor;

> He is as reflective as ever which not only worries me but his mother as well . . . I fear that the desire of retirement and quiet is growing upon him . . . this may be due to the warm weather or to the greater degree of diffidence as to his own abilities . . . he feels an unequality with those he meets, for he is silent and reserved in company – even beyond what he used to be and is little inclined to go from home or mix with the few strangers that come to us.

Though he realized that his own illness was reason enough for some of his son's increasing abstraction he did hope that his 'air of melancholy' would not become a permanent habit. Would not this hinder his success as a public man, he asked, entreating Dr Carpenter at the same time to do 'his best to counteract it'. And though his son's health had certainly improved since he went to Exeter, 'there have been several days on which he has complained of headaches, and after his rides he seems much more easily fatigued than a lad of his age ought to be'.

Bright comforted himself before departure by buying a globe in Bristol for his baby sister Elizabeth. It was accompanied, we are told, by two notes, one to his father and one to Phoebe, in which he said: 'this will give her a more accurate idea of the relative situation of Exeter. Be sure to explain the meaning of longitude and latitude. I daresay she will laugh when she sees the world turning round. Give my very, very best love to Mama and just as many kisses as you suppose I should give her if I were there.'

Bright remained in Exeter a further eighteen months. During this period there are only fleeting glimpses of him to be had now and again. In April 1807 the strictly prescribed daily ritual was interrupted by Mrs Carpenter's disappearance into the bedroom. A sense of expectancy took the place of the customary solemnity; and when Mary was born Bright's days became more packed than ever. Dr Carpenter took his wife to Dawlish and Dr Manning's devotion to the sick and poor of the parish left Bright with more responsibilities within the school. But it was good training, forcing him to ignore his lassitude and his headaches, which made him so often dull and unresponsive.

When Dr Carpenter was there, though still somewhat aphasic and nervy, he did put aside the book on education he was writing and turned all his energies to the needs of his senior pupil. Bright responded, but remained silent and reserved. Those who did not know him said he was sullen, while one of the day-boys even called him stupid. Dr Carpenter's seeming pleasure would give him confidence but the next day he would be utterly cast down by his own ineptitude; sometimes it took two or three tellings before he heard what somebody asked him to do. 'I confess I am baffled,' wrote Dr Carpenter to Richard Bright. 'He has many good parts though I do not rightly know myself how to bring them out . . . His observing in physiology and natural history, I have never seen a boy like him.' A local man, a Mr Bickland, had been brought in to take some of Dr Carpenter's classes in Greek and Latin. An understanding seems to have sprung up between him and the youth. And because of Bright's desire to improve himself in the classics, Richard Bright spared nothing to further it. 'My proposal,' he wrote to Dr Carpenter, 'is that you should consult Mr Bickland whether he would be willing to ease you constantly of the Classical department of Richard's instructions and allow *me* to make him such compensation as such sacrifice of his time and trouble will fitly require.'

It was originally intended that Bright should leave the Carpenters' household at Christmas 1807, but because of these arrangements for extra tuition he remained at Exeter until June 1808. That month Ham Green was undergoing some structural alterations and the whole family left for Worcestershire. Against a background of green slopes stood Welland Court, a tall rambling house of muted red which turned an indescribable apricot in the lowering sun. The pleasure of Bright at being there may be readily realized. The Malvern estate was, in many ways, as Phoebe said, 'their happiest of places'. On arrival the children would immediately set off on a tour of inspection to make sure everything was as they had left it, from a favourite gap in a hedge to the top stone of the cairn in the quarry. Nothing ever changed at Welland. The days of the week, too, were always the same. Mutton on Monday and the cheap-jack calling on Tuesday; bread was baked on Wednesday; tin baths were carried into the bedrooms on Thursday, carpets beaten on Friday; 'owd' Purser had to be visited on Saturday. There was holy worship on Sunday morning and Bible reading to the village on Sunday afternoon. On Sunday evening came the callers – local people like the whimsical Sir Isaac Heard, who sang love ditties to the ladies, when Bright wished to talk heraldry, but because he had lived ninety years he 'seemed unwilling to talk anything but nonsense'.

At Welland even a carriage in the lane was an event. Here there was no laboratory, no conservatory, no forcing houses; instead Richard Bright taught his children all about the land and its limitless possibilities. It was here that they learned of the rotation of crops, the pests in the pear orchards, the manures in the loam and clay. On Richard Bright's land there were no mud hovels, no ill-drained fields or communal tillage, no slovenly cultivators or weedy wastelands. There were neat homesteads dotted about the landscape and gardens with pinks and pansies and hollyhocks. The Enclosure Act had not deprived his labourers of their holdings – their cabbages, their carrots, their tethered cow. But if they owned pigs they had to have sties; the oxen had to be correctly fed; the geese and or goats were not allowed to wander at will by the village ponds. The crooked higgledy-piggledy hedgerows were straightened, lopped and 'interspaced with elms . . . trees, which I do verily believe to be best for breaking up the flatness of our land and, of course, [to] provide good planking for our ships'.

For Bright, Welland must have been an ideal place for reflection. He was probably going through a Romantic phase, for he was writing poems, several of which were found amongst his mother's letters. (Bright was never to lose his love of poetry. He educated his own children on the subject, and Clara was not the only one who said, 'I have not read it for Papa said there is nothing so bad for young people as reading bad poetry.') Only one poem was placed before the eyes for which it was intended. It was sent to his cousin Ann Heywood in place of a birthday letter and reveals an attitude of chivalry which Bright never lost (see Appendix I).

The atmosphere of cheerful reality which Welland imparted to the whole family could not but in the end be contagious, and serve finally to dispel some of Bright's melancholy. By the time of their return to Ham Green, his parents were happy to see he was in better spirits.

(I can find nothing in the family correspondence of 1808 referring to Bright's further education. Perhaps it was taken as a matter of course that he should matriculate at Edinburgh and follow the footsteps of his older brothers.)

The system of education was of a high standard at Edinburgh and what had attracted Benjamin's contemporaries Lord Palmerston, Francis Jeffrey and Henry Brougham also attracted Bright. Edinburgh was dominated by Whigs and Dissenters, who because of their liberal and religious principles were denied admission to the Universities of Oxford and Cambridge. Besides, Henry Holland was now there, having decided to abandon the counting house for medicine,[4] and Bright must have longed to have his companionship once more. Ever since he left Estlin's school, he had been rather lonely and friendless. Only in one letter written by Benjamin – who was now reluctantly studying commerce under his Uncle Benjamin Heywood at Manchester – is there a hint of Bright going to Edinburgh. 'I am most desirous', he wrote, 'to see Richard while he is at home and before being occupied with other matters. We have been a long while strangers and unless we meet soon, I may describe him so wrongly in my letters to Edinburgh, that he will be taken for an impostor.'

If Benjamin did manage to pay a flying visit to Ham Green there is no word of it in any of Sarah Bright's letters to her oldest son Henry, though she has much to say of Bright's coming departure. The last few weeks were passing quickly. There seemed too little time for the extensive scheme of study Bright had laid out for himself. As political economy – a new science – was to be one of his subjects for matriculation, he felt he should attempt to read Malthus's *Essay on Population*. But he could not resist the temptation to help his father unpack some new specimens of rock from the Hartz mountains, just sent to him in exchange for a barometer he had given a friend. They both spent many hours in the laboratory trying to identify them, so it was not until the evening that he had time for Malthus's gloomy predictions. All this did not make things any easier for Sarah Bright, who felt that Bright had many obligations to fulfil before he went north. He must write to Dr Carpenter to say how sorry he was that he was going to miss his visit to Bristol, and that he would not therefore hear his sermon at Lewins Mead, nor be able to congratulate him on his new hymn book. He must go and say goodbye to Dr Estlin, and he should go and see Captain William Gibbs from Topsham, who was staying at Clifton and asking to see him. There were invitations to Blaize Castle and Leigh Court, while Mr Ames of Clifton Wood was keen to show him some fine lava deposits he had newly acquired. Mrs Beddoes, (Ann Edgeworth, sister of Maria) too, wanted personally to wish him well in his medical career. She had some books to give him which the late doctor had himself used as an Edinburgh student. And, when he had listened long enough to her, there was Lowbridge waiting to give him an etching.

45

4

University
1808–1810

Richard Bright had given much thought to Bright's accommodation in Edinburgh. Henry had lodged at the well-known house of Mrs Flemming at 38 Hanover Street, while Benjamin had had a somewhat uncomfortable time at Mr Trotter's lodging house for students in Princes Street. Bearing in mind the retiring nature of his third son, he accepted gladly the offer of a room in a clergyman's house. Perhaps he hoped that the Revd Bob Morehead, an episcopal clergyman of many attainments, would encourage him eventually to choose the Church rather than medicine. If this was so, then he was to be disappointed, for not only was Bob Morehead much esteemed in the intellectual clubs of Edinburgh, but many of his friends taught medical subjects and the son of his greatest friend, the Revd Dr Alison, was a keen medical student. As soon as the front door was flung wide and Bright was ushered into the presence of the Moreheads he was given the position of a son.

No. 21 Hill Street is little different now to what it was then. It takes up the whole corner, stretching back to twice its narrow width. The front faces south on to a cobbled street and a row of modest dwellings. The house is an office today, but it still retains its eighteenth-century air, with its large, elegant Georgian door, its lovely old walls, its fire insurance plaque and eroded stone crest of crown and fleur-de-lys. Inside, the rooms are light and square, and the ceilings, chimney-pieces and fanlights are decorated with beribboned leaves of plaster. The hall gives a great sense of light, for the window on the staircase is as wide as it is long. It was in marked contrast to the austere Carpenters' dim rooms and curtained windows, here the sun streamed in, and in winter there were blazing fires and candelabra of candles.

The Revd Bob Morehead was considerate towards his lodger and always respected Bright's privacy. He remained in the background, a father figure, unobtrusively pushing him into the right places – St Paul's Rectory, Cowgate, for instance, the home of his crony, the

Revd Dr Alison, author of *Nature and Principle of Taste*; the chambers of his brother-in-law Francis Jeffrey, or the book-lined room in Castle Street where Walter Scott lived.

Bright, finding himself at last in Edinburgh, wasted little time in getting acquainted with it. Ever since war had closed the Continent, it was Edinburgh instead of the 'grand tour' abroad that had lured young men. Philosophy and literature had become indigenous to the place, the fame of its professors was widespread. We do not hear who it was that first steered Bright through the complexities of a university life. Was it Holland who took him in hand, directing him here and there? Did Benjamin's letters of introduction prove fruitful? Or did he just filter in on his own? In any case he enrolled under the dates of 1808/1810 in the Faculty register, buying the necessary tickets to attend a course of lectures on Political Economy and Moral Philosophy by Professor Dugald Stewart, on Natural Philosophy by Professor Playfair, and on Mathematics by Sir John Leslie.

The university system then was a lonely one: there was no collegiate life, no tutorials, like there are today. The students then went to their classes, scribbled their notes and returned to their lodgings to struggle on as best they could. This was not difficult for Bright, however, accustomed to Dr Carpenter's rigid timetable and his own solitary habits of hard work. Indeed he found that not living under a schoolmaster's eye, having to manage on his own and arrange his studies as he felt inclined, was 'a real source of excitement'. Again, he was fortunate in his professors, for where many were unapproachable, both Stewart and Playfair enjoyed a kindly intercourse with their students, inviting them into their homes, going on expeditions with them and generally enlarging their horizons and offering brilliant new ideas.

Professor Dugald Stewart's classes began before winter daylight hit the tower of St Giles, and Bright soon learned that to get a seat at all it was best to be early. His brother Benjamin had told him what to expect from this remarkable man, and how much he had 'shaped two tastes' and coloured his imagination. Now Bright in his turn was to find him quite as stimulating, as he grasped the principles of political economy, statistics and free trade, and became fascinated by the philosophical theories of Malthus, Franklin and Mirabeau. 'I wish', he confessed to his father in a letter, 'that I could have better appreciated the value of what you had told me once of these gentlemen.'

The Professor was asthmatic and, like the rest of the class, Bright found his struggles for breath painful to witness. On one occasion much later on, when he was a medical student and an invited guest at the Professor's breakfast table at Canongate, he forgot his shyness and was moved to give his own ideas of relief. It was best to inhale warm steam when in paroxysm of coughing, he said, and to obtain 'a fresh supply of air . . . at an open window'. He also believed that 'irritants in the air and peculiar conditions of worry could aggravate'. History does not record whether he gained for himself any respect, or whether he told those at the table that these ideas might have had their foundation in remembered impressions of Dr Beddoes' Dowry Square clinic.

Bright was attracted to mathematics and he seems to have found the large, florid Sir John Leslie a teacher of 'high order', for he carried off the top prize at the end of the session.

From John Playfair's lectures and talks on Natural Philosophy and literature sprang also an increasing interest in geology. Bright was one of the many students who gained much from the magic of this man's personality. Playfair stayed perennially young in spirit, and was perhaps the more conspicuous to admiring pupils for his flirtations with any attractive women that appeared in Edinburgh society. He would take his class on pleasurable excursions, some geological. The students trudged up the Salisbury Crags, up the volcanic steps to Arthur's Seat, then slid down to the waters of Leith. They tramped the footpaths of the Esk, the Almond and the river Forth. They climbed the Braid Hills and the Pentlands, and went as far afield as the Blackhope Scaur on the Moorfoot Hills. As the Professor insisted on careful observations, the mineral kingdom was exactly examined, while earth formations, the nature of springs and lakes, hill-pools and meres, 'most remarkable mines', chasms and quarries were explored in detail.

'When we return at the end of the day,' Bright wrote to his father, 'Playfair gathers us about him and we sit before a blazing fire consuming oatmeal and scrutinising our specimens.' The thrill of it all was stimulated by the playful controversy that was going on at this particular time, causing, Holland tells us, 'a minor and more whimsical disruption in Edinburgh society'.[1] Playfair advocated the Huttonian theory that the earth's crust originated through the action of fires; while his opponent Dr Robert Jameson, who taught Natural History at the University, was a Wernerian and like the German mineralogist considered the earth's beginnings to be aqueous.

The exact details of Bright's part in the controversy are not clear. More important than which side he took, however, is his thoughtful approach to the whole subject. Now under the influence of Playfair and later on under the direction of Jameson, he looked at both sides dispassionately, recording without bias. He studied geology, chemistry, physics, and ethnology for their important connections with medicine. Physicians used fossilized bones and minerals for treating patients and Bright drew where he could from all branches of knowledge.

In the highly charged atmosphere of Edinburgh University, buzzing with new ideas, with academic standards so high and Bright himself so keen to work, it was not surprising that within sixteen months he had not only got his first University degree, but had also gained a reputation as a promising geologist and botanist, a modest figure with an indelible impress.

Edinburgh was the only medical school that demanded premedical studies in science and the humanities; with these behind him Bright was now licensed to proceed towards a degree in medicine. The session did not begin till early autumn, and there is nothing in the family correspondence telling us what he did in the summer recess of 1809. It is unlikely that he travelled south – there were too many attractions to keep him in Scotland. He did plan a trip to the Inner Hebrides, but 'I have left it too late . . . after the month of August it is not easy to pass on to Staffa.' 'You must know', he wrote to his father, 'how ever since childhood it has been one of my dreams to get there.' He had read Boswell's *Tour of the Hebrides* and had listened with fascination as Joseph Banks described to his father the remarkable rock formations around Fingal's Cave.

John Davy was much with him about this time, and they became lifelong friends. Davy was small and spare, fair of face, with masses of dark hair and bright grey eyes. Brilliant and sensitive, he was also full of love for science and had all the Cornishman's honesty and imagination. He had a bent leg due to the mishandling of a greenstick fracture and his limp heightened the interest that was always felt in this brother of Humphry's. At this time, too, Bright was still seeing a lot of Holland; though now a third-year medical student his old Bristol friend gave him all the help and advice he could. His charm and grace made Holland one of the most conspicuous undergraduates of those years.

The three friends met in the evenings – sometimes at a club or a tavern, sometimes at the meeting of a learned society. The Speculative Society[2] was one of the youthful societies which sought to bring the student out of the isolation of his lodgings. It met at seven every Tuesday, and was much favoured by legal students and those of a literary bent. The proceedings began with a member reading out an essay on some controversial point. It was a wonderful school of oratory and a good debating platform. Bright later told his son Franck about those days of nervous suspense before his own first effort; the knowledge that under the famous chandelier of sixteen candles there could be present many visitors well known in the literary field, and that some of the University professors would occupy the special cane chairs reserved for the distinguished, can have done nothing to assuage his fears. In his brother's day, Walter Scott had been the secretary; now he came to encourage and to criticize, appearing sometimes with Jeffrey and John Wilson (the journalist and critic who wrote under the pen-name of Christopher North), sometimes with Brougham and Horner. According to the minutes, Bright acquitted himself well, but perhaps what he enjoyed most were the informal evenings in the rooms of his friends, infrequent as they seem to have been.

If Bright learned to speak at the Speculative Society, then he became a good listener in the drawing rooms. The Revd Bob Morehead tried to include him and his friends in their entertainments, but Bright's reserve was part of his personality and throughout his life he kept in the background. But, though often 'unhappy and ill at ease' we hear of him going to the house of the beautiful hostess Mrs Fletcher, where he sheltered behind the circle of 'pale-faced and reverential looking students'; and to the house of Mrs Apreece, a widow, vivacious, versatile and 'haughty'. The gatherings in her parlour included 'all the exciting personalities' of the day. At this particular time she was disturbing the heart of Humphry Davy, who kept interrupting his duties at the Royal Institution in London to come and see her, eventually deciding to ask for her hand in marriage.

*

At last it was October; Bright paid his fees and entered the Medical Faculty, putting his name down to do Chemistry with Charles Hope, Anatomy with Alexander Monro and Medicine with Dr Duncan.

Having been fired with the passions and exotic colouring of Dugald

Stewart's lectures, he tells us that it was strange to find himself in a world of bones, dry facts and clichés, with Latin names that were hard to learn. Alexander Monro, whose forbears had been anatomists of true worth, did little himself to stir up enthusiasm for the subject; it was the 'Preceptor' in charge of the dissecting room who taught the students most. If 'old Fyffe' was a 'horrid' lecturer, he was a marvellous anatomist and took infinite care to pass on his phenomenal knowledge. He made certain that the students knew everything about 'the part' put in front of them, making them demonstrate its functions and insisting that they went over the same ground again and again until they knew it.

Bright found each session fascinating. There were never more than ten students at one time and there was no dearth of material. Once the dissections were done and mastered, the students would gather around the fire, while the shrunken little man, Chinese pigtail hanging down his back, entertained them with stories about departed medical worthies. He was a poet at heart and out of his memory came many embroidered pictures: one of his favourites was about Dr Joseph Black, the famous chemist, who was found dead, sitting alone at a table, and so completely quiet was he at the end that a full cup of milk was found resting on his knees and steadied by his hand, and not a drop had been spilt.

Charles Hope, who taught Bright chemistry, had been Dr Black's most able pupil. His classes were popular, with hundreds of students. Bright learned from him about quantitative analysis and latent heat, and was excited by his practical demonstrations. The students complained continually about the lack of laboratory facilities, for Hope's working benches were available only to his assistants. Bright was 'one of the more fortunate'. This might have had something to do with his father's past friendship with Dr Black or his own friendship with John Davy, but it was more likely due to Bright's own aptitude for the subject. At this particular time, Davy was working with Hope to prove that attacks against his brother's theories as to the composition of oxymuriatic (hydrochloric) acid were incorrect.

Andrew Duncan, Bright said, was a 'fine teacher in the Institute of Medicine'. He considered practical work important at a time when few doctors who taught it did. Little contact with a patient was ever demanded, but his pupils got some experience in his city dispensary and the lunatic asylum he opened at Morningside.[3] It was he who started the practice of making medical students walk up to Arthur's

Seat to see the sunrise on the first day of May – and to this day the silence of the old town is yearly broken by the resonance of young men's feet. Bright soon realized that it was preferable to follow this practice than to suffer the alternative, which was a dull painful evening over a cup of tea at Duncan's house.

The pattern of Bright's life now changed little. From the time the servant entered his room with a can of hot water and raked over the ashes of his fire, to the end of the day when he went to bed, he worked. Little attention was paid to the allocation of the student's time, and so without the aid of tutor, or the relief of exercise – except going backwards and forwards to the college, before and after breakfast – he studied hard. He found medicine to be an exacting field, and the Revd Bob Morehead noted the anxious air it gave him, 'which I cannot tame'. He could not stop Bright running either, he told Richard Bright in that same letter. In the morning 'he runs to his lectures, in the afternoon he runs to the dissecting room . . . in the evening he runs back to his dinner, often eaten alone, reading as he cuts his meat and drinks his beer'. He was no sooner finished than he was up and running to some 'houff' or student gathering. He himself told Benjamin how he rushed to the Dispensary to pick up what knowledge he could, tripped over the apothecary's doorstep and fell into the wards of the Infirmary at the few hours open to students. He was interested in everything, and a gusto and curiosity which his father had feared he might never have carried him along at last. Actively employed in a curriculum recognized as medical, he tackled the theoretical with zest; and the little there was of the practical, with caution. 'My mind is now most upon books and my muscles grow stiff,' he wrote to his father. 'Everything happens here now more quickly and more intensely and with better order . . . I have purchased a lancet and a tongue scraper . . . give my very love to all.' His approach to medicine at this stage must have been more scientific than altruistic, and he was as fanatical in his attention to detail as he had been when collecting for his museum under his father's eye.

5
Iceland
1810

All that winter he was at his books. The Christmas break of a few days was devoted to seeking instructions in the wards, and he was even trusted with a midwifery case in a rat-infested hovel in the High Street. When spring came at last, a flood of light enveloped him at his desk as 'if he were in a cup of amber wine'. He became restless and his thoughts turned once more to Staffa.

But it was Holland who actually set things in motion. He happened to overhear that Sir George Steuart Mackenzie of Coul was about to undertake an expedition to Iceland for the purpose of mineralogical research, and to try to assess the claims of Werner and Hutton. For one reason or another his scientific colleagues had let him down and he was, it seems, finding it difficult to procure others of like mind. This was enough for Holland; never was his persuasive charm more evident than in his approach to the explorer. In no time at all Bright was involved and Sir George was not hesitating 'to meet their wishes . . . I know them both to be young men of very superior talents and acquirements, in a very high degree pleasing in their manners . . . I can easily number them amongst my friends.'

An outward bound mail-boat had been waiting at Leith for some time, and on the morning of 18 April 1810 Sir George Mackenzie, Holland, Bright and Mr Fell, an Icelandic agent, embarked, along with a number of cattle and an odd assortment of passengers. We only know the barest details of the voyage to Orkney, but we can safely assume that it did not take long for them to get to know each other in the confines of a small ship. Sir George, who had once burnt his mother's jewels to prove that diamonds were a crystalline form of pure carbon, must have cut a splendid figure, with his flowing dark hair and whiskers and fine linen. He had a commanding presence and his voice was 'clear and strong and sonorous'. There soon grew up an 'accord' between the three. They shared the same sense of comedy, each respected the others' talents, and all three were endowed with a good deal of commonsense. The two students sometimes pandered to the older man, as Bright told his father, but more often than not it was their ideas and not his that were followed in the end.

In calm and pleasant weather the ship furrowed her way to Scapa Flow, through the beauties of the Hoy Sound to Stromness. Here, they spent several impatient days awaiting the arrival of the *Elbe*, the ship which was to take them on to Iceland. An archipelago of fifty small rocky islands was a geologist's dream, but they dared not venture far afield for fear of missing the boat. They had to content themselves with the local coastline, finding much of interest in its 'weird, sculptured rocks'. The town itself was a collection of filthy crowded houses, the single street no more than a narrow lane where pigs and cattle were slaughtered, 'never cleaned save by rain'. Sir George also tells us that much of their time was spent in the comfortable inn, or the manse, where the Revd McClouston brought out his best brandy and his wife made them an 'excellent cinnamon water and posset'.

On 28 April they sailed north. Twenty miles on, the *Elbe*, along with several other ships bound for America, was becalmed and for many days, according to Bright, they 'floated on still waters under the splendour of a pale and pearly sky'. In 'drowsy langour with every flag drooping listlessly against every mast and every cloud loitering for want of wind to stir them', they waited. It was on 3 May that the wind filled the sails and with farewells sung at last across the water each ship turned its nose west and sailed 'gently out of sight.' Only Captain Liston of the *Elbe* set a course north.

After the safety and peace of a calm sea, it must have been frightening to be pitched with little warning into rough conditions. The weather became 'unsteady' and a strong wind overtook them. In the early hours of the following morning, at the height of the storm, as the ship was tumbled and tossed by a gale of vicious strength, an accident occurred: an elderly seaman aloft slipped on the ice-covered rigging and plummeted on to the deck. 'On hearing of this accident we got out of bed, and though it was hardly possible to stand, we continued to reach the place where he lay and to bleed him. He died in the evening.' With these few sentences in his book *Travels in Iceland* Sir George dismissed the whole event. But the incident must have had a profound effect on Bright, bringing home to him vividly a doctor's impotence. I can find no letter written by him at this date, but something of the depth of his feeling was expressed in retrospect. Half a century later, alluding to this event, he was to tell his son Franck how instinctively easy it was in youth to shrink from responsibility when feeling unequal to the occasion. He recalled also how some of his own loathing for the sea stemmed from that memorable day. For although they had done their best to save the life of the injured sailor, he remembered well the frustration, the inept bungling, 'the sadness and anger that filled us to see how the terrible pitch and toss and roll of the ship affected every single thing we attempted to do . . . the lack of co-ordination, when fingers trembled uncontrollably, when sitting was impossible'; when kneeling they were 'pitched forward' and when lying they were hurled in the opposite direction. They found they could do little but 'cling on to something and continually watch till his heart was stilled for ever'.

In those lonely northern waters it must have been wonderful suddenly to glimpse land. To Sir George, Bright, Holland and Mr Fell, standing together on the deck, scanning the long approaching coastline, Iceland was 'luminous and glowing like a sapphire in the distance'. As they gazed, 'dawn broke over the black rocks and through a haze of rising vapours' an iridescent glow rose slowly, changing the amphitheatre of mountains 'to ingots of silver and pink'. But, as the sun remained hidden behind the snow-caps of the north-west, they remarked on the lack of warmth and the inhospitable appearance of 'this black fissured shore'.

They landed at Reykjavik on 7 May and it seemed to the trio, impatient to begin their explorations, that all was one long altercation. In the absence of their host, His Excellency Count Trampe, it was Mr Fell who acted as mediator, trying to sort out the hindrances, excuses and delays which must have been utterly provoking to a party that could ill afford to wait around. They knew the Icelandic summer was short and their programme long.

It was the delightful, corpulent Bishop Gen Vidalin, magnificent in his threadbare coat, who was to provide them with horses, advice and information. He kept telling them to wait, saying it would be alright tomorrow, and tomorrow; that the weather would improve; that the grass would soon grow enough to feed the beasts; that the horses would soon be fit enough for hard work. . . . And so they had to wait.

Although Holland kept a journal, in which their day-to-day activities in Iceland were recorded, the material for this chapter has mostly been gathered from the pages of the book written by Sir George. He gives a good picture of those waiting days. It was bitterly cold and the ice lay four inches thick indoors. Established in the

Count's stilted house of wood and turf, with its open 'forge-like' kitchen, they settled down to work. Sir George, in one cubicle of the partitioned attic lumber room, sat with a map spread out on the table before him, planning different trips, and logging his daily meteorological observations. Holland, in another cubicle, wrote his notes on political matters, education and the diseases of the island – mostly pulmonary, though scurvy and leprosy were endemic too. He worked alongside the local doctor, Dr Klog, and helped share out the smallpox vaccine which they had been urgently requested to bring. He worked in the laboratory and dispensary and was appalled by the ancient equipment and medicines he found there. Bright, the youngest of the party, worked in the smallest cubicle. Sir George had given him the task of describing the flora and fauna of Iceland, so he wandered off on his own, with his 'knife, stick, hammer and specimen bag slung around his waist'. His sharp eyes missed little; he filled his notebooks with diagrams and sketches, pressed his lichens and preserved his plants. Mr Fell's task was to see whether the vegetable seeds Sir George had brought from England would grow in the loose ash which constituted the soil of Iceland. He seems to have spent a great deal of time watching the white turnips, peas, cress, mustard and potatoes. He also threw in some nasturtiums and lupins in the arid dust, hoping 'to surprise with their bright colours'.

While they waited they met some of the people of Reykjavik. They ate meals in quaint, odorous rooms under smoke-darkened rafters; they attended a seaman's funeral; they went to a wedding, and they themselves gave a ball for the ladies and were put out to see them dressed like 'English chambermaids' when national finery and colourful headdresses would have given glory to the occasion.

But all this hospitality only increased their longing to get started, and scientific projects were better suited to their mood. They devoted days to geological research, roaming east to 'the sulphur mountains' around Thingvalla – where solidified lava had taken on 'fantastic shapes and forms'; where 'trails of yellow mists lent an air of mystery and remoteness', and 'we were frequently uneasy when the vapour concealed us from each other'; where there was a 'sense of brimstone and fire' and such concealed activity that it gripped the three scientists in wondering fascination.

It is quite beyond our power to offer such description of this extraordinary place, as to convey adequate ideas of its wonders or its terrors . . . Walking over this soft and steaming surface we found to be very hazardous . . . the chance of the crusts of sulphur breaking, of the white clay sinking with us was very great, and we were several times in danger of being scalded and in trying to dodge the exploding jets of steam Mr Bright ran at one time in great hazzard [sic] and suffered considerable pain from accidently plunging one of his legs into the hot clay.

Sir George went on to say that Bright never once sought consideration or begged for rest as they continued to traverse the area. Neither did the discomfort of the burns seem to quell his enthusiasm. He took samples of the different clays – white, red and blue; he picked plants that were 'nauseatingly odorous' and helped scrape up the scabs and crusts of crystallized sulphur. And as they gazed at the boiling cauldrons, they wondered much at the islanders' lack of enterprise. A Joseph Priestley or a Benjamin Franklin would soon have alleviated the discomforts of their homes by having every room heated and every tap gushing with hot water. As they took samples of water for analysis, they found that with careful damming it was possible to 'wash their hands in a pool of tepid water, boil our cod in another and steam halibut or tusk in the next'.

Another day was spent at a small fishing village, Guildbag Syssel, on the southern promontory. Here, they took a small boat and shot out between the breakers to study the indented coastline, with its hanging cliffs of veined obsidian, greenstone and basalt, marvelling at the skilful way the cormorants caught fish and watching the bobbing red mergansers and harlequin ducks. And when they got out of the boat to walk on the cindery beach at Videö they found themselves in a thronging mass of eider ducks, the eider-down nests covering the wharf, the paths and even the doorsteps of the houses. The handsome drakes swung their bills to snap at the men's legs, while the sitting ducks allowed Holland and Bright to stroke their feathers.

By the end of May 1810, the grass was growing and the weather was fair. So, as the migrant birds arrived from the south, the party was at last ready for departure. For guide they took a priest, who could communicate with them in Latin, while Mr Fell joined them in one place or another, depending on the amount of work his shipping company had to occupy him. For their baggage they took horses. But they regretted the English saddle, for the Icelandic 'contrivance always proved troublesome. It consisted of wood, and rested upon four pieces of spring turf, cut from bogs; once loaded, it sent our tents, our change of clothing and our equipment slipping to the underside of the horse's belly . . . this continually caused irritating delays.' Then, again, the horses roped together in a line, were temperamental: if one slipped on a dangerous path it upset them all. But in the swamps of Mondervich they were totally dependable, 'carefully feeling the ground with one hoof before attempting to put their full weight upon it'.

The weeks of travel that followed – from June to August – might be described as a formative period in Bright's development. It was instructive and highly interesting. His inveterate curiosity and feeling for geology were to find the outlet they needed. For obvious reasons Sir George says little in his book about his companions, but he seems to have had a great liking for Bright. He makes little asides about him which he rarely does about Holland. Bright preserved a calm and considerate exterior, which Sir George appreciated, saying also that he was ever grateful 'for the cheerful and ready exertion he always displayed and the undeviating good humour with which he submitted to the cross-accidents which sometimes befell us'. He came to rely on him and once, Bright being indisposed, he and Holland visited Reikhold without him, 'leaving him behind with regret'.

Departing from Reykjavik, they trekked north, following the top of a great sub-oceanic ridge. 'Under a pale grey sky of rainbows . . . breathing incredibly pure air', they travelled through a terrain 'tormented, savage and of awful beauty'. Climbing all the time to a cinder desert 2,000 feet up, they made their way along steep alluvial valleys and came upon green glens of lyrical charm. They passed slag heaps, stunted trees of birch and willow lakes 'as smooth as steel', rivers that crossed and re-crossed and met in water falls.

Sometimes they travelled by rowing boat and studied the formations of ancient lava which had flowed down in places all along the coast. It had cut the perpendicular cliffs into wide fissures of filigree and blue-frosted grottoes. Stapi was an unforgettable place. The sheer beauty of it took their breath away. Columns of glazed ice rose from the chalky waters of the sea, piled in green and jagged heaps which 'moved and creaked with the tides'. In immense caverns they had to throw their heads far back to look at the simulated gothic architecture, gazing with amazement at the elusive blues and aquamarines of the icicles.

Sometimes they walked more than thirty miles a day. Once they were misdirected and took two days to do the eight-hour journey to Harvefjord. 'Thirst distressed us always, as we picked our way through grey wastelands, where swirling mists and suffocating vapours' alternated with a rude, driving wind. They were ever conscious of great subterranean heat as they stumbled over the blistered ground. At one point it had burst into small potholes and large caverns, glittering with crystal. There was an uncanny aura of emptiness when they reached the high ridges around Buderstad and they found the body of a dead woman in a deep chasm. The sinister feeling, as if something were impending, remained with them the whole way to the northern promontory.

As they proceeded the misshapen outline of Snaëfell Jokul 'rose ever before us' in startling clarity against an apricot sky, though separated from them by miles of ice-glazed slopes and snowfields. They camped in odd places, always remembered for a different reason – for honouring King George IV's birthday on 3 June; for the ducks gyrating under great waterfalls on the river Kald-aa; for the yellow poppy on a single stem growing on a dreary shelf at Klieblink; for the music of the lang-spiel at Akkraf; for the flags gaily hoisted in welcome at Olafsvick; for the great book sale at Oddë. Near Niardiuk Holland lost his shoes and near the same place Bright lost his coat. 'The soles of Mr Bright's shoes having been torn by the lava, he sat down to cut away the loose pieces which were a trouble. On rising he forgot to take up his great coat, which he had laid down beside him.' There could scarcely have been a stranger place to lose a coat than in 'this flat expanse of honeycomb lava and lichen': it should have lain conspicuous from any angle. But when he searched he seemed to be going round in circles, and in whichever direction he went he found himself always returning to the point where he had begun, which was where Sir George sat sketching. Finally, outwitted, he had to abandon the search.

At Olafsvick, they renounced their tents for the house of a Mr Clausen, where they rested for five days. He was a hosier and an owner of a salt fish factory, with an endless fund of interesting information about his country, its literature and its peoples. Mrs Clausen's inborn courtesy delighted them too, and the days passed easily. In the old church near the house the two medical students held a daily sick parade. Holland was the more knowledgeable of the two, but Bright, finding himself faced with experiences he was little fitted for, was 'gratified to find that he could stitch and treat unhealing sores' though spongy gums, scaly skins and fevers were another matter. They were all moved, it seems, by the plight of the islanders – their medieval superstitions, the total lack of luxury or comfort in their lives – yet they were astonished how well read the poorest of them were.

Despite the demands made upon them, Holland and Bright worked hard on their own projects. They perfected their sketches, too, some of which Sir George was to use in his book. Sir George himself was content to talk and to write, but neither student could rest till they had climbed Snaëfell Jokul,[1] though even the stout Icelander who undertook to lead them had so far never been higher than the margin of perpetual snow, 'as the sheep never wandered above that limit'.

If all the chances were against any party so ignorant as Bright and Holland, they did take a few precautions. They equipped themselves 'with an Icelandic walking staff, furnished with a long spike at the end, several pairs of Mr Clausen's coarse worsted stockings, hammers, specimen bags, a compass and thermometer, a bottle of brandy, with some rye bread and cheese'. Thus equipped, they set out at daybreak. Bright noted the piping calls of a horned lark and the style of three houses passed. Men in coloured caps hung over their horses and shouted to the guide that they would never do it. Nobody had climbed that mountain.

They took a straight line towards the snowfields that lay in the distance. Mile by mile the arctic willow, saxifrage and wild betony grew scantier, till at last, two hours later, they reached the startlingly white snow which lay in beautiful elliptical curves. Heavy clouds smothered the summits of the surrounding mountains; only the Jokul 'rose perfectly clear'. This was a good thing since now they became as competent as their guide, 'none of us three knowing which direction to take'. The deep, powdery snow somewhat encumbered their progress, but though the sun shone there was no reflective glare and their eyes were 'not dazzled so we entertained good hopes of accomplishing our purpose'. As they climbed they took temperature readings, tried to unravel geological problems, and rested to enjoy the strange silence, waiting for clouds to pass 'through whose picturesque floating arches we could spy the sea and further off still, the distant mountains on the other side of Breide-Fjord'.

With the acclivity getting steeper and the snow becoming deeper, they found themselves facing widening fissures. They chose to cross them with the help of their poles, rather than go a considerable way round. It was three o'clock in the afternoon when a chasm 'put a complete stop to our progress'. It was a formidable affair, Bright said in his written account of the climb, forty feet deep and six feet wide, and on the opposite side there was 'a wall of snow several feet above the level of the surface . . . and from where we stood we felt the lip to be undermined and we were afraid to approach the brink lest it gave way'. They sought to cross it elsewhere, and found a place with a mass of snow which formed a bridge, 'a very insecure one indeed':

> Standing on the brink, we cut with our poles three or four steps in the bank on the other side, and then, stepping as lightly as possible over the bridge, we passed one by one to the steps which we ascended by the help of our poles. The snow on the opposite side became immediately so excessively steep, that it required our utmost efforts to prevent our sliding back to the edge of the precipice, in which case we should inevitably have been plunged into the chasm.

On a tolerable bank of snow, with a sixty-foot perpendicular precipice on their right, they climbed slowly up to the eastern summit of one of the three peaks of the Jokul. They came then to a fissure so formidable in both width and depth that they had to abandon the last hundred feet of the actual summit, though they made several attempts to find a way. They were bitterly disappointed and even cheated of a view. They stood 4,460 feet above sea level, but low cloud and swirling mists cut them off from the sight of Greenland and the countryside below. There was one tantalizing moment when the curtain parted, revealing glimpses of a satin sea, but quite as quickly another cloud rolled up the side of the mountain. They then became anxious to quit 'our present situation . . . that we might repass the chasm before it was lost in mist'. But first they had certain observations to make:

> Our first object, however, was to examine the state of the magnetic needles, which Olafson in his travels asserts to be put into great agitation at the summit of this mountain, and no longer to retain its polarity. What may be the case a hundred feet higher, we cannot affirm but at the point we reached, the needle was quite stationary and, as far as we could judge, perfectly true. We then noted an observation of the thermometer which we were surprised to find scarcely so low as the freezing point.

Then 'after an application to the brandy bottle', they began with difficulty to retrace their steps:

> We found re-crossing the chasm a work of no small danger; for whenever we stuck our poles into the snow bridge, they went directly through. The first person, therefore, who crossed, thrust his pole deep into the lower part of the wall, thus affording a point of support for the feet of those who followed; Mr Holland, however, who was the second in passing over, had, not withstanding, a narrow escape, for his foot actually broke through the bridge of snow, and it was with difficulty he rescued himself from falling into the chasm beneath.

Scarcely had they passed the chasm when they became enveloped in fog. This, Bright said, 'made it extremely difficult to keep the track by which we had ascended the mountain'. But even at this point they stopped to make further observations: 'When we came opposite to a small bank which we had remarked in our ascent as being free from snow, we desired our guide to remain where he was, that we might not lose the path, while we went to examine an assemblage of loose stones. We found the bank to be almost entirely composed of fragments of pumice and volcanic scoriae.'

At about a quarter past six they arrived back at Olafsvik, apparently 'to the great surprise of all for we had not been expected back till the following morning'. The guide was particularly gratified with the exploit, 'having always been accustomed to look upon the Jokul as some invincible giant, but, we afterwards learned, he found considerable difficulty in making his friends credit his narrative of the ascent'.

It was with a sense of home-coming that they returned to Reykjavik to sort themselves out before further expeditions. Mr Fell's white turnips were now quite large, the potatoes were in flower, and bright nasturtiums wreathed the tentpole. Once again traversing the patchy snowfields of Thingvalla, they took a north-easterly direction. It was a trek of sixty miles to the world of geysers, up a strange valley of some considerable size, whose hillside slopes were 'like prison walls, whose river was gloomy and seeming lifeless'. After examining some of the fountains – of which there were many – they returned to the principal spring, the Great Geyser. The oval basin was full of hot water, and as they were watching a little of the water running out of it they were 'alarmed by a sound like the distant discharge of artillery and the shaking of the ground'. The water, after heaving several times, suddenly arose in a large column, accompanied by a cloud of steam, 'to the height of twelve feet'. A succession of such jets followed, then surprisingly the 'water disappeared from the basin and sunk within a pipe in the centre of it'. Intrigued, they started to try to unravel the whole amazing process. In no time at all they were deep into problems of hydraulics and the possibility of underground pipes and valves controlling these great natural effects.

They bivouacked that night at a distance of 100 yards. It was agreed that a regular watch should be kept, and that the one watching should wake the others at any strange sight or odd noise. Bright's watch commenced at dawn; before he left the tent he first laid on his bed his pencil and notebook and tools ready for the morrow's work. It was light enough to see long distances and to marvel at the 'beautiful variegated petrifactions everywhere around'. On the lips of every geyser there were the ossified deposits of splashed water 'spread out like so many cauliflower heads, all bronzed and luminous: there were petrified mosses and peat, and every spray of grass and leaf and twig of every stunted tree were marvellously sculptured as if in stone'. It was about four o'clock when Bright noticed some agitation and 'trouble beginning', and 'as the water started to simmer I gave the alarm'. In no time at all they were all jerked to attention by a new sound; this is how Sir George described what happened next:

From a place we had not before noticed we saw water thrown up and steam issuing with a tremendous noise, from a place within 50 yards of us which we had not before remarked. There was little water; but the force with which the steam escaped produced a white column of spray and vapour at least 16 feet high. We enjoyed this astonishing and beautiful spectacle till 7 o'clock, when it gradually disappeared. We conjectured this to be the fountain which Sir John Stanley has called the New Geyser.

They were almost defeated by the size and velocity of these violent blasts; all that weekend Sir George kept the two medical students working through various tasks. They had to check temperatures and measure distances, and throw stones into the still water to time the ebullitions as they occurred; they had to count every eruption, catching the wide-flung deposits and the falling drops of water. With acrobatic dexterity they slithered and slipped at the edge of cavities as they tried to bottle the vapours; always cautiously, they peered into every pipe, every new basin. Bright painstakingly picked at stubborn crusts and carefully gathered friable material, taking microscopic note of everything seen and numbering his specimens exactly. In the early hours of the following morning Bright was to be seen attempting to sketch the fountain throwing up a 'wall over ninety feet in height, and with the whiteness of a winding sheet', so powerful that, even with a strong wind blowing against the jet, it still remained perpendicular.

One day, Bright and Holland climbed the volcano Mount Hekla, which in medieval times was considered to be the gate of hell.[2] And, before they left this desolate area, Sir George was anxious to find the Icelandic agate in its native place. Bishop Gen Vidalin had told him where it could be located, twenty-three miles east of Hekla. Once more they found themselves in a plain of cavernous lava, a place of malevolence which Sir George found it difficult to describe:

> On ascending one of the rocky pinnacles we beheld a region, the desolation of which can be scarcely paralleled . . . its fantastic groups of hills, craters of lava, cracks and fissures, leading the eye to distant snow-crowned jokuls; its mists rising from waterfalls, its sinister lakes and its awful and profound silence, with marks all around of the furious action of fire – all combined to impress the mind with sensations of dread and wonder.

The sooner they found the agate the sooner they could turn their backs on this mournful spot. They were gazing up at a particularly massive black perpendicular rock when suddenly a single ray of sunshine pierced through the swirling mist and 'obligingly lit up a clear cord of ignateous rock'. There, unbelievably, was the obsidian. But even this moment of delight did not dispel the horror of the place, so it was with all possible speed that they filled their bags and retraced their steps west. Reaching the end of the valley with relief, they turned to look back once more and found themselves hypnotized: 'the longer the scene was contemplated, horrible as it was, the more unable were we to turn our eyes from it'.

The ship which they had hoped would take them to Edinburgh never reached Iceland. They descended many times to the quayside of Reykjavik to enquire about a boat, but the harbour authorities kept shaking their heads and had no comfort to give them. The delay was serious; none of them wanted to spend the winter in Iceland. Their money was gone and their clothes and boots had long worn out; both

Holland and Bright were worried about the immense distance between them and their medical studies.

While waiting they kept themselves busy labelling their specimens and packing them carefully into crates. It took time and thought to divide them up. Sir George was going to give the minerals to the Royal Society of Edinburgh and other specimens to private collectors; Bright had his father's collection to consider, as well as his own shelves; then there were the waters, soils, sands and lava deposits to go to Humphry Davy for analysis at the Royal Institution. All of them had purchased books, and Bright had to find space in his luggage for the Icelandic Legends he had brought for his brother Benjamin, the 'superb Icelandic Bible' he had got for himself and some manuscripts which had excited him. These can be seen in the Bodleian Library at Oxford.[3] Here, it is permissible to assume that he also acquired some Icelandic costumes, for many years later we are to be told that they were much cherished by his children when playing charades.

It was sheer good fortune that a Captain Butterwick brought his small brig, the *Flora*, into harbour. It was the only vessel to reach the island that whole summer. Everyone was sad to see them go while Sir George and his two students regretted taking leave of a people 'whose situation had often excited our pity, exposed as they were to severe privations from the nature of the soil'. On 19 August the three of them walked under an archway of flags and through a concourse of people to the quay. Then, with music, farewells and the cry of seabirds sounding in their ears, the *Flora* cast off and backed away from those unique shores.

They spent fourteen long days on tempestuous seas. Off Hoy Sound they were nearly shipwrecked in a wind that was reported to be the greatest ever known to have blown against the cliffs of Orkney. This time they spent two days at Kirkwall, then a boat that was to have taken them to Inverness was forced by the westerlies into Wick harbour at Caithness. Henceforward Bright was to have a real fear of the sea. He must have been glad to do the rest of the journey by land. 'From thence we went to Dunrobbin and crossed the Dornoch Firth to Ross, pursuing our journey by land to Edinburgh, where we arrived in health and safety after an absence of nearly five months.'

Rumours and reports of their adventures flew ahead of them. Edinburgh friends were agog; such an enterprising mineralogical research had not been undertaken since Sir Joseph Banks and Sir John Stanley had sailed to Iceland twenty-five years or so ago – and neither of them had returned with such excellent and new observations. Bright remained in that maelstrom of interest for as long as it took to re-discover the niceties of living, but he left most of the fuss and acclaim to Holland. He knew that his parents had been worried over his long and hazardous journey and he was anxious to get home.

I can find nothing in writing of what the three said to each other on parting, other than Sir George telling the two students to visit him whenever they found themselves in the Highlands. They had inevitably been drawn close and become attached to each other. There is little doubt that Sir George was indebted to both Holland and Bright. One gets a strong impression that much in his book on Iceland is taken directly from their notebooks. Later that year, when he was hurrying to finish it, he acknowledged with gratitude the help given him by Bright, 'who in the middle of his professional studies has found time to furnish me with real remarks of much useful information which, without his assistance, I could not have procured'.

The mail coach took Bright swiftly south. He gave expression to a little of what he was feeling in a short note to his brother Henry, telling him of his safe return. After the eternal barrenness of Iceland, every moment of that glorious September journey amongst the green hills of England was savoured, and he took pleasure, he wrote, in the rich colouring of cottage gardens. At Bristol he found Thomas, the family coachman, awaiting him at the Counting House. The well-remembered ground was soon traversed, and as he passed the Smyths' estate at Long Ashton he was amazed to see it enclosed by a new high stone wall, which ran part of the way along to Abbot's Leigh – 'a new and abominable practice which shuts out views from the road' was the way in which Mrs Barbauld described the new craze, when she visited Ham Green around this time.

At Ham Green he found little changed. Phoebe, in a delightful letter to Mrs Randolph, tells her something of Bright's homecoming: how Sam and Sally and Elizabeth watched his 'every movement'; how they struggled to sit next to him, and argued with one another as to who would 'carry his hot chocolate, books and quill' and who would help him unpack and arrange his treasures in his cabinet. There were affectionate outbursts between father and son over the geological material Bright produced and 'they were even up early the following morning'.

Although both Richard and Sarah Bright were anxious that their son should resume his studies almost immediately, he remained to celebrate his twenty-first birthday. Both parents found him changed. From a rather sullen, uncommunicative and generally unsatisfactory youth, Bright had turned into a man of enthusiasms. They regarded him with new respect for showing 'such physical endurance and stout spirit . . . and there is a poise that accords well with his inward emotions'. He was still quiet, still disposed to solitude, still gentle, but he was more forthcoming and more aware of the people and things about him. And, always balanced, he had about him now 'a philosophical equanimity' which both parents felt to be somewhat rare in one so young.

Richard Bright was afraid that the exactitude of being a doctor would remove or destroy this. Sarah tried to reassure him: she felt that medicine was the only work that could give her son true happiness. But his father remained uneasy. He saw before his son an arduous future; and he was even more anxious now, since he felt that the experience and knowledge his son had undoubtedly gained in Iceland would hardly be recognized by a faculty that had been from the beginning against such a serious interruption in his medical studies. He would have to work even harder in his new position at Guy's to prove to the authorities that he had the ability to make up the ground he had lost. These fears were reflected in a letter he sent to Dr Carpenter telling him of Bright's return. It is incredible to find that his son's decision to be a doctor – even at this late stage – remained incomprehensible to Richard Bright. But as he repeats his doubts one can sense a thread of longing – of a father's desire to share in his son's alien interest.

6

Medical Training:
Guy's Hospital and Edinburgh
1810–1813

In October 1810, Bright walked into the courtyard of Guy's. Built between Great Maze Pond and the Borough High Street, it stood then amidst breweries, coaching inns and galleries in an intricate maze of cobbled yards and narrow streets. Just nearby was the confusion of the waterfront, with its bear garden and theatre, and St Thomas's Hospital with its herb gardens and burial ground. The delight of the whole vicinity was the width of the river and the open sky above and London Bridge, which joined the great highway to Dover and the Continent with the city lanes of London.

The union of St Thomas's and Guy's Hospitals for teaching purposes, known as the United Hospitals of the Borough, occurred in 1769, and ended in 1825. Anatomical and surgical lectures took place at St Thomas's, while Guy's was allotted the lectures on Medicine, Chemistry, Botany, Physiology and Philosophy. Both hospitals were part of the voluntary hospital system of those times, whereby the financial generosity of hospital governors maintained the sick by charity, bred of genuine compassion. In choosing the United Borough Hospital to do his clinical studies Bright might have been following the example of Holland, or taking the advice of Dr William Babington, a famous physician, who had long been at Guy's and was known to Richard Bright. Or perhaps he was influenced by his father, who would certainly have found out the lie of the land and made contacts. On the other hand, it was probably a foregone conclusion, for not only did Guy's have strong connections with Edinburgh, but it was highly respected for its administration and its teaching and world-famous for its surgery under Astley Cooper.

The United Borough Hospitals was one of three medical schools attached to Hospitals, the others being at St Bartholomew's and the London. It was not a school as we understand the word today, but it was an organized opportunity for students to 'walk the wards'. Following the usual apprenticeship of five years with an apothecary or apothecary-surgeon (the general practitioners of the day), the

68

students came to the hospital to attend lectures, see operations and do dissections, thus making good the deficiencies in their training. The course of instruction consisted of two annual sessions of about six months each. There was usually a week's break at Christmas, and the dissecting room was closed in May at the beginning of the warmer weather.

The best way for students to obtain instruction was by assisting a surgeon or physician in the care of his patients and listening to his explanations and learning his cures. At Guy's the surgeons were allowed an apprentice and four dressers; a physician was assisted by a clerk. These were coveted positions and barred to those who could not afford to pay the fees. Otherwise the unlimited number of pupils with neither a special identity nor any personal status were mere onlookers, attending lectures, seizing eagerly the restricted time when access to the wards was granted, listening to a rare bedside disquisition or pursuing the surgeon, pushing and shoving for a place near him. Every Friday they crowded into the small operating room as an outer ring of beholders, the inner ring being the surgeon himself, his dressers and all his colleagues, 'there to support him in the ordeal or criticise his work'. On other days they besieged the dissecting room and suffered the bad stench as they fought for the least soiled gown and a place at one of the tables.

To become a surgeon was the choice of practically every student; the role of physician was unpopular, the work being considered too unrewarding and theoretical. 'You must know that surgery is at this moment rising very fast at the expense of medicine,' Bright had written to his father from Edinburgh, 'and we must do our best to keep our ground . . . I wonder much about its place in the future; its ultimate worth will depend on whether or not my generation can do better than the last.' Bright had wanted to be a physician from the start.

Bright's training differed from his fellow students', for he served no apprenticeship. He must earlier have conceived for himself a plan that after a year's clinical experience at Guy's he would return to Edinburgh and complete the course. After graduating he would seek the licence of the College of Physicians and then perhaps practise in London.

His entry into Guy's was somewhat privileged. He was accepted as a physician's clerk, paying £10 to serve under Dr Babington. And he was no 'rank and file' student lodging in one of the many houses near

London Bridge, but stayed in the house of the only resident officer, Dr Richard Stocker, the apothecary. This alone gave him considerable advantages and furthered his experience of practical medicine. Dr Stocker was highly knowledgeable, and though his official task was to dispense the medicines prescribed by the physicians, he was held in such high regard that he was left to decide many other matters pertaining to the treatment of patients. His duties were somewhat like those of a house-physician of today. He acted also as a General Secretary to the school, registering the names of new students in the Counting House and taking their fees. His son James – gentle and almost obsequious – was growing up to take his father's position in the hospital and was eventually to acquire the same intuitive skills. Bright mentions that he helped him tend the plants regularly sent by Phoebe – heliotrope, 'pot of roses', even *Lobelia splendens*, 'scarlet and from America'.

Bright appreciated his own exclusive role. He was treated somewhat to his surprise as a senior student, but with duties and rules clearly defined. He could not go out of the hospital without permission. He had to visit the medical patients daily, write up the features of each case, and carry out all Dr Babington's instructions. As all admissions were first seen by Dr Stocker he learned a great deal more as he trailed round behind him. He was taught to cup, and to apply poultices, blistering agents and leeches. He taught himself to smell, to listen and to feel with his hands, learning early that each patient has to be studied in his own particular way, that 'none could be measured with the same rule'. It was a time of few textbooks, no x-rays, no laboratory help and no technical aids, and as nobody stopped to teach much at the bedside it was largely his own observations that gave him his great skill in doctoring.

With the harmonious, scholarly, well-adjusted way of life in Edinburgh now but a memory, Bright must have felt the door to his past life had been slammed behind him. He was, as he said himself, 'extremely busy and confounded'. In a world characterized by disease and premature death there was much to unnerve him. He must often have felt defeated when he found that those whom Dr Babington had tried to save died one by one. On his many night vigils, as death became more familiar, we find him watching for the clinical reason with increasing attention; and the more he saw the more he wanted to know and to understand. He fought death hard, even at this early stage of his career examining 'that which was before him with an objectivity which almost amounted to genius.'[1] He coaxed a reluctant patient to take the treatment and when 'he bears the depletion so ill as necessarily in some degree to check its employment and when the alarming weakness in the powers of life take their slow course . . . then, as a tired man longs for sleep, let him sleep'.[2]

The wards were full of the best material possible for the training of doctors. Bright absorbed it all and got to respect the patients, however odd their character or strange their creed. He would study their background and behaviour, and was strangely content in spite of the many grim encounters. Some of the patients were humble people – blind beggars, idiots, cripples, outcasts brought in from surrounding gutters; some were hard-working and ignorant; some were intelligent – for governors often took advantage of an empty bed for a poor friend or relative. Although Lord Sheffield might ask: 'Can you as an extra favour introduce the mother into that nice place called Guy's',[3] most people were desolate to find themselves behind those dreaded walls. The chances of survival were poor. The danger of cross-infection was very great, and when the ominous word gangrene was whispered the patients 'gave themselves up for lost'.[4] (It was because people were so afraid of going into hospital that the Fever Hospital where Bright subsequently worked was called 'The House of Recovery' by the authorities.) In any case those that were admitted into Guy's were almost invariably too ill to benefit, coming too late for anyone to do much for them. Bright makes this point often in his case histories, which he wrote up daily.

But he cared much for those who suffered, and was worried at the ease with which he came to accept the cries and moans, the squalor and distress. He tried to see it all as part of a doctor's life, just as he accepted his own lack of leisure and sleep as part of his training. He concealed his feelings in the few letters he wrote to Ham Green at this period, telling nothing of the despair and despondency he must have experienced. Once to Phoebe he revealed his characteristic diffidence, when he confessed that he was often muddled in his thinking, that he dreaded to be confronted with a patient in the admission room 'where the name of the malady is unfamiliar to me and is described in terms which carries little meaning to my mind'. So he was working hard, he said, to learn how the body worked in health, while Dr Babington showed him the ways disease could disturb its harmony, for 'It is mortifying to know but vaguely the form and situation of an organ Dr Babington is talking about: hearing of its perturbations before I even know how it functions normally'.

It was Bright's affectionate habit to attribute his love of medicine to the influence of this wise and much loved physician. Dr Babington had been at Guy's for a long time. He was a father figure, with enormous charm, who gave the impression of being in league with the patient. He had impeccable manners, and in this he set an example to the surgical side, who were well known for their rude, rough and callous attitude. He was strict with his own pupils, insisting that they removed their hats on entering the wards, that they washed their hands and trimmed their nails; that they should – with a nod of the head – acknowledge every nurse and every working menial, just as every patient had to be shown all possible consideration. Once, it was said, when a surgeon heard one of his own students say to the patient 'Turn over, if you please', he laughed aloud. 'Surely', he said, 'you must have been a pupil of Dr Babington'.[5] The staff loved him for his gentle, caring ways, his simplicity of manner and his true humility. The patients loved him enough to waver and rally when on the brink of death, and when frightened became as wax in his hands. The governors, the Court of Committee and the College of Physicians loved him for the laughter he brought into their stuffy lives.

There was a succession of other interesting men at Guy's at this time, whose lectures made learning a positive pleasure. William Allen and Alexander Marcet taught Chemistry and Natural Philosophy. Shy Mr Cline shared the Anatomy classes with Astley Cooper, John Haighton taught both Midwifery and Physiology, while in the Practice of Medicine, besides Dr Babington, there was Dr Curry, an Irishman, who held the attention of all with his flowing speech and a wig that kept slipping off his head. A few hesitated about paying fees to hear Dr Cholmeley on the Theory of Medicine, while every sacrifice was made to attend the anatomy classes held by Astley Cooper.

What an extraordinarily attractive and stimulating man he must have been. He eclipsed them all. With his close-fitting buckskin knee-breeches, fine silk stockings, shining top-boots and silver buckles, worn to accentuate the shapeliness of his legs; with his snow-white cuffs and frilled shirt front – he was a dandy without a dandy's conceit. His lectures were more like a conversation than the conventional discourse. Looking benignly down, speaking with a broad Norfolk twang, rubbing his nose with the back of his hand, he kept alive the interest of every listener as the structure and functions of the body were clearly revealed. As an operator he was bold, quick and skilful; as a demonstrator in the dissecting room, he was patient, helpful and droll. As an entertainer in the little hut attached to his house at St Mary's Axe he was never challenged: here he fascinated all by his loquacity over the bodies of dead animals – whether it be rat, elephant, London sparrow or pet monkey belonging to a foreign sailor. When invited, Bright spent many an odd evening there; after the six o'clock round of the wards, required of him as physician's clerk, he was often to be seen rushing across the bridge.

Bright's interest in pathology had already been awakened at Edinburgh, but it was under Astley Cooper that he first began to grasp the possible importance of morbid anatomy in the understanding of disease. Pathology was to absorb him completely. Every organ that was put before him he examined and investigated in meticulous detail. It must have been with the same sense of the miraculous that as a geologist he had observed pieces of rock, tracing the delicate threads of imbedded minerals, that he now traced the capillaries in a section of liver, or scanned a valve in the vein of a leg or the larger ones of the heart. He spent much time at the drawing board, too, taking infinite pains in following such things as the convolutions of the brain, the organized tissues of the body, or the abnormal environments of a tumour. He would handle and paint in water colours the contours of a normal organ and then illustrate that same organ in its diseased state. And it was now, at the end of the year 1811, that he first drew a granular kidney. Though he looked at it with none of the understanding he was later to acquire, it seems that he carried its odd appearance for ever afterwards at the back of his mind.

Theory took up a small portion of Bright's day; lectures on midwifery started at an early hour in the morning and others followed. At 11 a.m. Bright reported to Dr Stocker at the dispensary and they walked the hospital together. Surgical and medical cases were mixed in the same wards, so little happened that escaped their notice, though surgical cases were none of their concern. Twice a week Bright awaited the arrival of Dr Babington's carriage at the steps of the Colonnade. On Saturdays physicians and surgeons came together and went in pairs to particular cases for joint consultation.[6] Hopeful of instruction, the pupils accompanied them in a stream – surgical pupils easily outnumbering the handful of aspiring physicians crowding round the beds, laughing and talking, quite regardless of the feelings or condition of the patients. As the days went on and the routine work became more familiar Bright began to blossom. His work was noticed by other members of the staff. He was soon recognized as the sharpest of observers, and got noted for 'his indisputable dedication to work . . . He is painstakingly honest and reports nothing that he has not noted himself.'[7] He remained always quiet, collected and courteous, entirely occupied with what he was doing. The shy and awkward manner that had once so dismayed his father was now concealed by his pertinent interest in all his activities.

It was not long before Benjamin Harrison, the Treasurer, having watched his progress and heard from Dr Stocker of his abilities, suggested that he was sufficiently qualified to dispense medical drugs and preparations. It was also about this time – 10 December 1810 – that he was elected a member of Guy's Physical Society, famous for the renowned scientists like Jenner who came to read their papers. He was proposed by Dr Laird and seconded by Dr Curry. This was an unusual distinction for a pupil only just into the third year of his profession and in his first year at Guy's. As for his proposer, little is known of Dr James Laird. One gets an impression of a lonely, kindly figure, who died comparatively young. He flits in and out of the Bright correspondence and was a frequent visitor to Ham Green, using an attic there to store some of his belongings. He seems to have kept a benevolent eye on Bright, both at Guy's and later at the Caley Street Dispensary, dragging him, too, for 'night rambles near the river'.

At first Bright attended few meetings of the Society and was 'fined for his absences'. But at last, and with some curiosity, the senior members attended a meeting in January to see what sort of paper this dilatory new member would read at his inauguration. How grateful Bright must have been for the lessons in oratory he had received at Edinburgh, for he acquitted himself triumphantly. He chose the subject of blood-letting, which had occupied his mind for some time. He could not reconcile himself to the idea that it was necessary in every case of illness. It was used to an excess as a cure, he said; only in certain cases of heart failure and in an acute lung disease when the sudden obstruction to the passage of the blood threw an increased strain on the heart was it justifiable to take away more than a few drams. In brain cases it 'should be adopted with caution', if at all, the application of leeches being sufficient. He stirred up enough interest to occupy the attention of the Society for all the four meetings held the following February. By March there were others besides Dr Babington prophesying that in no time at all they would see him on a lecture room platform.

It is not clear at what point Bright transferred his loyalties to the surgical side to gain experience. It must have been only for a short time, and if he was not entrusted to carry the box containing the applications for wounds as a dresser then he was a pupil assisting a senior dresser. Anyway, he soon became proficient in carrying out all surgical procedures, such as venesection, opening abscesses, and extracting teeth.

Shut away at Guy's Bright lived a life of great intensity. On the rare occasion when he felt free of his duties, he was never to be found in the customary haunts of the medical student, sharing snuff, black tobacco or a glass of porter at The George or The Ship and Shovel. The life most medical students led held no attraction for him. He was often shocked by their behaviour and was too conventional in his attire to emulate the artistic – wearing shirts open at the neck like Byron. The majority were wild and frustrated, being mostly under no jurisdiction and no set curriculum such as that enjoyed by the United Borough Hospitals; even if they were attached to a private school of anatomy, few teachers were really interested enough to guide them – and those that were had too many hundreds herded together to provide any individual attention. Most students lived in lodging houses under miserable conditions and the only common ground for professional discussions was the local tavern, where they bragged about what they saw and did behind hospital doors; or sometimes the dissecting room – and this, too, became a place of ribaldry, bred by familiarity with the objects they handled.

When he saw Bright's white face, Dr Babington tried to inveigle him on to the bowling ground or to join others of his age at quoits or cricket. He was himself no mean athlete and a good boxer. He was planning an elaborate gymnasium at West Green, his country home in Tottenham; and he liked nothing better than to share his own enthusiasm over it with his students. Bright was too much touched by the warmth of the elder man's concern to refuse outright, but he always had some legitimate excuse in the end. But where the Geological Society was concerned he did his best to attend, for geology still excited him. He had devoted several hours of the Christmas break (in 1810) to sorting out his geological curiosities. They presented him, he said, 'with a plentiful feast'. We can guess how he dusted, polished and arranged them before handing them over to the Society sometime in February 1811. According to the Transactions, not only did he give the selection once collected by him from the Liverpool area, but those discovered around Bristol on his teenage excursions with Holland. Then, that summer, he presented the Society with duplications of his Icelandic material. At the same time, on learning that Sir William Hooker had returned from Iceland (in 1809) with an incomplete collection of flora and fauna, he presented the grateful man with his own botanical collection.[8] Other than mentioning this to his father, Bright gives no picture of the encounter, neither can I find in any of the letters a description of a Friday evening in May the following year, 1812, when Bright not only met Hooker again, but Sir John Stanley, who had gone to Iceland in his own yacht in 1789. It was at Spring Grove, the small and beautiful country home of Sir Joseph Banks, and it must have been a delightful dinner with the four travellers discussing an island of shared enigmas. 'Possibly the four may never meet at the same table again, there are so many chances of their dispersal.'[9]

He and Dr Babington became two of the most conspicuous figures in the bright and animated company of the Geological Society. Bright read several papers that year. The first one, on the strata of the neighbourhood of Bristol, was informative, if rather dull. He had written much of it in his youth, when the environment of his home had been a favourite place of geological study. In July, he read another paper; this one excited more attention, being on the mineral products collected from Iceland. He confessed to have borrowed some of Sir George Mackenzie's observations, but he added his own, carefully accurate, giving his own evidence and avoiding the established dogmas and controversies of the day.

Otherwise Bright had little social life. He kept in touch with relatives – the Heywoods, at St James's Place, and John Birch, an active Member of Parliament, who was always complaining that his nephew's studies came between them. 'We have not seen Richard here for some days past,' he would tell his sister-in-law Sarah Bright. 'He is always a most welcome guest but he is so much occupied and his attention is so unremittingly with the profession he has chosen that we cannot expect to see too much of him. Depend upon it, if we live a few years, we shall see him near the top of the tree.'

Some time during that summer of 1811 Francis Jeffrey was in London and invited Bright to Duke Street. Of all his Edinburgh friends, Jeffrey was the one whose visits Bright welcomed most, but on this occasion the advocate waited, impatient, looking out of the window for quite a long time, reluctant to start breakfast on his own. 'Today, Dickie Bright not having come as promised, I went up to breakfast with Mr Simon and took him to see Lord Elgin's marbles,' he wrote to Marjory Morehead. One will never know what it was that stood in Bright's way, but there must have been repeated apologies and explanations on his eventual return to Edinburgh in October 1812, when he was invited to admire Jeffrey's new home at Hatton.

This time, Bright had to seek lodgings near the University, for the house in Hill Street was shut up. Jeffrey had gone off on a visit to America, leaving the care of his animals and the new house to the Moreheads. It was Bright's first experience of fending for himself and he did not care much for it. So he led a simple life, buying only the bare necessities, noting that tea, sugar and bread were costly, while beer, beef and butter were cheap.

Bright had now progressed more than half-way within the curriculum recognized as medical. The next stage was again theoretical rather than practical, and he was lucky enough to have some extremely able teachers.

There was Dr Gregory, who believed in vigorous treatments – purging powders and cold effusions, blisterings and emetics – and had definite ideas on fever and inflammations. There was the surgeon John Thompson, under whom Bright studied pathology and chemistry and with whom he made friends over the rare books in the University library. These two were friends of Jeffrey's, and there must have been many an occasion when Bright found himself sharing the same table as these three eloquent and learned men. There was the early morning rush to the botanical gardens at Leith for the botany lessons with Dr Rutherford. He was Walter Scott's uncle, and had discovered nitrogen. The elderly gout-ridden man took classes also in Clinical Medicine, making it clear in his beautiful language that he abhorred blood-letting and believed in medicines containing iron. Again he attended the lectures of Andrew Duncan; this time it was for Medical Jurisprudence, into which Duncan poured all his love of German literature, which gave Bright the urge to teach himself the language that he too might one day be able to converse in it. Dr Home took Materia Medica; he was a rare man who gave up much of his own time to help students become acquainted with drugs and their uses.

Bright must have missed the companionship of Holland, but he was so absorbed in his books that his absence was barely realized. He mixed with many interesting people at this time, like John Davy, Dr Beddoes' son John, Thomas Addison, and the dynamic Robert Knox. He spent time in 'two comfortable rooms in the Infirmary' with Marshall Hall, a physician's clerk. There was always a lot they wanted to talk about, to do with 'the many interesting cases under his command'. There was John Leech, too. 'This promising young man', Bright told his father, 'will be the first entomologist in the kingdom. It is wonderful with what ardour he pursues his science. I believe he is going to London with Sowerby to engage in a book upon the subject.' With him, Bright indulged his capacity for enjoying the naturalist's world, and together they went in pursuit of insects. Cramond apparently provided the perfect hunting ground, a long time being spent under the lime trees, on which 'every honey-dripping tassel had its clinging bee'. Like Bright, Leech instinctively eschewed society, but there were odd occasions when they met up at one of Mrs Fletcher's evening parties. It was at a concert at her house that he met John Constable, his future publisher, John Murray the advocate, 'already bringing much of Scottish law out of chaos', and Francis Horner. He was quite surprised, he told his brother Benjamin, when writing to him, to find that people were quite pleased 'to engage me in conversation . . . I get a certain notice for having come fresh from Astley Cooper's operating sessions . . . such is the lustre that surrounds his name.' Many of the older professors remembered him as one of the most popular students in the University. Bright came into a bit of glory, too, when Sir George Mackenzie's book, *Travels in Iceland*, was reviewed by Robert Southey in the *Edinburgh Review*. In it Holland got praise for his 'great ingenuity and research', but though Bright's 'lively account' of the excursion up Snaëfell Jokul was quoted in its entirety, Southey admonished him for not stating an opinion as to whether the perpetual snows on the northern mountains were just a covering or a large glacier. The book was a bestseller and by now in a new edition.

He resigned his seat regretfully from the Speculative Society. 'I found it impossible to pay any attention to the subjects,' he wrote to his father, 'and therefore could reap no advantages from it . . . Friday night I shall read two long papers of other persons' expositions at the Royal Medical Society – probably we shall do more than sit out the night [sic].' He was now President, and later contributed to it a good paper on gangrene.

On Saturday mornings he made his way to Dr John Gordon's School of Anatomy, where the wonders of the human body gripped him anew and every intricate detail of its machinery had to be mastered. Gordon, a warm and simple man, was an exceptional teacher; Bright became one of his devoted disciples, and talked about him long after the young man's death. Saturday afternoons were set aside for pleasure, depending much upon his inclinations. One Saturday, for instance, 'there was to be a great sale of valuable paintings in Edinburgh today but I did not see them'. Another was the 'day for celebrating the memory of Fox but I was not Whig enough to attend'.

Bright remained as much a part of the Moreheads' home circle as if he had been still their lodger. It was in the familiar drawing room, after their return from Hatton, 'with Mr Morehead reading a book and Mrs Morehead asleep on the sofa and myself comfortably by the fireside awaiting Jeffrey to take me with him to John Murray' that Bright wrote one of his letters to his father. Early in 1813 Richard Bright had written several times to ask about his progress and his plans for the future. He always showed great interest in the lives of his sons, but it was this doctor son of his with whom he had the greatest empathy. He was the one most in touch with scientific friends, the one most immersed in the subjects of natural history of which he was so passionately fond. 'How far I must go back in order to give you a continued series of my proceedings I do not know,' he began, 'but I know I must go back a great way.'

I have just dined with the Moreheads and take this opportunity to make my peace with you . . . I find competition for anything in the shape of situations in Medicine is so great that it becomes necessary to look sharp and to look a little into futurity . . . I have no doubt of the correctness of Sand's opinion as it respects dispensary practice. I am sure that as soon as a man has learnt what he ought to observe, it is the best school which he can find and I therefore hope for some time to give myself up to it.

But he could not agree with Sand so fully about the relationship between medicine and surgery:

The two professions are the same and indivisible. It is quite impossible to show the line between them, so much do they run into and depend upon each other. I conceive that the internal and external parts of our frame are regulated by the same laws, and what process on the outside we may see openly, we may infer from analogy to be going on within. Is the surgeon to have only the advantage of these external manifestations? Must the physician content himself only with conjecture and hypothesis? For my part I am very fond of seeing, and I never feel so well satisfied with myself as when I think I understand a surgical case.

By March he was working hard on his doctoral thesis. At the same dark hour of the early morning, when some of his acquaintances were abroad stealing along some graveyard wall to snatch a body for the dissecting room table, Bright was already up and studying his notebook. In its pages he had put down his observations on erysipelas, or St Anthony's fire, as it was known amongst the poor, a subject that had long interested him. Every case he had seen was described, and as time went on he put others in, dropping the subject under pressure of work, picking it up again, and adding to it from time to time. Now he took it up seriously again. Erysipelas is an infection of the skin characterized by an odd demarcated swollen area, red and shiny, with accompanying fever and malaise. It is caused by haemolytic streptococci and the site of entry can be as minute as a pinprick. Nowadays the condition is rare, since it is instantly treatable with penicillin or the sulphonamides. But in Bright's day such conditions were common, as toxins freed into the system caught hold and progressed unchecked. The course of the disease varied with the organ involved, the depth of the infection, and the direction in which it spread. Germs were certainly known of in Bright's generation – the Dutchman Leönwenhoet had described bacteria some time past, noting their multiplication in man, in diarrhoea and in putrefaction – but the science of bacteriology was unknown. There were no highly developed optical instruments such as are used in our laboratories today. The germ then was at much the same stage of discovery as the virus is today.

Bright was young when he first noted that erysipelas was possibly contagious: a careless nurse exposed to the disease carried it to another patient; a wife 'attending her husband very carefully, up with him for three nights in succession, felt feverish and I soon observed a swelling near the angle of her left jaw'. But it was not until he worked with midwifery cases at Guy's that he became wholly interested. Under Dr Haighton's instruction he saw how amongst women in the puerperium, erysipelas was more virulent and spread more quickly. Attendants who did not bother about being clean, failing to wash their hands as they went from one patient to another, 'fed the fire'.

To show that erysipelas was contagious, and that ideally cases should be isolated to prevent the spread of infection, was the purpose of Bright's thesis. Seeking material to support his arguments, he haunted the wards of the Infirmary, questioned his superiors, wrote asking his father to probe the Bristol Hospital Committee about instances where the disease passed from one to another, and wrote to more experienced doctors with whom he was acquainted – never failing to gain their assistance. Dr John Estlin found it common in Bristol amongst the fishermen and the dockers who loaded infected meat. Dr Henry saw it in the textile workers of Manchester, in spite of the new public health programme. York hospital was full of cases, and Phoebe, who was working in the Clifton dispensary, gave him a singular account of the 'misfortunes of medicine in Bristol with its plague of erysipelas'. But Bright was disappointed to find that no one mentioned any means they employed to prevent its spread, other than fumigating and white-washing walls. Eventually Bright amassed sufficient material, working hard to get the manuscript off to a printer late that spring.

Thinking then of his future he marked out in his mind 'a delightful course of study'. He applied for three posts that were all becoming vacant. One was Marshall Hall's post as physician's clerk in the Infirmary; the second was suggested by an old school-fellow, Gold, who was leaving the Westminster lying in hospital; and the third was at the Lock Hospital. All his hopes and doubts and fears found their way on paper to Ham Green, and few letters are more diffident. Underestimating his abilities as was his wont, he warned his father that he did not think he would even get as far as an interview. All that mattered was to gain further experience: 'whatever post I get before I am fit will be more pain than pleasure, more trouble than profit'. He was despondent, too, over his chances of getting a place in the final examination, informing his father that an average of 200 students failed every year to get their degrees.

7
The Caley Street Dispensary
1814

Bright graduated on 13 September 1813 with his thesis on 'Contagious Erysipelas', and some time later he returned to Ham Green. His first step on leaving Edinburgh was a retrograde one. He had been accepted at the Lock Hospital but, having a year to wait before the post was vacant, he thought to graduate at Cambridge as well. That October, 1813, he went to Cambridge with his brother Henry, who was a Perle Fellow, and they resided at Peterhouse. Bright was 'vaguely excited'. And though he enjoyed nosing round the old colleges and gravel pits, collecting flints for his uncle Serjeant Sam, he found the library there to be 'flat and toneless' ('the access to books was delightful at Edinburgh'), while the poor curriculum was hardly compatible with his wish to progress. Finding it all academically undisciplined and tediously restrictive, he did not return for a second term. Instead, at Dr Laird's suggestion, he started a working year in January 1814 at Dr Bateman's 'excellent dispensary' in Caley Street.

Bright took lodgings in Bouverie Street, just a few minutes' walk from the Dispensary. He had only 'to shoot, bob and duck' across Fleet Street, the 'busiest street' in London, then walk up Chancery Lane to Caley Street. He was comfortably situated, in a place of good repute, and although there was no servant he was well attended by the landlady and her daughters. His weekly bill with rent, coal and candles (8s.), shoe-cleaning (5d.) washing (2s.) and Italian lessons (7s. 6d.) came to 'always at least £2.2' a week. Breakfast was the only meal taken at the lodging, and as far as he could discover, from his own experience and from asking others, it was not possible to get tea or dinner in London under three shillings. There was only one drawback: the landlady did not rise early enough in the morning to light a fire in his room, and as it was bitterly cold he made this a good excuse for not rising himself. This obliged him to sit up later at night, and a late hour for him was but 'moderately well spent'.

But he was pleased with his room; it was large, with a round table on which to spread out his papers, and several shelves. There was little space for purposes of dissection, but his brother Henry had offered a small back room in his Temple Chambers. 'I have been doing nothing in the way of comparative anatomy,' he wrote to his father, 'Occupying my time more profitably . . . I can get subjects without difficulty . . . I saw two very fine specimens in a shop a few days ago and they asked 2s. a bird which I thought very reasonable . . . I am much obliged to Phoebe and Eliza for the present they sent me of the goat's head, it is a very nice addition to my sculls [sic].'

He was also surrounding himself with books. 'It will be by no means a pocket library, I think about eighteen or twenty folio volumes . . . for there are many books that a physician absolutely must have . . . though he, as absolutely, cannot read them.' He already had Galen, Hippocrates, Bonelius and Hoffman, Paracelsus's tomes on *One Hundred and Fourteen Experiments and Cures*, Lawrence's translation of Blumenhael's *Comparative Anatomy*, and books by Sydenham, Lommins and Lancisins. Now he wanted to buy books on scurvy, fevers, consumption, *Muscular Action* by Pugh, *The Anatomy of the Heart and Brain* by Ramsey, Astley Cooper's *Hernias and Fractures*, *Morbid Anatomy* by Baillie, and a book on *Fractures and Dislocation*. He thought that Adam's book on *Hereditary Disease* might be interesting in view of King George III's blindness and supposed mental disorders. Wishing to become proficient in languages and to improve his self-taught French and German, other books were added to his list of purchases. Books on religion, too, for he had kept the faith of his early life and was interested in religious philosophy. Bright, like his brother Benjamin, was a frequenter of bookstalls, often hanging around hoping to look over the expected new consignment. After consulting many catalogues, he decided in the end that it would be best to leave the list to the interested Dr Carpenter, who was in touch with all the booksellers in Bristol: he would not only get them at cost price but would see to their shipment.

Dispensaries played a regular and important part in the medical education of postgraduates, providing as they did unrivalled opportunities for the study of diseases. Unfortunately little has been handed down about them. Situated in the big cities, they were charity clinics sponsored in most cases by eminent men.

Bright's uncle, John Birch, was a subscriber to Caley Street, and as Richard Bright later wrote requesting a list, no doubt he also decided to contribute. Dispensaries served large communities, providing medical treatment, midwifery, drugs and advice, referring cases to surgeons where necessary. As much depended upon the calibre of the doctor in charge, some had standards higher than others. Bright himself had a poor opinion of some of the doctors who worked in them:

> Dispensary Doctors have great facility in giving names, they see a case for two months and give it a name in their catalogue to impress ... see to what absurdities this has led our friends at Clifton – out of 22 patients in consumption (which nothing can cure) they have cured 15 ... and it is singular if they have had two cases of catalepsy in one year ... it is a rare disease.

The Caley Street Dispensary was an orderly, harmonious place. Dr Bateman, who ran it, was extraordinarily knowledgeable about medicine generally, but on eruptive (skin) diseases of all kinds he was a rare authority. He was known to give lurid descriptions at the most inappropriate moments, most especially at table, when at the appearance of the first dish this usually reserved man would describe pimples, crusts, flaky skins and pus-filled bullae.

Bright quickly caught the rhythm of the place. Besides himself and Dr Laird, the physician, there was a dispenser, an apothecary, a surgeon and an accoucheur. Under the guidance of Dr Bateman he learned to recognize different fevers, which seemed to appear in cycles, and the many varieties of skin complaints, 'which cause such discomfort and aggravation unknown in hospital practice'. Under Dr Laird, a competent physician, Bright discovered the true extent of disease associated with poverty and overcrowding. Work commenced at noon, when Bright faced a slow and steady file of patient people. The afternoon was taken up with home visits, and the day ended at 5 p.m. when he had to submit a full report to his seniors. Most patients were treated there, a few were sent to hospital, and many too ill to attend were visited in their own homes. No patient was ever refused admittance, and some came from long distances and not from the area at all.

Bright found himself thrown like a swimmer into this baffling current. The district was an unknown world and, ever apprehensive, he struck out into an area of spreading streets – north to Russell Square, south to the river, west to St Martin's in the Fields and east to St Paul's. Though he got accustomed to the agglomeration of narrow lanes he never got used to some of the houses where the patients lived, and was always shocked and surprised to find behind the imposing façades a derelict, paupers' metropolis.

As that winter of 1814 was the severest ever recorded the Dispensary was busy. Cases of bronchitis and pneumonia, always prevalent in winter, had reached epidemic level. The waiting room rapidly filled up with patients and some who could not come by themselves were almost 'carried on the arms of another'. Bright must have seen many cases that he could not immediately understand, and have feared that his view might be only a guess or a 'spot-on diagnosis'. Bright observed each chest case with meticulous attention. These cases distressed him greatly, and he did all he could to relieve his patients' lack of breath. Inexperienced as he was, he showed great resourcefulness where treatment was concerned. He advocated oxygen and was thought a crank because of it. Instead of the cylinder we have today, he tried a pig's bladder full of oxygen, noting then a change in the colour of the patient's face and for a short time 'there were longer and deeper respirations'. Or if opening a window was not feasible, as in the case of Mr Wade, he 'diffused the air immediately surrounding the bed by my heating manganese in an iron retort to which I attached a pipe of sufficient length to reach the patient', but it was too late to save him. He tried it on Cathie Duncan, a local eccentric who plied wares of bread and crabs. She was scared of the contraption at first, but then admitted its beneficial effects. She was to gain Bright fame some years later with his marvellous description of her case and his drawings of her tubercular lungs. The oxygen revived old John Highal enough 'to produce a temporary excitement during which the eyes opened'. But he had too much fluid to allow full expansion of the lung and died in Bright's arms thirty hours later.

It was as a result of the autopsy on John Highal that Bright was able to publish abroad what he had been observing for some time: that this particular winter, with its icy air and stifling fog, had a peculiar effect upon the lung. The inflammatory condition found in both the lining and the air cells showed a form of bronchitis, quite distinct from pneumonia; in pneumonia the actual substance of one or other of the lobes of the lung is attacked.

When it came to examining the skin cases he worked hard to identify each one, though he was never excited by them. He studied those that were caused by ill health, recognizing those that were influenced by emotional states, or by irritants, and taking infinite pains to heighten morale. Doctors in those days were all psychologists, and Bright was no exception, always using the right words of encouragement and common sense, often changing despair to hopeful acceptance. The patients in the district all got to know this young doctor, who always paid the keenest attention to the smallest detail, the simplest complaint.

Bright exchanged many letters with his father at this time. While they reveal his vivacity of character and his conscientiousness about his profession, on the subject of his patients he was amazingly reticent. Instead he wrote about London. That winter it was particularly beautiful, and he got carried away writing about the mist-shrouded spires, the threatening skies, the ice-encrusted horse-troughs, the chimneys shapeless with snow and the few lovely moments of sun flung into an afternoon. For days on end it snowed and wagons were unable to move. In all the important streets workmen 'were employed in quarrying and carrying off in carts ice and snow which has put a stop to commerce'. Walking with difficulty on his rounds he saw not a single carriage. On his way to Guy's he noticed that when 'the water rises at high tide the ice breaks away leaving vast islands floating about the ships', while on his return at low tide, the river at London Bridge was 'spread like a white sheet connecting the two sides of the river to-gether', and on it were people and bivouacs and fires of steadily burning brilliance. 'I enjoy the novelty and beauty of the sight and never think of the misery and inconvenience which must accompany the cause.'

Much of his spare time, he told his father, was spent on learning languages. He sat down at his table, putting his watch down before him as he started. Ever since the time when Dr Carpenter had insisted on a timetable, from sheer force of habit Bright had daily planned out a course of study, and because he did not deviate from it he managed to accomplish an astonishing amount. In Italian 'he had overcome his first difficulties', and he was now concentrating on German. Comparative anatomy was once again occupying some of his time. When he was not haunting the home of Astley Cooper, he was attending lectures at the Windmill, where he was fascinated by Charles Bell's account of the nervous system. One night he went to the Geological Society – 'to renew his acquaintance with Dr Roget'; the next to Guy's Medical Society, where 'I generally talk, tomorrow I shall treat them by reading a case'. Otherwise, he had 'great satisfaction in having my evening to myself.' But he did see people.

He saw Leech, who had graduated at the same time as Bright, and had now put aside his insects to run the new zoology department of the British Museum. He saw Dr Rolfe who, like Cuvier in Paris, was working on the correlation of organs in animals. He saw Joseph Banks, who talked about Iceland and the 'interdependence of various parts of an animal's frame'. The chief wonder of one particular evening spent with him was

> 'a box full of a peculiar species of mouse which has been for a long time committing the most dreadful depredations on the trees in the King's forests in Hampshire. The damage was accredited to hares and rabbits, and a thousand other things, until these mice were found in the act of barking the trees. Thirty thousand were very soon caught in holes cut in their pathway. They are a species scarcely before known, or at least very rare in England – it is not Mus but Averline – or some such name like this. They seem more like rats without tails, and large heads, ears hidden in the fur.'

He disliked eating his evening meal alone and usually looked about for some companion, 'for of all the solitary things in the world, to be in a room full of persons talking to each other and to know no-one, is the most solitary'. His favourite eating place was somewhere near the Exchange, where his brother Henry often joined him. Sometimes he ate with James MacAdam of Bristol, a family friend and of road-surfacing fame, once with his brother Robert.

It was rare for the three brothers to be together, and they made the most of it on this occasion. Robert had just graduated at Glasgow University, hoping to enter the family business. He was on a visit of reconnaissance as a possible apprentice to the firm of Anthony Gibbs & Co. He had come unwillingly encumbered with Ham Green asparagus, which was to be delivered to Dr Babington. It was an embarrassment to the three of them, and for some days they did not know what to do with it. At Bright's suggestion 'they sent Robert to the Market' to see whether it was sufficiently scarce to make a present, and finding that it was very rare indeed, to be had neither for love nor money, it was despatched post-haste to the Doctor. Telling his father about this in a letter, Bright went on:

> Though a question has since arisen in the Court of Conscience whether we ought not to have considered it in the light of a marketable product of the farm, and raised two or three guineas

upon it in Covent Garden. The question was however indignantly refuted by the Court, and the Parties stand honourably acquitted – in truth there seems to be a little prejudice in this decision of the Court. A gentleman is allowed to sell his oxen, his sheep, his grain, his grass, but his Sparrow-Grass let no man sell – his apples but not his pine *apples*. However, I know a host of such prejudices; and where prejudice ends or reason begins it will be found no easy task to determine.

Bright had many family obligations. He visited Heywoods at St James's Place, where his aunt was unwell with abscesses 'forming in her ear', whence he felt unqualified to give his opinion or advice. He went to the Birches at Bedford Place to celebrate a wedding anniversary, and saw how the Ham Green gifts of a tea-service and flowers were appreciated; the flowers had arrived 'in good order and good spirits', but had 'drooped as soon as they found themselves in the frosty air of London'. The young Birches thought that the gardens at Ham Green 'must look very pretty with such nice flowers, and of course we had to assure them that you had no magic power to make lilacs blossom in the open air amidst frost and snow'.

By spring he was restless. His brother Henry had said that it was a pity at his age not to travel, now that Europe was open: Henry Holland kept writing and describing Italy; Andrew Baillie, a contemporary from his Edinburgh days, told him about schemes afoot for furthering medical education in Germany; articles in *The Times* constantly reminded him about the needs of the British wounded in France, while the medical journals were full of the new initiatives in the treatment of diseases which the conditions of the Peninsular War were producing. The more he thought about his own affairs, the more he must have felt as if he were caught in a huge net, unable to disentangle himself from the meshes. His life was already planned out for years ahead: a further year at the Dispensary would be followed by two years at the Lock Hospital, and if all things 'should fall out as he had scarcely a right to hope' he would then probably succeed Dr Laird at the Dispensary. If he wished to escape from the net then May 1814 to June 1815 was the only possible period. He was quick to put his ideas into practice. He immediately committed his plans to paper and sent them off to his father. 'It is my wish to extend myself beyond the limits of our little island', he wrote,

'for when I once settle, until I arrive at a height in the profession

88

which I can never anticipate, the town in which I live must prescribe my limit . . . I do not know how far it has ever come into your mind of late . . . that advantages, both real and in the estimation of the world, were to be derived from my visiting as a student some of the great continental schools of medicine . . . It is to me a very desirable object, and to see as I pass all that these countries can show me . . . It will be a means of acquiring the languages of these countries and for the general expansion of mind, and the delightful remembrances which remain our pleasant companions through life . . .

As far as the expense of such a trip was concerned, he was confident that 'a certain sum of money which you have chosen to call mine, I mean the product of the Icelandic journey, would completely cover the difference between a year spent in the way I mention and a year spent in London . . .'

If there was any subject that really distressed Bright, it was money. He was sensitive about being dependent upon his father, though he was not a proud man. But at this stage in his life he had to have his father's help. He kept a careful note of his bills, and each time he sent his accounts to his father he begged that the letter should be destroyed. 'I hope you will burn this letter together with all I have ever written to you with accounts in them. I detest the subject . . .'

Once committed in his mind to this new course, Bright felt better. He was relieved to find his father catching his mood – though he did insist on talking to Lowbridge about it, and to Dr Lovell (the family GP), while Bright must see that it was all right with Dr Bateman and that the 'Dispensary business would not lie too heavily upon Dr Laird'. Otherwise, he saw it as a wonderful project, even hoping that it might make his son more interested in current events. Richard Bright himself plunged immediately into the business of map-reading, hunting up addresses and writing endless letters of introduction. This kept him from worrying over the ill-health of his wife, who was suffering, according to Bright, 'from nameless feelings and unconnected symptoms', and though he felt that they might not mean anything now, 'they might become of greater importance'. He therefore advised that Dr Laird should be called in in consultation with the family doctor, Dr Lovell.

Bright's earnestness about anything that he undertook led him always into extra trouble; he was like his father in this respect. This time, having decided that he was sufficiently fluent in Italian, and that his German had improved, he changed his lodgings in order to assimilate better French – though he did this with a great deal of reluctance. He hated changes and unfamiliar surroundings; besides he was comfortable and settled where he was. His proposed new abode, being near Russell Square, was still in the Dispensary neighbourhood though it did mean a longer walk to Caley Street. But the chance of lodging with a French emigré was too tempting to ignore – and it was on the recommendation of Edward Kenyon, a lawyer friend of Henry's, who had himself benefited by Abbé Monsieur Marsnet's excellent tuition. So it was the middle of March when Bright had to face 'all the horrors of changing my habitation'.

He was settled and soon he discovered that Edward Kenyon had been right when he told him that he would 'observe a cleanliness which is seldom discovered in any French house'. Everything was surprising: the demeanour of the servant, Madame's spotless apron, the quiet manners and speech of the Abbé, and the piano music tinkling through the house.

Meanwhile he spent all his spare moments studying French, but when Phoebe reprimanded him for not writing his letters home in French we find him preoccupied with other matters: 'Tell Phoebe I am too unsettled, too busy, and the lessons with the Abbé are not proceeding as well as they did'. For it was now May and time was pressing – 'I cannot seek out Dr Randolph or Mr Ward today . . .' he wrote to his father. 'Sir Joseph Banks promised me last Sunday evening that he would give me two letters to Vienna and I hope to get introduced to Madame de Staël soon.' It seems that his mother's health had improved, and he wrote that he was 'truly glad always to hear of Mrs Bright's recovery'.

That May he was too busy to entertain a young cousin from Liverpool and had to leave Henry to take him sightseeing. Nor could he accompany them to see Kean, which was a disappointment for he dearly loved 'the magical spell' of a theatre – 'that wonderful stage'.

Then, suddenly, as his departure became imminent, Bright found himself caught up in a whirl of activity, passing from one influential person to another, attending a levée, getting a quite unnecessary passport. For Richard Bright of Ham Green was not having his son going anywhere unprepared or unwelcomed; he insisted that he should get a passport, finding that through his friend Francis Horner it could be obtained with no difficulty. He took infinite pains, too, in making contacts on his son's behalf. He got letters of introduction through Lord Sheffield, his old friend in the Board of Trade, and he wrote to all his European colleagues in the field of science and geology. Bright himself was surprised by the messages of good wishes, advice and information which reached him from all who knew him – even from people who did not know him all that well, like Mr Wardrop the surgeon, who told him about his experiences in Austrian hospitals. While some of his patients, hearing that their young doctor had a new excitement in his mundane job, wrote to ask that some expression of their best wishes should be conveyed to him.

Bright was soon able to write to his father,

> I do begin to think that everything will be very straight for me . . . I have been very busy in running about after people who tell me to come again. I breakfast tomorrow with Sir Walter [Scott] – this morning with Sir Joseph, who asked me what he should say in his letters of introduction. I did not know what to say but told him I had devoted my life to medicine and had made great acquirements in Minerals and had been in Iceland.

Bright thought it important before departure to confirm his appointment for the following year at the Lock Hospital. So, accompanied by Dr Laird, he called upon Mr John Pearson, who 'had not in anyway forgotten his engagement . . . and when I spoke of the possibility of my going on to Vienna for a part of the intervening time – his opinion was exactly in conformity with others that the advantage would be considerable'.

Bright had thought so long about going abroad for further medical education that he must have found it difficult to believe he was really going. The date of his departure is not known, but it was some time in June of that same year – 1814 – when, accompanied by a servant, he left Bristol and all that was dear to him.

8
Europe
1814–1815

It took Bright several hundred pages of a quarto-sized book to record his travels;[1] even then, a mere glance of his route on the map is enough to show that he left out more than he put in. He proved to be a wonderful traveller; his eyes were sharp, his appetite quickened at every mile; his head turned at every corner. He loitered contentedly, always on the look out for something rare and beautiful.

When Bright visited the Continent in 1814, Napoleon had just been exiled to Elba. Louis XVIII was on the throne of France, while Holland, Belgium and Germany were rejoicing in their new-found freedom. Bright never took much interest in politics and leaves the subject alone, but he does portray the restlessness that was everywhere. Every day he faced refugees trudging along the road and soldiers who had survived the horrors of war struggling back to their homes.

His first stop was Amsterdam, where with the help of a banker friend of his father's he completed the plan of his itinerary. As he went on to Rotterdam he learned about the reclaiming of land, the technical changes going on in the docks, where iron was replacing wood, the insect life of the peat dykes, and the birds that nested in the sand dunes. And he saw the Emperor of Russia, Tsar Alexander, in white chamois leather breeches and high boots, entering Rotterdam Cathedral to the 'thundering peals of the grand organ'.

He had a passion for medical experience, and wherever he went he visited the hospitals, introducing himself as a student and producing a letter of introduction. He studied for some time at Leyden, where there was a distinguished medical faculty. To Frankfurt then, and Leipzig, and, at last, Berlin. Coming from London, he was 'a kind of lion . . . for the English here are very popular'. The newly married Durnheims made a fuss of him.

It was through the Society for the Relief of Foreigners in Distress in London that Bright had met a clergyman of the German church, who had recommended to him this endearing Latin master. Professor

Durnheim taught at the nearby Gymnasium, and as neither he nor his young wife spoke English Bright was well pleased to lodge with them. A feeling of great respect bordering on affection developed between the three, and Bright's German improved quickly.

In Berlin he followed William Iffland, actor and playwright, to his grave; he discovered a second-hand copy of Adeley's celebrated German dictionary, which he was to treasure all his life; he met Dr Klaproth, small and shy, seer, philosopher and famous chemist, who had discovered the elements of uranium, zirconium, titanium and cerium, and who had in the shelves of his cupboards exquisite and rare objects in coloured glass; he saw Blumenbach's unique collection of skulls. When younger, Bright had made a prolonged study of this man's craniological work, and he was now glad of the opportunity to work in the post-mortem room of the hospital on the morbid changes of the brain. Under Professor Horn he also took the time to look systematically at the appearance of every organ of the body.

In Amorbach, a fashionable resort and a delightful old town, he met his sister Sally, who was studying German in a seminar for 'young ladies'. There, too, on a visit were Dr and Mrs Randolph, great friends of the Bright family. Dr Randolph had learned to love Saxony and its people when he was tutor to Frederica, Duchess of York, and was easily tempted back. The visit was an extremely happy one, and a letter from Ham Green announcing Benjamin's engagement to Elizabeth Heywood was an added joy.

'Even Sally's quietness was done away with when she opened the letter', wrote Mrs Randolph to Phoebe, 'your two doctors being on the mountains. We resolved to keep council till we all four assembled for I wanted to see dear Richard's face light upon receiving the news and we sent for a bottle of the very best Burgundy to drink all your healths.'

Bright had not intended to dawdle in Dresden, being impatient to get to Vienna, but he was captivated by the old town. He was quickly seized upon as a possible spokesman at the international congress taking place in Vienna, to represent 'that great and generous nation' – England, who would personally 'espouse their cause, preserve their national integrity and restore their own King'. It was difficult to extricate himself, until an amiable talkative local recognized Bright to be what he really was – just a student.

In Vienna, it was not long before Bright found himself in the centre of the stage – at the Imperial Palace or Bourg. Accompanied by a

Viennese gentleman with whom he had made a chance acquaintance, he went to an evening assembly. Here were gathered together monarchs, princes and foreign ministers; the proud Hapsburgs of Austria, the resentful Hohenzollerns of Prussia, the aristocrats of Britain. Round them revolved the hopes and fears of smaller states. Bright gazed with astonishment at those who were to remodel Europe.

Never was an assembly less ceremonious; everyone wore his hat; many, till the room became heated, their great-coats; and no one pretended to appear in evening dress, except a few Englishmen . . . My companion squeezed my arm, as we passed a thin figure with sallow shrunken features, of mild expression, with a neck stiff, bending a little forwards, and walking badly. 'That is our Emperor.' I shook my head and smiled. He was alone, and dressed like the rest. 'Pray allow me to doubt a little till I have some further proof.' – 'There, do you see that little man with white hair, a pale face, and aquiline nose? He was almost pushed down as he passed the corner, – that is the King of Denmark.' Again I shook my head in disbelief. 'Here the Emperor of Russia approaches.' I looked up, and found the information true. His fine manly form, his round and smiling countenance, and his neat morning dress, were not to be mistaken; they were the same which, some months before, I had seen in Holland. I soon recognised the tall form, the solemn and grave features, of the King of Prussia; and afterwards seeing these two in familiar conversation with the two monarchs whose pretensions I had disputed, was satisfied their claims were just . . . That short, thick old gentleman is the Duke of Saxe-Weimar . . . that is Talleyrand – the brightest spirit of all Napoleon's princes . . . In this way, for two or three hours, did we continue meeting and pushing amongst hundreds of men, each of whom, had he but made his appearance singly at a fashionable rout in London, would have furnished a paragraph to our newspapers . . . and titles to our bazaars. . . .

Bright went everywhere, 'talking with princes and flirting with ladies', from brilliant balls to banquets, from concerts to the art treasures of private collectors, from evening parties with their childish games and charades to the solemnity of the cathedral, where on Maundy Thursday he saw members of the royal family wash the feet of old men.

Meanwhile he did not forget his studies. He became intimately acquainted with Baron Jacquin and his aged father, a distinguished botanist who had been responsible for enriching the imperial conservatories at Schönbrun. He met the 'elder Franck, to whom the spread of clinical instruction in medicine owes more than to any individual'. He attended the general hospital daily, but though he worked under Dr Hildebrand, one of the more prominent professors, he learned little that was new. He met Dr de Carro, a fervent follower of Jenner, who had had the courage to experiment with vaccine upon his own two sons and had propagated 'the greatest discovery of the age' to the whole of eastern Europe and Asia. He worked with Professor Beer to remedy his lack of knowledge of diseases of the eye. He followed two surgeons, Rust and Kern, around their hospital and was interested to see that there were private chambers as well as public wards, and that a physician was detailed to taste daily the 'full diet, half-diet and low diet' before it was put before the patients. He visited the Lying-in Hospital for Women and was surprised to find that women from all classes of society could give birth to illegitimate children without exciting any comment, the baby being kept by the mother, adopted or sent to a foster parent. He also went to the Hospital for the insane, where he found that the theories of Pinel of Paris had not yet penetrated, for there were still the fetters, the violence and the cruelty.

*

With Easter over Bright was anxious to leave Vienna. The high nobility with their empty purses had already left, and the floundering Grand Court was about to depart. This time he travelled, not as a medical student, but as a geologist, botanist and writer. He had always wanted to write; as a boy of twelve he had secretly sent satire to his uncle Serjeant Sam for comments – 'no mortal sole has seen it'. But now the determining factor was Hungary itself. There had been no book written about this remote and little known country since Dr Edward Brown's visit in 1673, while Grellman had touched on it but briefly in his famous book on gypsies. Gypsies appealed to Bright's imagination, and the idea of studying the life of the nomad, his motivation, and above all his dialect attracted him greatly. Besides there was much to seek out in the geological field, while the few Hungarians he had met in Vienna, and their invitations, now acted as a powerful stimulus to his restless curiosity.

These travels of his were to make his name a legend, doing for Hungary what Sir Walter Scott had done for Scotland and Byron for Greece. He was to colour it and put it on the map, drawing attention to its geology, its beauty, its energy, the terrible callousness of its rich towards its poor. He was to give to the intellectual Hungarian the idea that their country's poverty, ignorance and sterility could be overcome if only they directed their energies towards raising the standard of living and improving health. Bright was even to suggest, at their request, practical plans for reform.

Bright's road took him to many isolated places, and the fact that he only begins to mention his servant at this period rather suggests that there were times when he felt lonely. Instead of the servant being a shadowy figure and taken for granted, he is now a companion, a good friend, saving Bright from numerous small worries and exasperations. Possessing the discretion of a good servant, he was never in the way and always there when needed. Throughout his travels, hostesses were to badger him as to the habits of his master – what did he like to drink and eat, and when did he want to wash – though many scarcely believed him when he told them that his master wanted to fit in with others and so was easily to be satisfied. He helped, too, to protect Bright from his somewhat untidy ways: loose sheets of paper fell from his pocket; notes, money, letters and pencils got mislaid; sketches slipped through the ill-fitting planks of country carts; beloved books toppled from his arms. He sat on his hat, tore his trousers, lost his socks – yet he could always find a reference in his notebook, and when asked to show his passport, even in the most remote and wild of places, he could produce it instantly. While he appeared vague and helpless to servants, and landladies, who always wanted to do things for him, there was nothing disorderly in his work or in his writing. He was carefully accurate in everything he said, verifying all his written statements again and again, noting only what was relevant, always meticulously correct in his observations.

Once in Hungary, Bright began to travel in a north-easterly direction, towards Pressburg, and then on into the Hungarian highlands. He was guided to some extent by the ancient maps of Dr Edward Brown, and in Vienna Baron Jacquin had given him some helpful information. But as he progressed from place to place, largely following his own whims, he took the advice of the peasants he met about transport and where to rest for the night. He was passed on from one landlord to another; having been welcomed in one castle, he

1. Dr Richard Bright.
By courtesy of Mrs Elizabeth Lloyd.

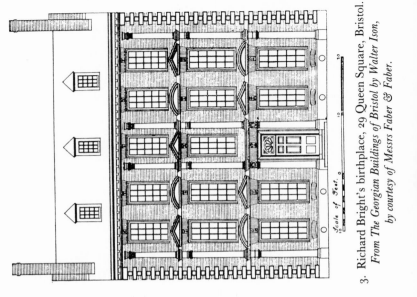

3. Richard Bright's birthplace, 29 Queen Square, Bristol.
   From The Georgian Buildings of Bristol by Walter Ison,
   by courtesy of Messrs Faber & Faber.

2. Richard Bright of Ham Green, father of Dr Bright.
   By courtesy of Mr T. Bright.

would go on to the next; he inspected Baron Brown's garden and cotton-spinning works one day, and the silk and mulberry trees of Perlac on another. From trade school to college, from hovel to tavern, through virgin forests and 'intolerable wastes of what could be arable land', he journeyed on. Everything was worth recording: the Tattersalls racing calendar on Graf Hunyadi's table, the Pannanian sandstone on the flanks of Szigliget Hill, the mistletoe surprisingly growing on oak trees, the warm springs of Glas Hutte, the male and female nudity at the Spa of Baaden and his prudishness in objecting to it; the clothes worn by the peasants, the hats of the men, and the stench of their hovels; the baubles and trinkets of the children, and their thin, dirty, exposed behinds; the Cyganys, with their over-powering smell, their snuff-making paraphernalia, their intricately embroidered jackets and their matted hair, felted into balls. He was always to point out that though it was anguishing to see the poverty, filth and nakedness of the gypsy children, be it at home or abroad, their intelligence and merry ways were very different from the apathy of peasant children.

He must have thought of his father and of his similar experiences when down the mines, as he watched the crude pumping machines at work and the human efforts made to extricate the gold and ore at Schenitz, the silver at Szent-Kereszt, the copper at Nensohl and the salt in Styria. When he came to write about the mines, his description of the process by which lead was extracted from ore shows his acute grasp of organic chemistry.

Arriving at Budapest in a storm, he saw the Danube in all its magnificence 'caught in the rays of a rainbow'. Later he viewed it from the top of Gellert mountain, where he sketched the panorama which lay below him: the castle, the water district, the river with its pontoon bridge and the hills of Buda in the background. It is one of many accomplished paintings to be found in his book. The name of Bright has never been forgotten in Budapest, and the pub where he drank at Pec opposite the hospital is pointed out to this day. Not far away was the house of Professor Kitzaibel who, holding Bright's arm 'below the elbow', led him round and round his botanical garden while they peered at the variety of plants grown on sandy soil and discussed the miracle of pollination and the wonders of grafting.

When he returned to Vienna, he learned of Napoleon's escape from Elba, and decided on a change of plan. 'Recent events in the South of France', he wrote, 'having deranged the plan which I had formed of returning to England by way of Venice, Milan and Paris, I availed myself of the delay to revisit Hungary and gratify my curiosity by obtaining some further knowledge of a country which had already so interested me.'

This time he went south, into a buoyant countryside of nightingales, hedges white with thorn, lilac, berberis and trailing vines. Again he dallied with the Cyganys. He loved to pick up a native on the road, and it was always 'the loss of so pleasant a companion' that hurried him on. He studied the plants and collected geological material. He stopped on sudden impulses to sketch, trying to catch the light on the broken summits of the Styrian Alps and the Schneeberg, 'whose snowy tops rose in beautiful contrast with the green plain of springing corn over which we were passing'. When he reached Keszthely he stayed for several days at the castle of Count Festetis, where he was embroiled immediately in all the business of the estate. In Hungary every castle had its doctor, its vet, its tutors and its priests. Here there were also professors of agriculture, botany and mineralogy, but it was Professor Liebald, the geologist, who attracted most of Bright's attention. They spent many days together exploring the spread of hills surrounding Lake Balaton, a large inland water of strange beauty. On Badacsony Hill Bright had 'seldom seen any substances more volcanic in their appearance than the mineral products of this hill'. On the edge of the lake he noted 'a peculiar sand' and saw pelican, snipe and wild duck through a screen of reeds and yellow flags; by night, when he crept away by himself, he heard the 'hoarse booming of the bittern' and gazed long at the 'reflections of the little fires kindled all along the banks to attract the crayfish'.

At night, with 'the croak of a thousand frogs' under his window, he worked hard at his book. He found it to be a dreadfully lengthy business writing down all the information he had acquired. There was so much of it: the curriculum of the agricultural school, and all sorts of details about forestry, the snail pens, the care of buffaloes and tortoises, and all the complicated business of making Tokay wine. As the objects of interest were endless, Count Festetis kept wanting to 'lengthen the period of hospitality'.

Listening to Bright talk about gypsy language – 'a subject of first importance in forming our conjectures on the origins of these peoples' – and realizing how interested he was in the use of ancient words, the Count arranged for him to spend a day with the head of a tribe already in the vicinity. It was a great disappointment:

For the elderly man who sat before me, clutching a stick notched with the number of his relatives and members of his tribe, was wholly inarticulate, with no understanding of traditional words. He who has wandered so far and so wide, but can neither describe what he has seen or does nor tell where his family come from; when asked for a word or a meaning of another word, he gives a sentence, and when requested to repeat it he gives a sentence a totally different turn . . . no one who has not had the experience can conceive how difficult it was to gain any intelligible information from a person so rude, upon the subject of his language.

Before leaving Hungary he was to collect quite a few words from the Cyganys, and when he finally returned to England, as he tells us in his book, he lost no time in seeking out a family of gypsies at Norwood

Having found them, I commenced my inquiries, without much expectation of success; but my doubts were immediately dispelled, and almost every word which I could recall, was at once recognised by the first gypsies I accosted. To find, crouched beneath a hedge at Norwood, a family who expressed their ideas in the same words as those with whom I had conversed but a few weeks before, in the most distant corner of Europe, and having no relation whatsoever to the languages of the countries in which they were respectively settled, gave rise to a singular train of feelings, and to a confirmed conviction in the fact, that they had been derived from one common stock.

Though specimens of the language which he had obtained from Spain were not so satisfactory upon this point, 'yet the perfect accordance which will be seen in a few cases, such as dog, bread, wine, an old man, water, child, the nostrils, the mouth, and some others, appear to me so convincing, that the circumstance scarcely admits of any other solution'.

If it was admitted that all the gypsies in Europe were the descendants of one common stock, it still remained to discover 'from what part of the world these wanderers have originated'. Their 'countenance, complexion, and habits of life' having excited a 'very general belief that they have originated from an oriental climate', Grellman's theory that they were Hindus of the lowest caste seemed to have 'the greatest weight of evidence in its favour'.

Where Bright first gained the confidence of the English gypsies can only be conjectured; Worcestershire perhaps, at pear-picking time, or the Scottish Highlands. Wherever it was, he found them 'conversible, amusing, sensible, and shrewd; civil, but without servility; proud of their independence; and able to assign reasons for preferring their present conditions to any other in civilized society'. They were 'strongly attached to each other, and free from many cares which too frequently render the married state a source of discontent'. He saw much that was good in their lives:

> I leave it to those who have been accustomed to visit the habitations of the poor in the metropolis, in great cities, in country towns, or in any but those Arcadian cottages which exist only in the fancy of the poet, to draw a comparison between the activity, the free condition, and the pure air enjoyed by the gypsy, and the idleness, the debauchery, and the filth in which a large part of the poorer classes are enveloped.

When the time arrived 'to quit a country' in which he 'had been received with the greatest interest', Bright had little idea of what his visit was to mean. He had contributed himself, by example and by influence, much to medicine and hygiene, and to the development of peasant life, while he had revolutionized the prevailing views about the treatment of prisoners. Though the felon was to find his prison yard as confined as ever, his irons were abandoned and his conditions improved. Bright's book was a bestseller in Hungary; many years later a plaque was placed on the walls of Count Festetis's castle in Keszthely in recognition of his influence.

*

Bright first heard of the Duke of Wellington's great victory when he was but a few days' distance from Brussels. A travelling coach, festooned with bunting, passed them on the highway, on the sides of which was chalked 'Great Victory', 'A Wonderful Battle'. He was then in such a hurry to get to Waterloo that he forgot to notify Ham Green of his intentions, and, his whereabouts being unknown, his parents actually advertised for news of him.

Everybody went to Waterloo. The aftermath of battle brought curious visitors. Some sought information about their wounded kin, some came as sightseers, some were refugees. But all found Brussels, as undoubtedly Bright did, euphoric with victory, humming with life through its thousand rooms and stifling its sorrows at the hundreds of unidentified dead.

At that time the army had no organized medical corps, no smooth-running hospital system. Each regiment had a doctor, a dresser, a couple of orderlies if they were lucky, and a mule with two panniers to hold medical supplies. Under fire these doctors looked after their wounded with great devotion, collecting them up as they fell, to await an ill-spared bullock cart to take them to hospital. Little thought was ever given to ensuring that medical supplies reached the hospital, or that the army surgeons, apothecary, physician, dressers, and six 'hospital mates' (today's orderlies) were available and waiting in the commandeered building.

Bright had often heard how overwhelming the problems of caring for a sick army were. Dr Franck, a friend of his who had held the post of Inspector General of Army Hospitals during the Peninsular Campaign, was dispirited and ill. Dr James McGregor, another friend, was doing a bit better; with his caustic comments and shattering candour, he was able to exert some influence over the Duke of Wellington, and attempts were being made to improve the inadequacies of the medical service. Thanks to him, too, the work of army doctors was at last being recognized and mentioned in official despatches. Bright found McGregor employing his energies in a confusion of scattered hospitals, raging against officialdom and the poor sanitation, jibbing like an animal before the smell and putrescence.

Bright was never to lose the memory of what he saw, and never thought of this time without a great sinking of the heart. He picked up all the threads of medicine again in the various hospitals, both French and English, he was directed to. He kept encountering friends from Edinburgh: John Davy, Robert Knox and his admired and loved teacher, Dr John Thompson. From Guy's had come the surgeon Thomas Calloway and three pupils, Aston Key, Henry Cooper and Henry Wakefield. They had been sent by Astley Cooper to work as a team, and were put under Army Staff Medical Officers, eminent men like Guthrie and Henner. But it was not long before this competent team merited a hospital ward of its own, and it was mostly alongside those from Guy's that Bright threw himself.

In the grimmest moments of fighting the soldiers might have been fearless and unfaltering but now, lying on the thin palliasses, as the effects of diluted spirits and opiates wore off, they could hardly control their agony and fear; they had no wish to die in the portals of safety. The Guy's team was popular, for the wounded, both from hearsay and experience, preferred to be cared for by gentlemen – men whose education had rendered them kinder in manner than some of those who had sprung from obscure origins, whose ways were brutal and ignorant. They loved Henry Cooper. Sweet-natured, humorous, and looking absurdly young with his pink cheeks, open countenance and blue eyes, he was everybody's favourite. His uncle, Astley Cooper, thought much of him and was training him to follow in his own footsteps. He could not know then how illness and death were to shatter his plans. Henry Cooper, at twenty, was now experiencing more than his uncle, doing the same work, had experienced in a lifetime; nobody who watched him could have guessed that while he chattered and strapped a man to the table, it was with an anxious dislike of his profession.[2]

Aston Key, also young, was immensely confident. He was a good-looking boy with a nervous twitch on one side of his jaw. He strode about in a blood-spattered apron, holding a cigar between his thumb and little finger; he would point, with majestic air, to the next soldier to be laid upon one of the tables that had only just been cleared and washed down. A bit of a dandy, he operated in the most unsuitable of silks and ruffles. Speed was everything in those days before the use of anaesthetics, and though much was necessarily sacrificed to that Key was carefully accurate. Henner taught him a lot about extracting shot from the abdomen, manipulating joints and joining broken bones. But he was a rude and impatient man. Guthrie condemned him as one of those surgeons who performed amputations indiscriminately, especially on the upper limbs, and for being too proud a learner.

Bright, at twenty-five, was older and acted as a mediator. He helped others, like young Cooper, to hold firm and he was useful as an interpreter. He concerned himself with all the medical sick, treating dysentery, pneumonia, rheumatism and tetanus. Sometimes he acted as a dresser watching out for hospital gangrene, helping the surgeons extricate bullets, holding tourniquets, stitching and administering drugs. His good-nature was boundless, and in his quiet way he had an enormous influence on those around him.

He found so much of professional interest in the wards that he was detained in Brussels some days beyond the time when he was expected at the Lock Hospital. Before his departure, he went like everybody else to survey the battlefield. In front of the old mill at Mont Saint Jean he saw the blasted elm tree under which the Duke of Wellington had conducted the battle. The tree was to be bought by a patriotic Englishman for 200 francs, and it is said that a pair of ornate black chairs was made from the trunk and presented to George IV when he was Prince of Wales. Bright himself picked up a bit of charred wood; much later, he had a snuff box fashioned out of it which he gave to his father.

It was late at night when Bright arrived back at Ham Green. Some time in October (letter undated) Elizabeth wrote to her brother Henry: 'Write to you I must . . . Dick breakfasted with us this morning . . . Mama has not recovered her surprise . . . he is grateful he says to find so little changed here.' Bright himself tells us that it took him a long time to absorb all the family news. He thought his mother far from well.

The main burden fell on Phoebe. She, now thirty, seemed to have given up all hope of marriage; engrossing herself in charitable enterprises and the new Clifton Dispensary down at Dowry Square, she was content. His younger sister, Elizabeth, took him by surprise. She was immersed in a classical education advanced for her age of thirteen, and he found her delightfully full of affection as she kept running to do things for him. She was greatly looking forward to Benjamin's wedding, when she was to be a bridesmaid.

He found his father full of energy; he travelled long distances to attend meetings, and now that Lowbridge was getting old he spent a lot of time in Bristol. He was looking forward, he said, to the day when Robert, now in Spain, would be sufficiently informed to take over some of the business. He was absorbed, too, in re-arranging his 230 geological specimens, for Professor Werner had suggested that he should organize them so as to illustrate the latest theory of the earth's beginning.

9
Fever
1815–1820

Bright had long been expected back at the Dispensary, and so was able to spend only a few days with his family. Caley Street had been an old friend to him; now, on his return, it looked dingy. But he was surprised by the warmth of Dr Laird's welcome and his acute interest in what he had to say, though Dr Bateman he found sadly changed. Instead of the odd, silent and reserved manner which had often before been a barrier between them, he now showed gratifying pleasure at Bright's re-appearance. He was feeling ill, he told Bright.[1] His digestion and headaches were troubling him, and the gradual failure of the sight of one eye was worrying him exceedingly. The fact that he was famous for his book on skin diseases and that the Emperor of Russia had insisted on a special edition made no difference to him; he was too unwell to care.[2] He clung to Bright but he had to move on to his next post with Dr John Pearson almost immediately.

Bright invariably sought out the best teachers, and John Pearson was no exception. There was no one at that time who knew as much as he did about syphilis and the treatment of it. So Bright settled down to learn all he could from him.

The Lock Hospital was a busy place, devoted as it was to that most ancient and terrible of diseases, with its ravaging tricks, and its way of disappearing, only to appear again later; bringing rashes, swellings and destruction of tissue, ultimately it attacked the brain cells, and led to death. The hospital had its own unique atmosphere; the temperamental patients, constantly soured by fear and by the treatment, often made it difficult for the doctors to carry out any systematic study of the disease at the bedside. Syphilis was such a complicated subject, and mercury such a tricky treatment, that Bright was glad that John Pearson was there to back up his slow and fumbling feelings about the cases he encountered. As syphilis attacked the brain he was both disappointed and frustrated over the rule that because the cause of death was known no autopsies were to be done. He was not at all convinced that the viscera were not affected by **venereal** disease. How could anyone know if no complete **examination** after death had ever been made?

Thomas Addison was one who shared his view. From Edinburgh, this brilliant young man suddenly appeared and joined Bright, as a pupil to John Pearson. He later worked at the Dispensary under Dr Bateman. He was quite as enquiring as Bright, quite as certain that there were realms of medical thought about which the profession was entirely ignorant, and quite as determined to prove it. Addison was an imposing man, with his swaggering gait, his long arms hanging loose. He resembled some 'sad melancholy beast',[3] with his firm jaw, beautiful hazel eyes and proud, interested look; he seemed out of place in the confined streets of London, and was always telling his friends how much he missed his home in Cumbria.

A newcomer to London, he was always alone until Bright befriended him. The few words exchanged between them as students in Edinburgh now provided the foundation for a relationship which, in later days, was to be of wonderful benefit to Guy's Hospital. They were both tenacious and thorough, neither attempting to break new ground until the subject in hand had been mastered. They were both ambitious, not for fame or financial benefit, but for the boundless knowledge the profession offered. Medicine was the sum and substance of both their lives. Addison was four years younger than Bright; having himself a rather unfortunate manner, distant and formal, which made his patients uncomfortable in his presence, he envied Bright's natural ease with the sick. And Bright in his turn was to envy Addison his marvellous rhetoric, and the way he gained because of it the heart of every medical student. As a lecturer and teacher of practical medicine, he was to have no rival in Britain.

Many interesting people surrounded Bright at this time: Constable, the publisher, talking about his book on Hungary; Leech, sadly showing now slight oddities from the slowly developing tumour on his brain; Arthur Aikin, secretary to the Society of Arts, talking of lecturing on chemistry at Guy's; Humphry Davy, tempted away from his wife's world of wealth and position, now working on a miner's lamp; Michael Faraday, working at the Royal Institution. Dr Babington invited him to lecture on the volcanic areas of Hungary at the next Geological Society meeting, and to talk about his experiences in the Continental hospitals at the next session of the Medico-Chirurgical Society – or, as it was to be called later, the Royal Medical Society – an influential medical club which bridged the gap between physicians and surgeons and which was to bring Bright into contact with all the medical men of the day. Phoebe came to London and stayed with the Birches, and Bright at last met Benjamin, his favourite brother, again.

Then, one evening, at Dr Babington's table, Bright caught up with Henry Holland, also just back from his travels. He had been chasing the butterfly '*Parnassius phoebus golorionnis*', named after an admiral, his companion – explorer of Nabokor's river. His delightful company must have brought back vividly the active student life they had once shared in Edinburgh. His path and Bright's now rarely crossed. Holland's attitude to medicine was different to Bright's: it was always to take him to splendid houses, blazing with lights; he moved only in the most dazzling and cultural circles. All he wanted, he told his friends, was £5,000 a year and women's favours.[4] He would select his clientele from the classes who were normally absent from London during the summer months, so that he could travel. Those who knew his worth must have been saddened to see such an intelligent man cut himself off from all real involvement with medicine, and from all the advances of those exciting times. But 'he waives aside our discouraging opinions', Bright told his father in a letter. Holland apparently did not envy him having to work amongst the 'obscure and dirty', amidst the inevitable wrangles of seniors full of out-of-date notions and prejudices, while he himself enjoyed the pampered, well-fed background of the privileged, assured always of the gratitude and adoration of trusting relatives.

In the spring of 1816, Bright was quite suddenly appointed assistant physician at the Willan Fever Hospital. It was through the work of the dispensaries that this isolation hospital had been set up in 1801. Dr Bateman, then a young physician, was working under Dr Willan at the Public Dispensary; faced with a succession of epidemics, and lethal illnesses like dysentery, typhoid and consumption, both felt it was imperative to have somewhere to put these patients, whom the general hospital refused to admit. Dr Bateman had long been in charge of the hospital, and was still the senior physician there. Now, undermined by ill-health and overburdened with work, he felt that Bright would supply those qualities of order and method, patience and perseverance, which he felt himself to be lacking. He admired his pupil's clearness of insight, sound judgements and sense of proportion. He had noted how well the young Bright had grasped the special nature of contagion, and how in looking after fever cases the patients' circumstances were always relevant. Bright realized that the conditions found in the tenements would favour an epidemic; he would teach others to look at everything as a possible carrier of infection.

Confronted now with the 'dismal world of poverty and ignorance', Bright fought courageously against prejudice and hostility. He helped his patients to face the stigma – the haste with which friends and neighbours took themselves to a safe distance. Many of his contemporaries ridiculed the idea of contagion, insisting that there was nothing to be done about a case of typhoid, measles or diphtheria, and that the public should bow to the inevitable, but Bright believed firmly in cleanliness and hygiene.

The Fever Hospital, small and neat, built in the solid Georgian manner, stood near the new monument of George IV – where King's Cross Station stands today. It was an austere place, with its square entrance, its wooden boards scrubbed white, bare of furniture except for a carrying chair, with a movable lining, in which patients for admission were carried from their homes at the expense of the hospital. A small stone corridor, arched in the gothic style, led to the single cell-like rooms allocated to patients in the different stages of fever. Somewhere in the whitewashed shades lived the inspector responsible for the care of clean clothes and stores; while the matron, also in residence, superintended the domestic arrangements and 'so many ordinary nurses as was necessary, together with a porter'. The number of beds occupied was always unpredictable; sometimes it was few, sometimes so many that 'extra attendants were demanded as the Committee shall think requisite'.

Bright considered himself fortunate to be moving in this orbit; the Fever Hospital had the same reassuring feeling of care about it as had the Lock and other small hospitals run by concerned doctors for specific purposes. Whereas in the larger city hospitals, like Guy's, a governing authority held all the power, decisions here were left to the doctors, who had the support of a thirty-two-person committee, which met monthly at the Freemasons' Tavern. Bright, throughout his life, did his best to attend.

The work was demanding, and it was part of Bright's job to see that the stringent rules were observed: windows had to be kept open, floors mopped daily, utensils washed immediately after use, clothes soaked, blankets changed, the rooms aired with the correct amount of vinegar and camphor. Those in intimate attendance had to learn to hold their breath and sit on that side of the bed where the current of air 'carried off the infection vapours'. Measles, scarlatina, whooping cough, diphtheria, typhoid, gaol fever (typhus), cholera and smallpox – Bright became familiar with them all.

He soon became popular in the district, and respected for his devoted work and his sense of humour; it was not long before every overseer, watchman and parish officer was on his side. They learned quickly that there was little chance of getting round him. He smelt out all duplicity, all mishandling, soon sensing instinctively when the powdered nitre and vitrio logiac acid were mixed in incorrect quantities, when a teacup full of vapour was not moved from one sick-room to another. So they became cooperative, informing him of a house where a case of fever was suspected; they were conscientious over the fumigation of contaminated rooms and personal effects; they made a point of accompanying him on his house-to-house visits, where daily he had to explain the way a sick person with a contagious disease should live. But it was difficult to advise extreme cleanliness when the nearest spring was several yards away; or to insist that the child with measles should not be in the same bed as the child with scarlet fever and the mother coughing blood, when there was only one bed; or to recommend extra nourishment in a pauper's home. If the conditions were particularly bad, his supporters helped him to evacuate the unwilling individual; and if the home was more affluent, they would stay to show relatives how best to protect the household. For his sake, too, they took an interest in keeping the registers and statistics up to date, and helped arrange autopsies.

Bright spent many an evening at work on his book on Hungary; whenever the opportunity arose he attended Guy's Hospital. Astley Cooper was performing some operations which had never been done before, and his dressers were often seen kicking the boxes of sawdust under the table to catch the dripping blood while Astley Cooper removed aneurysms and tied the aorta with his customary speed.

That winter of 1817 several cases of typhus were admitted into the hospital. Knowing the nature of this 'gaol fever' or 'ship fever', as the public called it and having seen its devastating effects in the gaols of Bristol, in the cells of Hungarian prisons, and at Waterloo, Bright tried to galvanize his staff into greater activity. Day by day, doctors in general practice began demanding beds at the Fever Hospital; in no time at all the outbreak had erupted into an epidemic. Starvation and overcrowding were the main contributory causes, and as the poor in wintertime sought warmth from the bodies of their neighbours and spurned ventilation the illness spread with frightening speed.

Bright did not spare himself; he shut himself off from his friends and filled the hospital corridors with extra beds. During daytime none of his patients escaped his vigilance, and at night he never knew what calls might be made upon him. His young assistants and the nurses, experiencing an epidemic for the first time, relied on his friendly and experienced guidance. He had to do much of the practical nursing himself but he was never once heard to complain. He became exhausted and his nerves reached a pitch of untoward alertness, but he ignored it, denying himself 'the repose and care which it required'. He said nothing of his own headaches and feelings of chill, until one day he was so prostrated with fever that he could not get out of bed. Within eight hours he was seriously ill.

Illness is an essential experience for a doctor, and afterwards Bright was the first to say that it had been one of the most important events of his life. Overwhelmed now by weakness and an oven-like heat, he resigned his body to outside care; investigation was no longer his province.

When his anxious father came to see how he was, he was worried by his son's appearance; he went to see Dr Babington and talked to Dr Laird and Dr Bateman. There had never been any absence of skilled help, but now two young doctors, whom Bright had known in Edinburgh, came to share the nursing. Dr Tweedie is mentioned in a family letter as being the most constant, sleeping by him on a lounge chair at night. In an agony of feeling for his beloved son, Richard Bright sent for the family physician, Dr John Estlin, and also Dr James Cowles Prichard, from Bristol Royal Infirmary, who took the first available coach from Bristol.

The typhus fever had by now run its allotted course, but instead of his temperature dropping as expected, it kept rising and there were signs of pneumonia. Apparently Bright lay in a stupor by day and raved by night, and Dr Tweedie had to 'struggle with him'. Dr Prichard was known as a ruthless physician – he belonged to the 'depleting school' and believed in drastic procedures[5] – so Bright would have been bled again and again; cold compresses would have been placed on his shaven head, and cups on his chest; purges would have been given to deplete his guts. There was no aspirin in those days, but other antipyretics were given: antimony, ipecacuanha and juborandi. Other measures, too, were employed to reduce the high fever, but instead of the ice-packs and cold-sponging of today his body would have been wrapped in a sheet soaked in alcohol. He continued to be dangerously ill for some time, but he seemed to resist the pull of the drifting tide. Then, as he got better, dry towels replaced the wet ones, sleeping draughts the stimulants, soothing ointments the cupping, leeches and setons; gruel and sago were given instead of wine and poppy seeds. No doubt Phoebe took the place of Dr Tweedie – Phoebe who, according to Henry, 'never takes care of herself and thinks herself made of different material to anyone else so she can never be ill . . .'; and no doubt delicacies poured into the hospital from well-wishers.

But no sooner had Bright recovered than we learn how he discovered the difficulties of convalescence: the selfishness, the irritability, the weakness, the way one 'got easily upset by the kindliness and thoughtfulness of others'. It must have been during the process of recovery that Bright learned to appreciate the comforts and discomforts of an invalid's life: how significant was the fragrance of Balsam of Peru, and tissane tea at daybreak, how specially disappointing it was to get arrowroot when one had hoped for beef-broth; how much the weight of bedclothes mattered, and the annoying tangle of shirt-tails; how sore the lancing wounds were and the pressure areas. Convalescence was a time of constantly expecting but being continually disappointed. He never forgot these things – which were not mentioned in medical books until he himself wrote about them some years later. It was largely because of these experiences that he was to become so beloved as a physician. Patients were always to say they preferred Dr Bright to other doctors because he understood exactly how they felt.

Amidst a roomful of Ham Green blossoms, he continued to improve. He was up and kept in a chair for some time before he was allowed visitors, but when the longed for visitors did come he tired quickly. He gave Benjamin a long list of books to procure from the library, yet when they arrived 'they did not provide the long anticipated delight'.

Eventually he left the Fever Hospital for Malvern. Here, at Welland House, smelling of beeswax and lavender, he was cossetted back to further strength. Harvest-time was spent at Ham Green, where he found himself well enough to enjoy the sight of wagon teams hung with ribbons, and wains packed tight with children. The village boys wore beaver hats, and the girls white socks and sandals, all given to them for the occasion by Bright's father – who was overjoyed to have his son home and well.

Worried over the long overdue book on Hungary, Bright tried to write, choosing, as was his habit, the hours before others were awake. But he found that instead of writing he simply followed the inclinations of the moment. He wandered to Pill and idled with his father's tenants, sharing their concern over the price of wheat and potatoes, or accompanied his father to the Hilhouse Dockyard to view Willie Miles' new ship, the *Helen Percher*, a small experimental steamship, in the last stage of completion.

Once in the city of Bristol, Bright was touched at the sight of the familiar; he had almost forgotten the beauty of its quaysides, its toppling houses and hillsides. He went to see Dr Prichard, and Lant Carpenter, now at 2 Great George Street, and his cousin Lowbridge – whom he was never to see again.

Once back in London, in spite of his mother's protest that he must never return to that 'abominable Fever Hospital', Bright resumed his routine work. At Dr Laird's insistence his duties were severely limited, and he was able to concentrate on finishing his book on Hungary. He had to involve his family; he sent chapters to his father, who thought Bright had given considerable 'rein to his humour and sprightliness' and that his characters were worthy of Chaucer; he got advice from Benjamin, who edited it and helped him choose the sketches. Being now an established book collector, Benjamin was recognized as an adviser to the publishing firm of Constable. They were always asking him to correct articles and read proofs, and now he could act as liaison between them and his brother. There were many delays, as letters were sent to and from Hungary, as data and information were checked and rechecked. Then the artist, Craig, fell ill, 'indeed near dying': it had been Constable's idea that each chapter should be headed with a vignette by an artist of their choosing.

A letter dated April 1818 hints that the book was at last almost ready to be launched:

> We now enclose a proof of the last vignette . . . This one, now sent, is not done by Craig, but by a person of the name of Austen . . . It will oblige us your returning this work and your remarks as soon as possible. It is now the only circumstance in the way of the book coming out, the proofs of the Index were procured this morning and meet due attention . . . signed A. C. Constable.

Greatly relieved to have finished the book, Bright received gratifying news from Constable in Edinburgh that sales were going well even before publication. The *Edinburgh Review*, too, was already praising the work of such 'a very amiable and intelligent man, who has observed with the utmost diligence everything remarkable that came within the sphere of his observation'. But when in June 1818 the weighty quarto of 600 pages was first seen in the bookshops, it was the London publisher, Longman, who pronounced that it had become an immediate bestseller.

Travels from Vienna, through Lower Hungary, with some remarks on the State of Vienna during the Congress in the year 1814 brought some renown for Bright. He seems to have been somewhat surprised by the number of papers and periodicals that carried good reviews, but apart from this Bright himself tells us nothing about its reception, nor does he mention the financial rewards. It is only from a letter written by Harriet Gibbs to George, her husband, that one learns that Longmans gave him £500 for the first edition, after which he was to get something for subsequent ones. 'Perhaps, you had better not say anything about Dr Bright's book as it was told me in confidence by Phoebe.'

It is his father who tells us that Bright ignored the acclaim, the physical languor of convalescence curbing his enthusiasm over other people's impressions. He was praised by the reviewers as a traveller: 'it is impossible that the travels of such a man should not be interesting.' He was praised for his descriptions, for his 'tenderness and subtle humour', for his domestic scenes, for 'the beauty of many of its written passages', and for his intelligent appreciation of situations. But most attacked him for the multiplicity of the subjects chosen. There was too much information, too much to digest – geography, economics, local customs, religion, agriculture, politics.

It was as well, perhaps, that Bright did not include the material he had also gathered on Hungarian literature. It was apparently his intention to publish this at a later date, together with further suggestions on hygiene in Hungarian prisons. As it turned out he became too deeply involved in his profession ever to find time to do this.

It was characteristic of Bright to accept criticism; his lack of confidence made him feel that what others said was usually justified. In this instance it was his father's susceptibilities that were most affronted, for, as he told his son, he saw no fault in being a persistent investigator. Bright had identified himself with Hungary, and such success as the book achieved must be because of this.

*

'I have seen Dick's lodgings, which are exactly as they ought to be, comfortable and small. Two drawing-rooms and a high closet with best bed chamber over the dining-room'. Where these were is not mentioned, but presumably they were somewhere close to the Fever Hospital.

It was rare to have his father in London for a visit of any length, and Bright saw him whenever time allowed. He would call on him at Holdings Hotel in Hanover Square at breakfast-time, before the routine of his busy day at the Fever Hospital began. Invariably he found his father in the middle of a letter to his mother: 'While I am writing this Dick has come in for breakfast.' Sometimes, arriving just as the coffee was being put on the table, Bright found there was already a little party there. His father's friends, delighted that he should once more be amongst them, had called on him the moment he had set foot in the hotel. Humphry Davy had appeared first, carrying him off immediately to Albemarle Street to be introduced to Michael Faraday. Isambard Brunel and Willie Vaughan had come, too, but 'in order to see Sir Joseph Banks he had had to go to Soho Square', where 'He found the old man in a wheel chair, knotted with gouty tumours'. When entertained by Dr Babington and Dr Franck, 'we talked of Dick and his prospects'.

It seems that his father needed to talk to Bright at this time, and was always grateful to his son for being such a good listener. For he was not only in London to see his friends; he had legal matters on his mind, and these were what he wanted to discuss with his son.

In March of this same year, 1818, Richard Bright's second cousin, Richard William Meyler, had fallen off his horse while hunting and died intestate. Through his mother Sarah Meyler and as 'heir-at-law' he had inherited all the landed property – the estates in Jamaica and in Pembrokeshire, and all the copyholds and freeholds of Crawley Manor and the Worthy manors of Hampshire. But a large tribe of Welsh Meylers, who had all been faithfully looked after up to the third and fourth generation by a succession of Richard William Meylers, now felt that more was still due to them and started lawsuits. Although they had inherited all the personal wealth, they now claimed all the landed property as well. Indeed, so keen were they to have it that one relative, it was reported, was to be seen 'stooping and scooping up and carrying off the very gravel off the drive at Crawley Manor'.

But the story has no place here, and the Meylers' tenacity and deceptions, plots and forgeries – the altering of a name and date on a tombstone being one – must remain untold.[6] Only the part played by his four older sons and the way they supported Richard Bright need be mentioned.

That April Richard Bright consulted his sons, and for many years to come all threw themselves wholeheartedly into the dispute. Henry dealt with the legal aspects of the cases; while Benjamin and Robert (after his return from Spain) carried out the necessary travel and investigations. Bright, always too busy to play an active part, added his passive support whenever solutions were called for. The following October the Brights were to win the first lawsuit, but the Meylers were persistent; they brought five lawsuits altogether, all unsuccessful. The last was heard in 1829, by which time Richard Bright's legal costs had amounted to £20,000.

Towards the end of that April (1818) Richard Bright left London; gouty attacks in his legs were troubling him, and he longed for his wife and 'Phoebe's treacle possets'. Though seemingly inexhaustible his exertions had at last forced him to his bed, and Benjamin feelingly declared that 'some ardent spirits are better in bonds than at large'.

In June Robert returned from Spain and stayed with Bright for a few days. He was in high fettle and Bright listened eagerly to what he had gleaned on Spanish gypsy lore, and their dialects, in relation to their Hindu origins. Then, in July, came the news that Lowbridge was dying. Bright was sad on his father's account, for the sense of loss he suffered was very great. He had been Richard Bright's oldest and closest friend and colleague.

In August Dr Laird, observing Bright's pallor and low spirits, suggested that he might perhaps benefit from a change of climate and some further work abroad. Bright's illness had broken a thread in his life. He had mechanically picked it up again, but he had lost his former joy in his work. He had developed his own vehement convictions about medicine, and was longing to put them into practice, but he had few facilities and too little confidence, and felt he must bide his time. He had come to realize that to control or to alleviate the symptoms of a disease was not enough; more work had to be done in interpreting the physical signs seen at the bedside, and in relating these signs to the state of the organs revealed at autopsy. Every organ should be scrutinized, as the French chemist Laënnec in Paris had done when working on the lung. Having himself become interested in the widespread malady of dropsy, Bright had already began to form the notion that it was in some odd way connected with the functions of the kidney. But the gaps in his own knowledge were as yet too great, and the facilities for research too poor, so once again we find him crossing the Channel to seek out more information in a wider field.

He went to Leyden, Gottingen, Frankfurt, Munich, Innsbruck and Freyburg, and wherever he went he visited hospitals and post-mortem rooms. It was the practice on the Continent for every corpse to be examined, so greedily Bright learned what he could. While everybody else was still studying the liver, which had always been considered the seat of all illness, and all tempers, Bright was having a closer look at the kidney. He had never forgotten the look of the first granular kidney he had seen, as a medical student, in a patient who had died with dropsy.

He enjoyed speaking German, Latin and French again, and wherever he went he was taken notice of, and included in the medical brotherhood, finding lodgings in doctors' houses and finding everywhere aims and interests identical with his own. He travelled always as a student; it is abundantly clear from his writings that he regarded himself still as a learner. That autumn of 1818, his medical quests were temporarily abandoned as he journeyed to Aix-la-Chapelle to join his sister Sally and the Randolphs once more. Here, there was another Congress going on and Bright recognized many of the crowned heads of Europe, but he only 'slightly enjoyed the fun'. They all spent Christmas at Amorbach, where he found the Duke of Kent to be 'an affable sort of royalty', and as ready to talk about his clocks as he was to listen to Bright's views on hospital reform and to give his promises of help. (The Journal of the Dowager Duchess of Saxe-Coburg-Saalsfeld mentions a Dr Bright being with Queen Victoria's parents, the Duke and Duchess of Kent – 'an ugly boy but most pleasant'.)

Most of the following spring Bright disappears from sight, as his curiosity and spirit of adventure took him along 'the old imperial road', through the Simplon Pass and the Tyrol and into Italy. Like many other travellers, one never finds Bright going the same way twice; he preferred always to return by a different route. On this occasion he stayed at the Great Saint Bernard convent, leaving its gorges and thundering waterfalls for the mountain slopes of Mont Blanc.

Here, alone, somewhere near the Grands Mulets, an adventurous urge led him up the steep slopes, and on to the ledges, ribs and crags. But this time he seems to have been more keen to spy out the alpine flowers in their gritty crevices than to collect geological specimens. And when he was not climbing he took his brush and painted, leaving a remarkable record of de Saussure's hut 'where the study of glaciation began' and a few other shelters then in existence, at a time when organized mountaineering was unknown.

In Geneva he sought out his old friend and teacher of chemistry Alexander Marcet; he then went on to Paris, fulfilling a promise that he had made to himself back in 1813 'to see a little practice in Paris'. It is obvious that he found his encounter with Pierre Rayer rewarding, and Rayer was no less attracted by Bright, who was four years his senior.[7] Both were interested in pathology and it may well have been Bright who first sparked off Rayer's interest in nephrology. It was Rayer who was first to acclaim Bright's original discovery, using the term 'Maladie de Bright' before anyone else had thought of doing so. We do not know who else Bright met in Paris, but he must surely have visited both the Jardin des Plantes and Cuvier's great museum of comparative anatomy.

On his return in the summer of 1819, his father asked him what he thought he had learned from this journey abroad. Bright found it hard to reply. He had studied cretinism in Austria, goitres in Germany and chest diseases with Laënnec in Paris. Meeting this 'simple and austere' and somewhat shy man from Brittany had left him with no doubt about his greatness. It was not that he was particularly learned – indeed he had himself confessed to his ignorance about other parts of the body. But on his own subject, the chest, he was 'a master'.

On the whole there seemed to be little to choose between hospitals abroad and those to be found in Britain. He had been somewhat discomforted by the rudeness of the doctors towards the students: there were too many kicks on the shin, 'too many snarling and crude rebuffs'. He thought, too, that there was 'too much unsuitable discussion carried on in the patient's hearing'. In medical circles in Britain there was more interchange of ideas and observations. On the Continent he had found little pooling of knowledge, no sharing of resources, little generosity. Doctors delivered their 'opinions in such dogmatic confidence as to deter a pupil like myself from asking a second question'. Neither Richard Bright nor his son could then know how many of the Continental men he had met would seek him out at Guy's in the days to come, many crossing the channel just to do him honour.

He returned to London, to the Dispensary and the Fever Hospital, much refreshed, and this time it was easier to face the defects and miseries of others. Dr Bateman's retirement had brought much additional work, but this did nothing to lessen the secret longings he had not only to spend more time on pathology, but to be given a chance to teach. He was dissatisfied with the existing education for the medical student and felt ready to help in achieving a new and better system.

Family affairs kept interrupting his work, and his love for his family often overrode his own yearnings. For much of this time he made himself available to Benjamin, who was anxious and unhappy about the health of his young bride. Said to be more like Sarah Bright than her own mother, and possessing all the charm and grace of her aunt, Elizabeth Heywood was the most popular of all the cousins. And the fact that she had never seemed delicate before made her illness all the more distressing and difficult to accept. Benjamin took her to Bath, but Elizabeth's increasing breathlessness troubled their peace. It was there that Phoebe stayed for a while to help her brother. The Revd Joseph Hunter was constantly around. A friend of William Hazlitt, an eminent antiquarian and something of a bibliomaniac, he was an intimate friend and correspondent of Benjamin's. The hundred or so letters exchanged between them, now in the British Museum, testify to their immense shared knowledge of literature in Shakespeare's time.[8] Hunter was equally devoted to the Heywoods and immersed in a book about Oliver Heywood, a divine of the reign of James I, whom he considered to be *the* connecting link between early Puritanism and 'modern dissent'. But, distraught and unhappy, Benjamin was unable to appreciate his company and found it difficult to concentrate. 'Mrs Bright does not make much progress I am afraid,' he wrote to Hunter, 'and now my sister has left us, I am more constantly her companion. Will you call as you pass tomorrow or call and drink tea at half past seven tonight.'

Bright travelled to Bath whenever he could, but there was little that could be done for Elizabeth. She died on the last day of May 1819, aged twenty-three, after only six months of marriage. Benjamin was left desolate, as were both families. It was left to Bright to write letters for his brother, and amongst them was one to Joseph Hunter: 'At the request of my brother Benjamin, I write to inform you of the sad and melancholy event which has occurred to him on the death of his wife . . . My brother is in sad distress as you may well suppose and feels how immensely you will sympathize in his distress.'

Bright himself had met Hunter, and had told Benjamin how amused he had been by 'the parts he played, never seeming to be himself . . . surprising his children by being the Black Prince or Hereward the Wake'. Bright felt that at this sad time Benjamin should be encouraged to be in his company. He was glad to see how Joseph Hunter felt for his bereaved friend, how constantly he wrote to him, how patiently he sent him books, or posed controversial questions. Benjamin was certainly grateful, but at the same time told him that 'literature and criticism' were not much in his thoughts at this particular moment. But Hunter persisted, and eventually achieved much more than Bright could have done. At long last Benjamin wrote, 'thanking God for minds that recover by the elasticity of which we know not the construction. They may fail and flag again and again but the latent power is still there. I am grateful to you, my dear Sir, for thus exciting it.'

The winter of 1819–20 was another severe one. This time we hear that the Floating Harbour at Bristol was a sheet of ice, and covered with skaters – amongst them 'flies sister Elizabeth'. There was much excitement as Henry was being put forward as candidate for the Whig interests in Bristol, along with his friend Richard Hart-Davis; all their friends rallied round to help with canvassing. Robert reported to Bright that 'we had a rough night, our opponents having beaten in all our windows and so on, and we have eleven in limbo – some heads are broken, but precautions will be taken by the Mayor and we think all will be comfortable again'. No doubt Bright was glad not to be part of it. But the Brights were popular in the neighbouring villages, and in Bristol itself intense loyalty finally helped to secure the majority of votes. Henry was to be a successful Member of Parliament intermittently for many years, and an admirable representative of Bristol trade interests. In London, Bright was the first to congratulate his brother; with his advice Henry was able to get the conditions of prisoners and the health of Bristol seamen improved, and the status of medical students in Bristol raised. Bright had intended to hear

Henry's maiden speech, he wrote to his father, but he 'was detained at the Fever Hospital and it was Sam who heard the "Squire's" impassioned pleas for the Western Union Canal Bill, stressing apparently very much the fact that it would give work to many of the unemployed between Bath, Bristol and Wales . . . two and three members congratulated Henry, telling him it was well done. He is quite delighted.'

In this same letter he told his mother how good it was to have Sam staying with him, and how much he appreciated his lively company at the dinner table. Sam, now twenty years of age, had finished his formal education and chosen commerce as a career. While he was awaiting an apprenticeship with the Liverpool branch of Gibbs, Bright and Company he gave his opinions as to how Bright should decorate the house he had by now leased in Bloomsbury Square.

No. 14 is one of the few original houses of that period left in the square. It is a house of great character, large and in the Adam style. Two of Sam's friends – the scholarly Cosmo Innes[9] and John Powers, the soldier – 'are as pleased with it as I am,' Bright told his father. One Christmas Sam had taken them both to stay at Ham Green; the whole visit must have left a lasting impression upon Cosmo Innes, for he invariably ends his letters to Sam sending 'thousands of love to all your family', and seems to have been involved in all the family happenings.

It is thanks to him that we learn that Bright was nominated for the Royal Society about this time, March 1820.

There are no letters about Bright's personal life at this date, so we do not know who acted as his sponsor nor what won him election as a Fellow – presumably it was his work on Hungary. Sir Humphry Davy had now taken Sir Joseph Banks' place as President, widening its horizons and bringing many more literary men, artists and foreigners into this selective world of scientists. Bright must have been pleased that his industry and intelligence had been recognized by London's most exclusive society, but he makes no mention of it.

One day in July, he wrote to his father, 'Now, this good evening, I shall dine with Dr Laird.' The evening proved to be one of complete surprise. There were no vacancies on the medical staff at Guy's, yet he was to be appointed as assistant physician. A new post had apparently been created just because, as Dr Laird told him, there was 'this suitable candidate available'.[10]

10
Martha
1820–1823

Bright resigned at once from the Dispensary, but agreed to remain on the Committee of the Fever Hospital. Now, plunging back into the life of Guy's, he was delighted to be part of this great, old establishment once more, to be back in its corridors, its wards and its lecture room, where, 'packed like herrings in a barrel', he had enjoyed some of the happiest years of his student life. There was no courtyard, street, shop or waterside stair in the neighbourhood that did not conjure up some recollection of those youthful days.

He was soon to be aware of changes that had occurred in the hospital. The many practical reforms talked about by the Treasurer, Mr Harrison, when Bright was there before had now been put into practice. There was a marked improvement in hygiene, increased efficiency in the departments and stricter discipline. You no longer had to use fists to get what you wanted done, and the general rowdiness was gone. Harrison had been in power long enough to identify himself with everyone in the building, and he really cared what happened to the patients. He was domineering, but he was at the same time diplomatic in his approach; he did little without first consulting the Governors of the Hospital, and even if there was opposition he was usually able to bring them round.

Many of Harrison's imaginative ideas met with opposition from the medical staff, too, for they were backward-looking, resisting every change. For this reason Harrison must surely have welcomed Bright's return, knowing him to be a young man who shared his own visionary outlook, and his desire to revolutionize medicine. Astley Cooper must also have been glad to have him back. He had always been a good friend to Bright: at his first appearance as a student he had penetrated immediately the youth's diffidence and reserve, and Bright never forgot it. In Astley Cooper he found someone to whom he could express his hopes, and confide his difficulties with his senior physician, Dr Cholmeley.

There was little love lost between Astley Cooper and Dr

Cholmeley, who was a difficult, quarrelsome man, jealous of Astley Cooper's success and popularity. Years ahead of his time, the surgeon could not tolerate those – like Cholmeley and William Black – who clung to the past. Dr Black was the other senior physician; his only interests were his pet canary and his barouche, which he drove about in all day. Neither of the senior physicians was seen much in the wards yet both were possessive and touchy over their patients, begrudging the slightest interference. Eventually, though, Bright's devoted industry was to be recognized by both of them. In the preface to the first volume of his *Reports of Medical Cases*, he says: 'I must confess my obligations to my immediate colleagues Dr Cholmeley and Dr Black; not because they have been more willing to assist me than others, but because without their kind and ready permission I must have been deprived of many of the valuable facts and illustrations which have been largely drawn from cases under their care.'

At first Bright wisely remained in the background. For the next two years he was quiet and unobtrusive, doing many of the things he had done as a physician's clerk, though he did them now on his own authority. His main concern was those patients belonging to Dr Laird, and as he was a good deal at the Dispensary a good working partnership developed between them. Of all the physicians Bright was the one most often with the patients. He was continually 'doing duty for my colleagues amongst the outpatients': continually being asked to look at one patient or another, to advise a dresser or oversee a nurse, and so the other members of staff grew to depend on him. It was never his way to harangue and accuse his assistants. He liked rather to reprimand as he praised, to agree with them and yet to indicate what he felt would have been the better course.

Bright had an astonishing memory. In his case reports he tells of several instances when walking through a ward he would recognize an old patient, whether his or another's. Now he was startled to come across several familiar faces remembered from his student days. Mrs Willoughby Taylor, again covered with blisters; Mr Willie Brookes, the sawyer, whom he remembered for his ice-cold extremities, which, as he had found out, 'no vinegar friction could warm'. Here he was again in agonies with colic and in the care of a raw attendant who did not know how to make a poultice. Then there was the dissolute baker Brookes, surprisingly still alive. His wife had put roast onions on his discharging ear. Now he was lying in the 'general purposes ward' in a coma. Finally there was Mrs Beal: he remembered how he had once 'run his finger round the tumour on her arm'; now it was rotten with gangrene.

One of the first things he did was to find a room of his own where 'he could think', where he could house the material he collected because it was likely to be of use to him in his studies, and where he had table space enough to do his own dissecting. It had to be a room near the Hospital, for, as he explained to his father, with the pressure of work increasing all the time, living in Bloomsbury Square had created problems. Walking to Southwark took too long and going by boat was no quicker. He tried hiring a horse, but 'the charge is enormous'. He had even proposed that 'one of Henry's horses shall stand at livery as usual during his absences that I may use him', but this arrangement seems to have been unworkable. He says nothing about the whereabouts of the room he procured nor about its amenities: only that here he was going to study every organ of the body. 'Utility is my first object . . . and the work which I now commence will not, in theory at least, be thoroughly completed until every disease which influences the natural structure or originates in its derangement has been connected with the corresponding organic lesion.'

Bright now became more and more engrossed in the struggle against disease and suffering. He sought out every observable phenomenon during life and tried to piece the whole together after death. It was fortunate for him that none of his seniors cared much what happened to their patients once they had died; none of them considered that morbid anatomy had any direct bearing on their work. It was in this area, therefore, that Bright had the field to himself, and early in the morning, before the ward rounds, it was in the post-mortem room that he was usually to be found. This gave him an hour or two in his room before he had to return to Guy's. He was careful never to miss an opportunity to do a post-mortem, and he became fanatical in his attention to detail: each specimen was beautifully drawn and carefully described. He talked little about his work, and few were interested.

It was in the Babington home that Bright seems to have found his relaxation. Now that Bright was eligible for private practice, Dr Babington might have been anxious to introduce him to more people – though this was definitely not the side of the profession he wished to pursue, as he must have told Dr Babington many times. In any case the Babingtons had an enormous number of friends, and Bright was by no means the only young doctor to be asked to an evening meal, or to spend a day at West Green, their country house at Tottenham, where 'in the heavy sweetness of Madonna lilies' and at the spot where a broad ha-ha separated the field from the garden, Bright, like everybody else, had to 'show the extent of my athletic qualifications'.

Mrs Babington seems to have been a delightful person, full of solicitude for everyone. Two of her children remain shadowy figures, but Benjamin Guy stands out as an attractive man and a distinguished oriental scholar. When Bright met him he had just returned from Madras with his young children. He had lost both his young wife and his own health out in India, and now he was destined to be a doctor at Guy's and to become Bright's devoted friend. Martha, the youngest daughter, spontaneous, vivacious and charming, undoubtedly dazzled both Bright and Sam.

There was no definite moment when it could be said that Bright fell in love with Martha. Indeed it was Sam who was first carried away, and it is from his pen that we get a vignette of the ball held by the Babingtons in January 1821.

It was after a musical evening, which they left at eleven, that Sam and Bright went on to the ball, where, 'surprisingly to relate, we danced the two year old Lancers'. Sam, knowing but few people, at first found it 'bad fun'. But some time later he had a dance with Martha ('Miss Angel B'), after which 'it was all perfect happiness and we did not get home till half past four'. Seeing them together, Bright must have feared that at thirty-two he was too old, too dull, for her.

Two days after the ball, Bright found love dominating everything at Ham Green, where he went for a short holiday, the first for eighteen months. He got there in time to celebrate his parents' anniversary; they had been happily married now for thirty-nine years. The village bells were rung and gifts exchanged. Bright had with him Sam's present to them, a brass inkstand 'with as many kisses as there are knobs on it and a wish that it may sometimes be carried by Mama into her dressing room when she goes to bed'. It was an especially happy occasion also because Robert had just announced his engagement to Caroline Tyndall. This was considered a most suitable match: the Bright family had known the Tyndalls of the Fort for 150 years.

His thoughts preoccupied by Martha, Bright gave himself up to the festive atmosphere, delighting in the high spirits of his father and Robert's radiant happiness. To his family it still seemed miraculous that the one-time retiring, morose young student was now an enthusiastic doctor, determined to share in all their interests – the wedding preparations; his father's geological quandaries; the choice of coloured silk for the tapestry his mother was weaving; the new treasures purchased by Phoebe for the hot-houses; Benjamin's struggles to wind up Lowbridge's affairs; the trimming of Elizabeth's plain muslin dress which 'had to be used as a ball gown, it being too extravagant to wear her crepe at a charity ball'. And one day, everybody else being out, Elizabeth even had 'Dick all to myself and playing chess he gave me checkmate twice'.

Otherwise he was devoting all his attentions to hospital affairs and his amusements were few. By this time he was holding classes on Botany and Materia Medica every Tuesday and Thursday. Deeply absorbed in medical research, he dismissed all else from his mind. So when that August, 1821, his sister Phoebe wrote proposing that she and Elizabeth should visit him he was appalled. Fond as he was of his sisters, a visit was the last thing he wanted at this particular time. He felt he could not face Phoebe's meddling in his affairs, her kindly cross-examining, her time-consuming questions, her well-meant suggestions; while Elizabeth, 'dear as she was, would only brush and polish my old hat over and over again until it shone and would want to see all London through my eyes alone'. Had Sam still been there to act as escort, had Henry not been out of town and their relations in the country, the idea could have been entertained. So he wrote appealing to his father:

I have been a good deal perplexed how to answer as I most certainly am not prepared for such a visit which under present circumstances would be most irksome to me and unpleasant to them. I have found it necessary for the more wholesome occupation of my mind to enter of late much more busily into the perusal of those professional studies to which my connection with Guy's Hospital gives me access . . . I intend at present during this autumn and winter to let a good many matters of theory and practice pass through my mind, and to see what use can be made of the hospital. It is a fine institution and it ought to be able to inspire those who are actually connected with it with some ardour.

Little is known of the progress of his love life. Meals at the Babingtons continued to be interspersed with his studies. But at what point their relationship blossomed, at what stage his feelings for Martha began to dominate everything else, we will never know.

Bright continued to hide his emotions from his own family for a long time, and the Babingtons seem to have remained ignorant.

Modest and lacking in self-confidence as he was, Bright must have found it inconceivable that Martha should love him enough to want to marry. It took him far longer than most men would have before he decided to ask for her hand in marriage. Perhaps it was the electrifying news of his brother Benjamin that shocked him into a more decisive course of action. For Benjamin quite suddenly announced to an astounded, and unsuspecting family that he was going to marry, in June of that year, 1822, Mary Elizabeth, the daughter of the Revd Rowe of Lewin's Mead. Apparently he had flung himself at her feet on the rocks of the Cheddar Gorge. Immediately after receiving Benjamin's news, Bright's visits to the Babingtons became more frequent. One evening he lingered on 'because he found himself unable to take his leave'; and when one afternoon he took her to a concert it suddenly seemed possible that she might actually love him in return.

When they became engaged, Sam noticed that Bright was overwhelmed with such joy that he remained unembarrassed by being the centre of attention. 'Dick says he is a fortunate man in possessing such a Helen.' Martha seems to have tendered her advice over any little problem that arose in the decorating of Bloomsbury Square, and most especially concerning some cabinets that Bright was considering having made to house his geological collection. In a letter to his father dated 23 July, Bright wrote: 'I intend to have this rather expensive job because I shall have the lower part filled up with drawers for minerals, insects, shells etc., as the fancy of myself and my wife may direct . . . '

There was no one more loved and respected in the City of London than Dr Babington, and so, under the gaze of a delighted public and a mass of friends, they were married at St Mary's, Aldermanbury, on 14 August 1822. Martha, as his wife, conferred on him, Bright said, 'such happiness as falls to the lot of few men on earth'.

We have no description of the wedding, no account of the honeymoon, and no portrait of Martha. We have to be content with the knowledge that she was very young, with an eager, childlike quality, vivacious, amusing and enchanting. As a doctor's daughter, she must have understood Bright's need to work, his long absences, his preoccupied silences, and she was probably a good listener. For as long as she could remember, she must have been involved in the affairs of Guy's Hospital; she might well have been taken to the Treasurer's house at some time or another, or perhaps to one of the wards on Christmas Eve, with a parcel under her arm.

In her own home, geology was often discussed and it was taken for granted that medical matters would arise in conversation; the occasional patient would be mentioned, the methods of other doctors talked about. But in the presence of non-medical friends, her father had been adamant that 'nothing relating to his professional work was to be mentioned', either at the dinner-table or anywhere else outside the hospital, so Martha was well aware of the need for discretion; she never repeated the confidences which must have come to her through her husband's work. By nature Bright himself was both reticent and discreet, so they probably did not discuss medical matters a great deal.

Marriage must have been a warm and vivid interlude in his life, short as it was to be. Undoubtedly, Martha enriched Bright's life, gave him new colours, sharpened his senses and brought out in him much that had been imprisoned and unguessed. On visiting Bloomsbury Square, Henry found 'Dick was sparkling . . . and is less diffident about his work and worth'. Harriet Gibbs also found him changed. When she called on the 'happy pair' one afternoon, she thought 'the doctor was much less restrained and so perfectly affectionate . . . it was quite delightful to see them together'. Even at Guy's the students noticed something different about him; always observant before, one of his pupils now commented that 'every button on his coat might have been an eye, he saw so much'.

Up to this time Bright had found his greatest fulfilment in his work: now marriage brought domestic responsibility, companionship and physical closeness. He and Martha went everywhere together. The family at Ham Green 'adored her', and when she was introduced to the Heywoods in the north she conquered them immediately with her 'wit and charm'. They had mutual friends in the medical world, and hovering in the background there was always Dr Babington. One gets the impression that Martha was his favourite child and that he became devoted to his son-in-law, zealously promoting his advancement and slowly coming to depend on him. He who had directed Bright as a pupil at Guy's now consulted him as an equal. They discussed difficult cases. They met at Geological Society meetings and at the Medico-Chirurgical Society gatherings, where Bright must have felt gratified to be related to one whose presence added so much to these occasions. We are told by Dr Brodie that apprehensive moments were always spent before a meeting wondering if Dr Babington might have been detained elsewhere.[1] The sound of the carriage wheels 'would instantly dispel the increasing gloom' – Dr Babington himself being wholly unconscious of all this.

The winter of 1822 was a busy one for Bright and he was often kept late on the wards. But Martha, who must have inherited all her father's unselfishness and intuition, seems to have made things easier for him by never begrudging him the time needed for his hospital work; by understanding the unforeseen situations; and by sensing his unspoken worries when his conscience demanded that he should attend to medical matters. At about this time he became involved in a case of mercurial poisoning. This unusual case filled in the gaps in the knowledge he had acquired at the Lock Hospital and established without doubt the fact that the minutest amounts of mercury absorbed by the skin over a period of time could have fatal results. At autopsies, too, he was always to find traces of mercury in the brain, in the kidneys and in the liver.

'A man and his wife applied for advice . . . they were sallow emaciated and enfeebled.'[2] In their eyes was an uneasy distress, in their gestures an eager meaning, which Bright found difficult to interpret. 'They were unable to stand steadily and could scarcely speak intelligibly' for the rattle of loose teeth and the ulcers on their gums, and 'from the constant agitation into which they were thrown the moment they were addressed, or attempted to articulate . . . on the least emotion of mind, all their symptoms were greatly increased.' They could not co-ordinate their movements, and as soon as 'they were desired to do anything with their hands, it was evident that they had no power of directing them: thus instead of taking hold of the proffered paper, they caught at it with spasmodic jerks, and when at last the paper was seized, it was crumpled in the hand.'

They refused 'to leave their habitation or occupation' and be admitted to hospital, and as Bright thought them too ill to attend out-patients, he had to go out of his way to visit them every evening before he was free to return to Martha. The couple lived and worked in a room of a shabby house, in a labyrinth of unwholesome streets. The walls and ceiling were greasy and 'all the implements, the tables, and the man's hands were discoloured by the particles of the metallic oxide, and the air of the room was close and fetid'. For their livelihood they procured the leather bags in which quicksilver had been imported, and by means of a vice extracted it 'from the very pores of the leather'; every globule found was treasured, every speck collected, and through the skin of their hands the particles were ingested into their system. Bright was astonished at the speed of the discoloration, the depth of absorption, the effect it had on hair, nails and mind.

'Of course no remedies could be of any avail while they persisted in breathing this polluted atmosphere: and the woman died worn out by the irritation of the skin. The husband then consented to come into hospital' – though it had taken a long time to persuade him. He became agitated, swaying round the room, stuffing his mouth with leather, trying to convey also that he could not find the necessary money to pay the fee for the towels, tin pot, knife, spoon, earthenware plate and sheets which the hospital provided. But, as he often did, Bright paid the fee himself; and under 'the total change of air and great attention to the state of the bowels, the tonic remedies, and ammonia and other stimulants he left the house cured. Three years afterwards I met him in the street, full of health and gratitude: he said on leaving hospital he had gone into the country, where he was pursuing life as an agricultural labourer.'

Strangely enough, it was while attending to this case that Bright learned of the death of Dr Bateman in Yorkshire. It had been indiscriminate taking of the blue pill, containing mercury, that had precipitated his demise.

It was in this same week, at Dr Babington's request, that he went to see his old chemistry teacher, Alexander Marcet, who had been ordered to bed that Monday with angina. He was on his way back to Geneva, having spent some time with Humphry Davy in the Highlands. He wished, he told Dr Babington, to congratulate Bright personally on his marriage. But it was not until Saturday that Bright found the opportunity to visit. When he arrived at Coram Street he learned that Dr Marcet was better and was getting dressed. He was ushered into the little sitting room to wait, together with Dr Roget and Leonard Horner, who were discussing Castlereagh's suicide. They all turned round simultaneously at the sound of the door opening to welcome their old friend, but almost at once their gaiety gave way to shock, for Dr Marcet had fainted as he was putting on his coat and now lay unconscious at their feet. They tried 'every method to revive him' and restore his circulation, but sadly they had to abandon all attempts and turn hastily to the stunned Jane Marcet, limp in her son's arms.

4. Ham Green, the Bright family home.   *Watercolour by N. T. Stones.*

Physicians at Guy's Hospital who influenced Richard Bright.

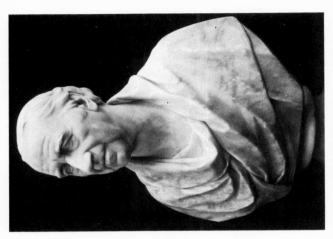

6. William Babington (1756–1833).
Marble bust by W. Bennes.
By courtesy of the Special Trustees, Guy's Hospital.

5. Sir Astley Cooper (1768–1841).
Engraving by S. Cousins after painting
by Sir Thomas Lawrence.

As a physician, Bright watched life inflict appalling punishments on individuals. He was ever weary of death and of saying goodbye to friends, and could hardly endure the ultimate experience of witnessing a patient's final hours. The dead played as large a part in his thoughts as did the living, believing as he did that 'we are truly no more pardonable in attempting to forget a friend who is dead, than we should be in forgetting one that is absent'. In his evening prayers he never forgot a lost friend. He had an implicit belief in after-life, taking comfort from the words of St John, 'There will be no death, the new thing will be life eternal.' Side by side with his science and art went a simplicity and devoutness in religious matters which always supported him. Brought up as a Dissenter, he rejected some of Christianity's theology, so his son William tells us, but he accepted and strenuously 'practised its ethics'.

It must have been a time of great happiness for both Martha and Bright when she became pregnant, when they planned their future together and looked forward to the birth of their child. Martha wanted a son and 'wishes him to be called William', after her father. Richard was to be the child's second name, after Bright's father.

We do not know what went wrong on 30 December 1823, leaving William Richard an exhausted bundle in his father's arms, nor why, five days later, Martha died. On a bitterly cold January Tuesday, 'in terrible silence', they carried her to the church of St Mary's and buried her in the crypt, below the spot where but sixteen months before she had been married.

Bright fought self-pity. 'Consolation', he said, 'was sought in forgetfulness and in a constant succession of changes.' But it must have been an agonizing time, with pictures of Martha multiplying in his mind, returning with dread to the house 'where she invariably waited for me', to an empty hall and the echoing cry of the baby. So he made a point of working late or going to the Babingtons – as bereft as himself – and he was often seen in the newly opened Athenaeum – the club thought up by J. W. Croker for artists and literary men and others dedicated to the life of the mind. Bright was proposed by Humphry Davy and seconded by the founder. It was a sign of success to be one of its forty members, and it gave one the opportunity to meet almost everyone of note.

His loneliness was 'greatly eased' by the presence of his sister Sally; she had just returned from Germany, and now stayed at Bloomsbury Square for long periods as a substitute mother for Willie. She was rather a silent girl, which suited his disposition, and 'though he is occupied in his own thoughts, he keeps seeing to my ease and comforts . . . we talk in German sometimes'. She gives us a picture of empty Sunday afternoons when Bright tried to 'get to know his son', holding one-sided conversations with him; and tells us how he 'wished him free of swaddling clothes and to have him tumbling about the rug'.

Benjamin, too, tried to be attentive, but was 'much harried in every direction possible' with settling his second wife, Mary Rowe, and baby son of a few months in 9 Lower Cadogan Place.

Writing to Dr Babington in January 1824, soon after Martha's funeral, Richard Bright had expressed the fear that his son's bereavement might cause him to isolate himself and squander his talents. But the opposite happened. Bright sought solace in activity and worked harder than ever. The Hospital, busy and alive, helped to fill the emptiness in his heart. If marriage had added something, then its loss did the same; and once the stupor and suffocating grief had been absorbed, he became the kind of man Guy's had been waiting for.

II

Reports on Medical Cases
1824–1827

Bright's generation had grown up in a changing world, a period of expansion in every field. With the ending of the Napoleonic Wars new ideas were surfacing all the time, in religion, agriculture, industry and education. Only in the lofty rooms of the College of Physicians and in the exclusive oligarchical club of the College of Surgeons had the clocks stopped ticking. Things, they said, were all right as they were. Of course, they knew all about poverty and overcrowding, and the diseases attendant upon them: they knew that infant mortality was high and the general state of health of the population appalling: they knew that there were people living in fetid dens, bringing up hungry and barefoot children in shocking and repulsive surroundings – but the dispensaries and the apothecaries took care of all this. Admittedly, there were the quacks and charlatans, but the public was gullible anyway. Besides, the Apothecaries Act of 1815 was beginning to take effect, stopping the prescribing and dispensing of drugs by unqualified persons, and insisting on examinations to deal with the frauds.

Though most members of the Royal College of Physicians ignored the rising tide of new ideas which threatened to engulf their world, there were a few experienced physicians like Dr Babington who were ready to assimilate them, and a few keen young doctors like Bright with the vision to realize that medicine had to progress – 'its ultimate worth', he wrote, 'depending upon whether my generation could do better than the last'.

These young men – Bright, Davy, Addison, Roget, Bostock – were all of the Edinburgh school; having had the best medical training then available in Britain, they realized that scientific thought and methods must replace the complacent lack of curiosity of the past. Illness must no longer be regarded as the plight of the sinful, remedies no longer taken from the housewife's cupboard; a swelling should no longer be regarded as being due to an 'ill humour' of the body, the brain was not a big gland, and outward deformities were not the work of the devil.

131

They found support of a sort in 1823 with the launching of a new journal, *The Lancet*. In its first publication its editor Thomas Wakley embarked on a campaign to abuse the medical profession and its practices. This encouraged all those who were eager for reform.

Bright had little quarrel with the academic side of medical education: standards were high, though the degree of proficiency required by the odd assortment of examiners was low. But he was acutely aware of the need to improve student education on the practical side. If, as he later wrote in his 'Introductory Lecture to his students', a naturalist lectured in the museum, and a botanist led his students to the fields, so should he, as a physician, lead his class into the hospitals. Both at Guy's and at Edinburgh he had experienced a state of affairs distinctly at variance with his own deeply held ideas of fair play. The student paid his fees and attended the lectures, but often the professor did not appear, sending his demonstrator instead. There were times when the surgeon avoided surgery and had forgotten the anatomy learned in his younger days, while the physician strode past the beds, his disciples trailing behind, 'not once opening his mouth'.[1] Dr Black, for instance, had not been seen in the lecture room for years, and on his weekly ward visits was often to be seen waving his hand at a questioning student to force him out of the way. Aston Key, by now considered an able surgeon, was seen more than once 'running for it' at great speed out of the wards and away from the patient awaiting the knife, his legs clad in 'brilliant blue velvet', murmuring something about the odiferous smell of the patient.[2] All this provided the stimulus Bright so needed at this time. It was not only his great compassion for the sick and his enquiring mind that prevented his being completely overwhelmed by the loss of Martha, but the preoccupation with reform which increasingly took hold of him.

It was fortuitous that in 1824, his first year of being a widower, Bright was appointed as full physician, on Dr Laird's retirement through ill health. Sad as he was to take leave of 'a true friend', it is impossible to think that he faced the future other than with joy: he would now have his own patients to treat in his own way, using his own initiative. At almost the same time Dr Babington resigned from his lectureship and Dr Cholmeley proposed to Bright that he should take his place and go into partnership with him as joint morning lecturer. Again Bright must have been delighted, for he had been longing, as he told his father, to teach Practical Medicine. Every

Monday, Wednesday and Friday he was now to be found at 10 a.m. sharp standing before the 'upturned faces of his young friends'. He had to pay Dr Cholmeley £700 for this privilege, £500 more than Dr Curry had asked when Dr Cholmeley had purchased the lectureship from him. Harrison, the Treasurer, objected strongly on hearing about it, 'considering this an unwarrantable and unjustifiable demand, but at length reluctantly conceded on condition that Dr Bright should take all the risk of loss upon himself, and stipulate not again to dispose of the lectures'.[3] It was not long after this that Harrison, after having to pay the £300 which Dr Addison could not afford to give Dr Black for his lectureship, stopped the traffic in lectureships. Lecturers were then nominated and appointed by him.

At this time the training of medical students went little beyond attendance at these lectures. The practical work in the dissecting room under the eyes of a surgeon was not obligatory, and few physicians ever gave clinical instructions at the bedside. So it was not long before rumours began to spread that Bright was taking his few students into the wards, that each patient was getting a hearing, and that Bright was doing 'outrageous things'[4] like undressing patients, poking and prodding, using his hands as might a surgeon in an attempt to discover the exact situation of a gland or a lump or the exact location of a particular pain. The students were used to seeing a physician place his ear against the walls of a fully clad chest, but Bright would always remove their clothing, never deterred by 'obesity, foul breath, fumes of tobacco, beards or a racking cough'.[5] What was more, he was using the new and suspect method of percussion, beating naked people about as if they were toy drums. More outlandish still, he used a stethoscope – that instrument thought up by some peasant, that foolish toy, 'that capital bouquet holder', as Dr Cholmeley once called it, when he was rebuking Bright for using it.[6] But Bright never seemed to consider what other people thought of him; he thought the stethoscope a tremendous thing, and had by now almost come to depend upon it when trying to interpret a peculiar heart-beat. He even took pains to show his astonished students how to palpate a liver in the presence of dropsy:

for this purpose the attention of the patient must be drawn away if possible to prevent the almost involuntary tension of the muscles . . . and then the point of the fingers being placed on the surface, by a quick movement are brought down with the integuments so as to displace the fluid and receive the impulse of the liver; and then taking advantage of a favourable moment the irregularities of the surface may be felt.[7]

He made his pupils take specimens from the patients – something unheard of before – of blood, sputum, excreta, pus and urine; it all had to be examined, described and analysed 'in whatsoever room or space they could procure, even taken home if necessary'. Every specimen of urine had to be examined for the presence of albumen, and perhaps of sugar; for this nothing more than 'a candle and spoon was needed . . . take a small quantity of urine in a spoon and hold it over the flame of a candle. If albumen be present, you perceive before the fluid reaches the boiling point that it becomes opaque. . .'[8]
On the subject of blood-letting he was equally revolutionary. 'Bleeding', he said, 'should be adopted with much caution.'[9] He surprised his young critics in Outpatients by not depleting 'a man whose body was constantly under the stimulus of drink'; how else, they wondered, could he hope to get rid of the patient's intake of gin?

He also told his pupils to look out for those sores which were produced by irritation – 'of urine constantly trickling over a part, saliva drooling from an open mouth or the pressure of one foot against another'[10] – all of which, he pointed out, in a case of high fever could produce 'what the French call "La pourre lieu" ' [gangrene – the rotting place]. These same pupils must have wondered, too, why he insisted on cleaning a dirty mouth or washing out an eye when there was delirium which he himself said 'often closes the scene of life'.

At first, all this must have occasioned ribaldry and ridicule, but it was not long before Bright had devoted followers who understood his thinking and supported his investigations. Fired by his imagination, many of them were even beginning to demand amenities of their own; they wanted a laboratory, and a chance to do post-mortems themselves.

His friends saw little of Bright that year, his family less. In May 1824 he took his son to be christened at St George's, Bloomsbury, and in June he was observed in public for the first time when he joined the grand assembly at the opening of the new building for the Royal College of Physicians in Pall Mall East. He went more from a sense of duty than anything else; he felt he should support the President, Sir Henry Halford, who had devoted a great deal of energy to converting the old, inadequate premises into something more akin to the grandeur of its members.

Otherwise his hospital duties absorbed him totally. His work developed slowly, as he continued to fill his notebooks with his observations; ignoring the head-wagging of his elders, he continued to defy the standard practices, always renovating, discovering and proving his cures.

One other thing that he did become interested in was the growing disagreement between Astley Cooper and the authorities of St Thomas's as to who should succeed him on his retirement. His nephew, Bransby Cooper, whom he had nurtured and trained, was his own choice, but the Governors of St Thomas's favoured their own surgeon, one James South. Bransby Cooper was a warm and honest man and a careful and competent surgeon, though he lacked self-confidence, something which was attributed to the brilliance of his over-shadowing uncle. To Bright, Astley Cooper was the sort of man who made doctoring a delight, and he liked the solid, broad-chested Bransby Cooper; he was always on their side. Mr Harrison believed that a complete break from St Thomas's would be the right answer, and Bright was one of those who supported him. Thus the partnership of the two schools under the name of the United Borough Hospitals came to an end, and a separate surgical and medical school at Guy's was founded. Once the decision was made the plans were drawn up and building begun with amazing swiftness. Harrison insisted that the students' life should not be disrupted, so the new dissecting room, the large museum and an anatomical lecture theatre were built during the holiday months.

Guy's suffered little from the rupture; the reputation of its lecturers remained still the highest, and Astley Cooper was a Guy's man anyway. Though he operated little in the Hospital now, wanting time, he said, to devote to his wife and his farm at Gadesbridge, he returned to tender his advice from time to time. Everyone was delighted to have him still about. He had been knighted by George IV for removing a small cyst on his head, and was also in continuous demand in private practice. He remained a good and steadfast friend to Bright. One memorable evening some years later he was to present Bright with a claret jug of considerable worth, which, he said, was nothing compared to the value of Bright's gifts to Guy's.

By October 1825 the new school building was ready to receive students. With the establishment of Guy's separate medical school,

Bright's name was entered for the first time in the new prospectus as a full lecturer in the Theory and Practice of Medicine. There were two other new names – Thomas Addison and Thomas Hodgkin, both men of the same high calibre and pioneering outlook as Bright, who shared his conception of the responsibilities and aims of a physician. Addison, who had already worked with Bright both at the Lock Hospital and at Dr Bateman's Dispensary, accepted the post as lecturer on Materia Medica and Pathology at Guy's with delight. Weary of sexual disorders, though still passionately interested in skin diseases, he flung himself back into general medicine so enthusiastically that the opposition he had encountered to his appointment as assistant physician soon proved to be unjustified. Some had apparently objected because he had not been trained at the United Borough Hospitals.

Hodgkin, like Bright and Addison, had studied for his MD degree at Edinburgh University, and like them he had practised in London, obtaining the Licence of the College of Physicians. Brilliantly educated, able to assimilate languages effortlessly, serious and studious, he was a young man of many talents. He clung to old-fashioned manners, sprinkling his speech with 'thee's and thou's', and was conspicuous by his sombre dress and the round hat of the Quakers. He was appointed Demonstrator of Morbid Anatomy, and his neat notes can still be read in the 'Green Inspection Record Book' which he was the first to institute. It was with his help that Bright was able to widen his pioneer work in pathology.

As curator of the new museum his work was outstanding. Sir Astley Cooper had accumulated a great collection of specimens, all of which were housed in the museum at St Thomas's, and as the authorities refused to part with them Hodgkin had to work hard to fill the cabinets from scratch. He went after everything that was interesting and unusual, displaying both skill and knowledge in the material he amassed. The glass jars, arrayed in tiers on shelves, were arranged in such a way as to illustrate each disease as it occurred in the organs and tissues of the body – a unique method never before considered.

As an ardent investigator himself, Bright contributed many specimens, appreciating the rich material which Guy's provided. The 500 beds were a 'repository' of every disease. Few patients were admitted in the early stages of disease and many were terminal. The ships brought many suffering from tropical diseases and the highway from the Continent brought cases like hydrophobia and tetanus.

Bright was slowly acquiring a Thesaurus-like knowledge of medicine, and he had a retentive, photographic memory of cases; trained in every sphere of his profession, he now felt himself to be capable of unravelling the mysteries of disease.

While the life-style of his senior colleagues continued unchanged, Bright carried out an astonishing amount of work. He always arrived at the Hospital early, for this was 'his best time of day', when his eye was at its sharpest and his mind at its clearest. In addition to his demanding day-to-day schedule – the ward rounds, lectures in the morning and evening, the clinical teaching, the demonstrations in Outpatients – he plunged into research and worked hard at pathology. But to his patients watching his every move he was no exploring scientist. You have only to read his case reports to learn of his kindliness and compassion. He went round the wards 'with a flask of port in his pocket and leisure to sit and watch'.[11] He always found time to change a poultice or a sheet, or pound a pill. Each patient must have longed to hear his reassuring voice and to feel the comforting touch of his hands – 'large hands with unusually long thumbs', that were gentle with everything they touched.[12]

To his weary students, staggering under the load of his instructions and teaching, as they gave treatment and watched reactions, studied drugs and assessed results, saw the data piling up, the drawings, notes and specimens flowing out of the mortuary – to them he was both a doctor and an investigator. Sometimes a pupil was careless or sloppy, but grumpily they all adopted Bright's methods. Though some complained that he kept them unnecessarily long at a bedside, others became suddenly fired with enthusiasm and followed him as a dog follows its master. In the end they were all to realize the inestimable value of his teaching, the immensity of his work.

It is unlikely that he discussed with his students or with anyone else what he was investigating at this time. From October 1825 to the summer of 1827 he worked ceaselessly at research: the tremendous task of detecting, in every case of physical disease, the nature of the primary cause which had determined its onset. He scrutinized the patients' history, circumstances, signs and symptoms, and continued his investigations by means of chemical analysis; and at death he compared and correlated the progress of disease as observed at the bedside, with the facts evident from the autopsy. Any organ of the body, Bright thought, might reveal the cause of the symptoms. Nothing like this had ever been envisaged before. Painstakingly, methodically, he collated and condensed all the material he and his students collected, remaining cautious until all could be brought to an irrefutable conclusion.

Bright worked under immense difficulties, difficulties which today would be regarded as insupportable. His patients were scattered in all the different wards of the hospital, where conditions militated against systematic study at the bedside. The wards were overcrowded and restless; the stale smell was stifling, the noises distracting – the shouted confusions of the very ill; the inane chattering and screams of fear and delirium; the coughs and groans; the furiously energetic scrubbers with their tin pails; the shouted altercations of the poultice makers; the unceasing sound of hurrying feet. The lighting, too, was inadequate for a keen observer; on a dull day it must have been difficult to discern the blue lips, the pinched, white nostril, or the jaundiced skin. Nor could the intricate dissections have been easy, performed as they were by flickering candlelight.

Another trial must have been the dearth of post-mortem material. As far as his own research was concerned, Bright found the task of asking reluctant relatives for permission to carry out autopsies both distasteful and difficult. Sometimes it involved him in a visit to a patient's home, where precious moments were wasted. The microscope was not the instrument of precision it is today, nor were there the modern methods of fixing and preservation; there was no refrigeration, and laboratory techniques were limited, too, with histology very much in its infancy. There were no x-rays, no scans, no pyelograms or cardiograms, nothing with which to measure blood pressure or gauge the cerebral spinal fluid.

Although Bright came into contact with all manner of disease he was during this time taking particular note of cases involving the thorax, like bronchitis, pulmonary abscess and gangrene of the lung; inflammation of the intestines also interested him. He described accurately a case of tuberculous laryngitis and tracheitis, and discovered the cause of glycosuria – sugar in the urine – in themselves very considerable achievements.

Dropsy was, of course, another condition that particularly interested him. It was, he said, in 1811 that he had 'first observed the altered structure of the kidney in a patient who died dropsical'.[13] Now at last he had the opportunity to do intensive observations and investigations on his own cases. It was a common and distressing complaint in those days and he must have longed to find a cure. The public knew the condition as 'the dropsy', the doctors as anasarca; today it is usually called oedema. It is a collection of fluid in the cellular tissues of the body, or in a serious cavity – ascites, for instance, is dropsy of the abdominal cavity, hydrocephalus is water on the brain, and pleural effusion is fluid in the lung. It was considered then to be a disease, but Bright in the course of his researches found it to be symptomatic of many other afflictions and always connected with the kidney.

'I have still the slight drawing which I made then,' he wrote.[14] But this 'slight' drawing of a diseased kidney is exquisite in every detail, the organ looking like live material rather than dead. All his anatomical sketches, which can still be seen today at the Royal College of Physicians, show his fine draughtsmanship and the superb accuracy of his observations. They are quite as good as those done by the Says – father and son – the fine professional artists whom Bright was to employ in later years, 'owing to pressure of work'.

Bright concentrated his attention on twenty-three patients who he suspected had kidney damage, noticing in particular in which cases of renal insufficiency dropsy occurred. Dr Bostock, a chemist, helped with the chemical analysis of the patient's blood and urine and, following autopsy, with histology of the tissues. Out of the twenty-three, seventeen were to die; he was then able to handle each organ and study it minutely. But each of the twenty-three patients was important; each made medical history.

There was Daniel Peacock, who attributed his illness to drinking cold beer when it should have been hot, and Elizabeth Stewart who, having trudged from Deal to Gravesend in wet clothes, blamed her swollen legs on the fact that she had drunk too much water. There was John MacDonnell, a pitiful youth of fifteen years, who meant a lot to Bright – 'my true friend'. He did everything he could to save him, but 'his weakly constitution for [sic] his many hardships from poverty' had left him with a granular kidney, and a liver, which, when dissected, was found to be tougher than 'boiled udder'. There was Willoughby Taylor, a parish patient, and Thomas Holbeach, whose swelling legs 'increased beyond whatever I saw'. There was Francis Fish, who had been exposed to all degrees of inclement weather as he regularly beat the featherbeds of a broker. After treatment, his swollen thighs fitted his trousers and his waistband met in the middle. There was William Brooke, whose output of urine was increased by diuretics from half a pint to four pints. There was Thomas Drudgett, the cabman, who was obliged to spend his evenings quietly at home, being too discomforted by his swollen belly and his inability to button up 'the knees of his small clothes' to go out, and the butcher 'of obliging disposition' whose illness, he said, was due to his 'libations of purl' taken at an early hour in the morning, when the hot beer with gin might have been better had he taken it at night.

But of all his patients Bright was above all indebted to the pitiable, whimsical, intemperate sailor, John King. It was this man who, as the first classic case of interstitial nephritis, was to influence the course of medicine so profoundly. Daily, in his weakening state, as his life slipped away from him, Bright watched over him, fed him with oysters cut up into tiny portions, and spooned wine into his mouth, holding his wrist till the end. In his life John King had provided Bright with all the essential symptoms – pericarditis, oedema of the lungs, pleural effusion, a large heart and ascites – and at death he had shown the same generosity, giving Bright the chance to correlate all these things with the conditions he found in the kidney.

He had discovered something which was to make his name famous for ever. Many people might have rested content at this point, but Bright worked on, searching for yet more granular kidneys and further derangements.

By the spring of 1827 he had finished writing up all the cases of special interest, and at last in August the first volume of his remarkable book was published. It was called simply *Reports on Medical Cases, selected with a view of illustrating the symptoms and cure of diseases by a reference to Morbid Anatomy*. He dedicated it to Benjamin Harrison and William Babington with sentiments of the most heartfelt esteem. In the preface he says:

It is my wish, in thus recording a number of cases, to render the labours of a large hospital more permanently useful, by bringing together such facts as seem to throw light upon each other . . . to connect accurate and faithful observation after death with symptoms displayed during life must be in some degree to forward the objects of our noble art . . . Amongst the observations contained in this volume there are some of which I must bear the responsibility alone. Such are the statements and conjectures regarding the dependence of a peculiar class of Dropsies on the disease and irritation of the kidneys; . . . There are other subjects, on the contrary, where I write with confidence, because borne out

by the testimony of my contemporaries . . . I may truly say that I
have met with the most cheerful compliance in all my wishes from
everyone connected with our establishment.

It is a remarkable book, quite distinct and original. Bright is careful
to report only what he sees, and to give credit to any medical
authority writing earlier; he is always ready to acknowledge help from
his colleagues or from anyone who presented him with a case. He has
a literary facility all his own, and a remarkable ability to give
articulate expression to what he saw and felt. His absolute familiarity
with anatomy was crucial, but it is the joy of his discoveries which
makes his book a memorable one.

Each case he writes about is a separate story; some are short, some
long, all are gripping. Each disease is carefully described – its cause,
its progress, its treatment, whether it developed gradually or
suddenly and unexpectedly. Each patient is vividly portrayed. His
anatomical descriptions and his hand-coloured plates are perfect,
and his fame as a pathologist could rest upon these alone. But it is his
dedicated study of his twenty-three kidney patients that really
excites. Remarkably, his descriptions of them are still quoted in
modern textbooks, and three of the original kidney specimens can still
be seen in the Gordon Museum at Guy's.

His account of nephritis is complete; to this day, no errors have
been detected. But from all his meticulous work on nephritis it
emerges clearly that he was not able to find a certain cure, and this
was a matter of infinite distress to him. 'I wish that I were now able to
add any thing completely satisfactory to myself with regard to the
mode of treating these diseases of the kidney,' he wrote.

It will be very obvious from a review of the cases I have cited, that
they sometimes present difficulties so formidable as to defy the
ordinary means of cure: indeed I am inclined to doubt whether it be
possible, after the decided organic change has taken a firm hold on
the kidney, to effect a cure, or even to give such relief as may enable
the patient to pursue for a few years the occupations of life: where,
however, the mischief is less rooted, we may undoubtedly do much.
In the treatment of the disease, . . . we have two distinct indications
to fulfil: – we have to restore the healthy action of the kidney, and
we have to guard continually against those secondary conse-
quences which may destroy the patient at any period of the disease.

No one since Harvey had effected so great a revolution in medical thinking, yet recognition for Bright came tardily. His colleagues at Guy's barely noticed the book's publication – though this was due perhaps to Bright's own reticence and deprecatory attitude towards himself. The volume was a harbinger. It was only a first step in his self-imposed task, for what he had done in the work on dropsy he wanted to do for other diseases in like manner: 'the work will not be complete until every disease which influences the natural structure, or originates in its derangements, has been connected with the accompanying organic lesion.'[14]

It was an expensive book, printed on paper of a quality unknown today, and it is doubtful whether many of his colleagues ever took the trouble to glance at it, let alone study it. But there was some interest shown, and slowly his work penetrated the medical world – though it was on the Continent that he first received real recognition. Dr Babington was warm in his praise; Mr Harrison valued it as a service to the Hospital; Dr Abercromby, in Edinburgh, was deeply interested, and Dr Gregory was quick and proud to give his one-time pupil the support his work at first required. Meanwhile Dr Christison, junior to Bright but already a name in Edinburgh medical circles, looked again at his own cases of albumenuria and quickly confirmed the accuracy of Bright's findings on renal disease. News of his growing reputation reached even his father.

But there were many who begrudged his success. Even Astley Cooper criticized the miscellaneous arrangement of the cases – a fact which Bright was to take to heart when it came to publishing the second volume. There was incredible ignorance, too. One small faction alleged that, as all the dropsy cases were Guy's patients, taken from the low neighbourhood of Southwark, it was solely a disease of the labouring classes; and, should an affluent person be afflicted by dropsy, then it was not the same disease as that described by Bright. There was even a court case in Edinburgh, alleging that the testator could not have died from Bright's disease, for it was a disease unknown to 'the middle ranks of life'. It was not until late in 1829 that Bright's disease was recognized 'in all stations of life by all medical men and only in too great abundance'.

12
Eliza
1825–1828

During those years of 1825–7, while Bright was amassing his material at Guy's, laying the foundations of the discoveries which were later to immortalize his name, there was also a slowly developing romance with Elizabeth Follett. They had known each other as children, but we will never know how this schoolday acquaintance was renewed. It seems that William Webb Follett and his younger brother Spencer visited Henry's chambers a good deal about this time. Both the Follett brothers were studying law and were probably in need of Henry's experience. And, where Webb went, Eliza usually went too, for she adored him. There exist a few letters that touch on this, and from these we get hints of male voices interrupting one another in the Temple, with Bright and Eliza in the background.

However consumed with work, Bright always took time off for relaxation; life to him was a mixture of work and pleasure. The time he spent at Guy's was never enough for him to do all that he wanted, but he was never one to grudge a holiday, and was easily lured away. The summer holiday of 1825 Bright spent at Ham Green, joining his sister Sally who was looking after Willie at that time. His mother was unwell, 'unusually indifferent' to everything. Bright seems also to have paid a visit to Welland Court with his father. It is at Easter 1826 that we hear, in a letter written to his father, all about his visit to the Folletts at Topsham.

'Passage' (or Follett Lodge, as it is known today) had been the family home since the first Folletts, natives of Normandy, had come to England in Henry II's time. Eliza's father, Benjamin Follett, was a retired captain of the 15th Foot Regiment and carried on the old family business as ships' chandler and timber merchant. He had married an Irish girl, Ann Webb of Kinsale, and they had a family of six sons and two girls.

'Goat's Walk' seems to have been Bright's and Eliza's favourite spot; it is often mentioned in Eliza's love letters. It was a narrow path along the water's edge. At high tide a vast expanse of water stretched

143

before them, while at low tide the tortuous channel of the Exe was winged with sea birds plummeting down on to cushions of sea-pink. Here they would watch the bare-legged winkle gatherers, dressed in striped skirts looped to the waist. Their wind-ravaged faces arrested Bright's interested attention, and Eliza soon discovered it was the same when they met gypsies, or talked to her father's men in the timber yard. Exploring with him was a wonderful experience. He was always stopping to pick a flower, to identify the sound coming from a bush or to scoop up the clay where the river Clyst met the solid wall of the old Bridge Inn. Walking along the road where the Romans had marched, he would always find some evidence of their existence and of their battles.

Of Eliza's appearance one learns little. There are portraits of her brothers, and one can assume that both she and her sister shared some of their good looks. Eliza, in one or two of her letters, hints that her looks provoked admiration, and one has the impression that she was attractive. According to Mrs Follett's recollections, Bright's gentle disposition as a boy had endeared him to all the Folletts, and it seems they found him delightful this time, too, and his visit was a success. He proposed and Eliza accepted.

Before the wedding, there were all the family visits to be endured, and Bright gave a few dinners to introduce Eliza to his more intimate medical friends. Then, in July 1826, they were married in the old church of St Marguerite at Topsham. Nothing remains of the day, nor of the honeymoon: no sketch or letter tells us who attended the ceremony, nor what the couple did or where they went after it. We know only that the shutters of the Bloomsbury Square house were closed long enough to have the chimney-sweeps in, and that Bright's book was occupying much of his thoughts.

The old house at Bloomsbury Square now came to life again. Eliza was 'delighted' with the large drawing room, the light, airy landings and the large book-lined study at the back of the house, where she often sat. Bright had set aside a certain sum of money for her to decorate the rooms and make any alterations, should she so wish. But Eliza was reluctant, not wishing to disturb any old associations he might value. Only when it came to fitting in Mrs Follett's large Irish dresser did they have to decide to alter the dining room.

There were at first some difficulties with the servants. They made Eliza feel 'uncomfortable', but since she had come they all grudgingly had to 'make the best of it'. The cook, Anna, seemed glad enough that there was once more a mistress in the house, but with Jones, the valet, it seems that Eliza needed to tread warily. She noticed at once that he was a man 'who saw to his own comforts'. He had taken over many of Martha's duties, waiting up for his master, helping him to get to bed, wishing him goodnight. Often he lingered, Bright's boots in his hand, his jacket over his arm, and feeling the need of something kept 'the unwilling doctor chatting'. In the morning, too, he would shake the folds of his cloak, twirl the doctor's tall hat, tender advice on the day's weather, and remind him of his appointments, before watching him mount his horse or set forth to walk.

It must have been hard for Sally, too, so much her brother's confidante, to relinquish charge of Willie's nursery life. She had, with the help of Susan the nursery-maid, looked after him, on and off, for nearly three years, and she was devoted to her undersized, delicate nephew, with his curly fair hair and beautiful eyes. To Eliza, there was something 'wan and wistful in Willie's small face', something strangely old-fashioned in the way he sat, with the rapt attention of a sage, brooding over his toys, but she grew to love him with all the love she had. People soon forgot that he was not her own child. 'I was about to say YOUR little boy,' wrote Dr Laird, 'but if he follows up to his early promise he must, by this time, have become a great favourite with you.'

For quite some time people respected their need for privacy, and the month of September 1826 was a solitary one. At times Bright went to work in his study or drove to Guy's to see to the management of an acute case, but Eliza saw 'that it cost him dear to tear himself away from me'. It was the same with her. If she read or played with Willie or passed the time sitting on the piano stool, she did so only because these occupations 'were concerned with you' and won his approval. He would organize treats for them. One Sunday, they hired a carriage and took Willie to see his grandparents, the Babingtons, at Wood Green, Twickenham. There, each room and each article of furniture must have recalled what Martha had once been to him and what he had lost. One instinctively feels that Bright never totally overcame the sense of grief caused by Martha's death. Again and again in his writings[1] you will find that no death of anyone deeply loved – especially his children – ever seemed to 'sever his communion with them'. But if that first love was always to lie dormant as something special, in the subconscious mind, it never interfered with his life with Eliza. He made her the centre round which everything revolved:

every thought of hers was understood at once, every feeling shared, and when she became pregnant that September every wish of hers was gratified. Eliza was a loving and comforting companion, but she was of a fussy disposition, demanding more attention and greater sacrifices than the selfless Martha.

Although every moment Bright could spare was taken up by his book – sometimes Eliza awoke in the morning to find him gone, snatching a few quiet hours in his study before breakfast – he was for that first year of marriage extraordinarily considerate. He attended fewer meetings, and tried not to leave her alone for long periods during the day. Accustomed as she was to the life of a small place like Topsham, surrounded by family and friends, it took her some time to get used to the more formal and lonely life of a doctor's household. She looked forward to the visits of her brothers, Spencer and Robert, and constantly worked herself into states of anxiety over Webb. She had never really got over the suicide of her brother Charles, even though it had happened six years before (1820). Bright welcomed them all; Bloomsbury Square was to be as much a home to them as it was to his own brothers and sisters.

Anticipating increased expenditure, Bright now found to his surprise that 'he was spending only half as much as before', and that his affairs were no longer in disorder. His wife was certainly a good manager. He was touched, too, by the efforts she made to anticipate his wants and to get to know his simple habits. When in his company she found 'his calm strength, his reserve of manner easier to bear', she told her mother, than the polite chatter of the drawing rooms he kept encouraging her to enter. But when she did find herself in the presence of his medical friends he was proud of her – and 'his praise gives me such pleasure'.

Christmas 1826 found Bright once more in consultation over his mother's bedside. Eliza remained in London with Willie, and Sally attempted a portrait of her nephew, painting it to surprise her brother. Sarah Bright, suffering most probably from cancer, thought it ridiculous that Bright should leave his bride when she had the benefits of Dr Prichard's purges and Dr Estlin's theories, while Dr Laird kept writing to her and recommending the Bath waters. Bright was reluctant to leave his sorrowing father, but Richard Bright said it would only worry him more to have him staying there when he knew that his own patients were awaiting him. But by 11 March (1827) he was back again, and with his four brothers carried his mother to the family vault in Brunswick Square. Her death was a great sorrow to them all. It was not reported in the *Bristol Mercury* until a week later.

March 18, at Ham Green, after a protracted and painful illness, the wife of our respected citizen, Richard Bright, Esq; in whom was united all the accomplishments and virtues which can adorn and endear domestic life, and constitute the perfect gentlewoman. She was a humble and pious Christian, and has ever been universally respected and beloved; and her memory will long be cherished in the hearts of her surviving family and friends.

In May Bright and Eliza lost their first child. For Eliza's sake Bright was glad of the distractions which were provided by the arrival of the Heywood cousins, descending on London for the season. Sam Bright came too, escorting his future mother-in-law, Mrs Jones – and it was Bessy, his fiancée, who of them all helped Eliza most to get over those first 'feelings of motherhood which had taken hold of her so powerfully'. Sam insisted on Eliza accompanying them in their London sightseeing, and she found Bessy charming 'with an unlimited capacity for enjoyment'. London never ceased to amaze her. 'Regent Street was surely the finest street in the world'; 'the Regent's Park – had it really been a barren swamp' – and 'now the most beautiful, most cultivated and romantic land ever conceived?' The streets abounded with palaces she had read about in *The Arabian Nights*, while nothing equal to the shops in the Burlington Arcade was to be seen in Liverpool.

Another interruption was provided by Serjeant Sam, Bright's uncle. Disturbed about his health, he 'did me the honour of consulting me', as Bright told his father. His not feeling fit, he said, had nothing to do with the loss of his sister, though it had been a severe blow. Lack of energy seems to have been his chief complaint. He could not see why he found distances to be so great. The effort of getting from place to place was such that by eleven o'clock, when the fashionable world came alive, he was quite out and fit only for his bed. Bright upbraided him for what seemed to be an unreasonable expectation since, being seventy-five, he could not hope to be the same uncle who had once played bears under the table with them all when they were children. What a likeable man Serjeant Sam must have been. King George IV once said of him: 'There is not a better man on the face of the earth.'[2] 'After our consultation', Bright went on to tell his father, 'Uncle Sam stayed on to sup with us . . . how gallant he was to both Bessy and Eliza, revealing all that charm that had won him his early successes . . . he darted from one subject to another making us laugh and telling us about Madame Patti's voice and how sorry he was that the ballet was no longer included in opera. . . ' It was Eliza who was to recall later that year, in September 1827, when Serjeant Sam died on the circuit at Haverfordwest, how he had been the 'life and soul' of that party, behaving more like a wildly happy boy visiting London for the first time than an elderly uncle with a faulty heart.

After the emotions and upsets of the last few months, little else disturbed the even tenure of their lives. Bright was giving more time both to his book and to his patients. Eliza continued to put everything in order for him, changing the flowers on his desk, asking Anna to choose his favourite dishes and making a fuss of Willie. When it came to the afternoon, this being the time he tried to keep for his home life, she waited expectantly for him. He would then return to Guy's for his evening rounds, after which they would talk in the drawing room. She made him tell her what he had been doing. Even so she was always conscious that there was a special department of his mind to which he was unwilling to admit her. Sometimes his medical activities were beyond her understanding, and on occasions she plied him with questions which he seemed disinclined to answer. In the letters she wrote to him she often expressed her regret at not being able to share the joys and vexations he experienced in a world that was remote and alien to her.

Many of Bright's patients were causing him anxiety at about this time, so it was something of a relief to him when Eliza went on a visit to Topsham, taking Willie with her. It also gave him an opportunity to finalize the mezzotints for the first volume of his reports.

Having looked forward for so long to being with her own family again, Eliza was surprised to find how hard it was to bear the wrench of separation. 'Anna declares I look 20 lbs better,' she wrote to Bright, 'and my father follows Willie as he runs about with his watering pot, trolley and set of tools.' But the old familiar surroundings, once so beloved, had lost all their savour for her. In her letters she poured out her feelings. Separation, she wrote, was quite unlike anything she had felt when parted before marriage. 'You ask me how much I wish for you. It is impossible for me to express how much I long for you every hour in every day. . . I wish for you quite as much as you could wish, much more than I ever did before we were married, for every day has made you dearer to me. . . ' The next day she wrote again: 'This is the day of your botanical party. I hope it will be agreeable and I hope and trust that the book is finished and that you my best beloved husband are ready to set off to come to me.' A week later she asked him, 'How long do you think it will be before that book is finished? . . . That everlasting book. . .

In July she took Willie to a lodging house in Sidmouth, where she enjoyed the fresh apricots and longed for Bright to get there in time to enjoy them – 'Tell me what preparation is necessary for us both before we go into the sea.' She told him she had a fixed routine, and somehow managed to get through what was perhaps the worst time of the whole day, the long evening. He was more necessary to her than air and water; and why was he still so 'horribly hard at work'? But he did not forget their wedding anniversary, and sent her 'a beautiful amulet and a small shapely bottle containing smelling salts'. These she might have found necessary to use when she learned that there was little hope of him joining her in Devon, and that she had to face Ham Green without him. It was a visit to be especially dreaded; indeed, though the Bright children were always to adore staying there, Eliza herself was really only at ease at Ham Green when Bright was with her. She never cared what impression she made on others herself, but she suffered greatly when it came to her children, wondering how they would acquit themselves under the critical gaze of Phoebe and Sally.

Apparently Eliza was not the only one to dread visits to Ham Green. 'By a lucky mistake of the Brights I am released from my engagement today,' wrote Harriet Gibbs once to her husband George, but a few days afterwards she was exclaiming, 'but when there it was impossible to be more kindly treated than I was.' On the other hand Bessy always loved her visits, declaring more than once in her letters to Richard Bright that she found 'a day at Ham Green is always three hours shorter than ever it be in my own home or anywhere else'.

Perhaps it was Phoebe's rather intimidating presence that put people off. She ran a most comfortable home for her father, her brothers and their wives, giving much thought to the children's pleasures and treating all visitors with consideration. She placed stoves on the landing, had fires lit in every room, arranged a vase of flowers on every bedroom chest; warm stones were always available for cold feet, fans for hot days. A carriage or horses to ride were put at the disposal of visitors, while they always left for home laden with provisions for the journey and plants from the garden. A more selfless, kind and dedicated person would have been hard to find. As a canvasser, whether for the election of a doctor to a consultant's post in the Royal Infirmary, or pushing one of her brothers as a Parliamentary candidate, her enthusiasm was always intense. No one supported the rights of the poor more ardently, no one bullied, cajoled and encouraged the sick as she did; no one poured more love into the well-being of their own family. She must have been an extraordinary personality. Slim and graceful, capable of exerting great charm, yet she was moody and aggressive. She found it hard to be polite when she was bored; the family all suffered in turn under her critical and dogmatic ideas. When she was with her Eliza lost all her self-confidence: it was hard to find that whatever she believed to be her best efforts were met still with Phoebe's disapproval.

On this first visit there was jealous contention over Willie; having known the little boy for longer, Phoebe and Sally could not help feeling they had priority, especially when matters of his education arose. At Topsham, Mr Follett had told his worrying daughter that it was not necessarily the best thing for a mother to teach her child. Having 'no pretensions to being blue, nor the least wish to be so', Eliza admitted that she did not like teaching children. In fact Willie had stubbornly refused to learn his letters from Eliza's father, so it had been left to Susan to teach the boy. 'I am however, thought a very wicked person for letting Susan teach him,' wrote Eliza to Bright. Phoebe maintained that no servant girl 'should be teaching *your* son. . . I said that *you* were pleased with my present plan and that is *my* chief wish. . . However, to keep the peace I have stopped his lessons altogether. . . only then to be examined and cross-examined about him by Sally, who wants to know why he was not saying his lessions. . . What a misfortune to any poor child to belong to such a learned family.'

Poor Eliza. All this must soon have been forgotten, however, for the next letters she wrote were much more cheerful. Her father-in-law kept planning excursions for herself and Willie, to the Gorge, Clifton and Pill. She had taken several walks in the woods with Benjamin, 'who is the pleasantest person I meet with because he talks to me about you and is very kind'. There were busy evenings with dinner parties, Eliza 'was sorry to say', for like Bright she was not particularly sociable, but she enjoyed the evenings spent with Robert and Caroline at Abbot's Leigh. And there were quiet evenings when 'nothing was talked about but bones, old teeth, caves, grey marls, blue oophytes, green sands, tetrocytes and a variety of names too hard for your foolish wife to attempt to remember'.

For Eliza that autumn seemed endless. All the time she was hoping Bright would appear, as was the whole family. 'You seem to me', she complained, 'most horribly hard at work.' She had no idea that books were such a labour to publish. On the last day of that long October Eliza wrote her final, desperate letter to him: 'a hope that has been my comfort for the last two months is now gone and I am sadly miserably disappointed. . . when you write to your father I wish you would say that you cannot spare us any longer than the end of this month. . . that the first of November you have desired me to set off to you. . .'

Back at last in Bloomsbury Square, in the face of her husband's welcome Eliza's reproaches remained unspoken. Once more together happiness, Eliza said, 'lifted them high above all else'.

The winter of 1827/8 brought cold and sleet; bronchitis complicated the condition of many of Bright's patients, already sick with some other complaint. An outbreak of gastric influenza absorbed his attention. Because of severe vomiting, 'the tincture of opium, the simple effervescing saline draughts and brandy' that he gave his patients were not being tolerated. He worked late and this upset Eliza. It was the first taste of what her married life was to become. She was accustomed to his returning from Guy's at the same time every evening, calling out to her as soon as he entered the hall, glancing into the nursery where Willie slept, going downstairs again to check that the garden door was locked. Eliza mentions this in the letter she wrote to her mother; otherwise they are taken up with her own concerns: a visit paid by Webb, a consultation with one of the best accoucheurs, the arrangements being made to procure the best midwife to attend her.

On 25 July 1828 Anna was born, and soon after this Eliza took Willie and the infant to Topsham, where they were to remain under the care of Susan and a new nursemaid, while she and Bright travelled north to attend Sam's wedding. This was their first trip together since their honeymoon. She found herself facing the intimidating experience of meeting more of the family and their friends with unusual calm. It was Bright who said that he was dreading the 'full impact of relatives'.

They were received everywhere in Liverpool with unfeigned pleasure. Elizabeth, Bright's youngest sister, had long awaited their arrival. Bright was, she said, the one object of her thoughts. She had written many letters to Bloomsbury Square telling Bright and Eliza about the preparations being made, and now, bubbling over with excitement, she took them round to see her friends. All that summer she had stayed with the Jones' at Lark Hill. She was to be the chief bridesmaid, and they were thankful to have her as their house slowly filled with visitors. Their younger daughters were away at school and Bessy was at Lupsack Hall near Wakefield introducing Sam to the Gaskells. Elizabeth was a capable girl, witty and attractive, with the same dark eyes and hair as her brother Dick.

As Bessy was the oldest and the favourite of four daughters, Hugh Jones, a successful banker, was determined that the wedding should be one to remember. It was certainly a big occasion. The Liverpool Heywoods had put rooms at the disposal of most of the visitors from North Wales, Bristol and London; while the Manchester Heywoods filled their home at Hope End.

The many elderly relatives were delighted to see Bright. Sarah Bright's two elder sisters, Phoebe and Anna, or the 'old Aunts' as they were affectionately called, felt reassured at having young Dick back amongst them. He could advise them as to whether a lobe of brimstone kept in the pocket or a cramp bone would ease their aching joints, and tell them whether reading by the 'new gaz' was harmful, and what measures should be taken to improve the condition of Benjamin Arthur, the elder brother who was suffering with water in the sac of his heart. The young Heywoods were delighted with the presents he had brought, and they in turn showed him the latest dance steps. He would be dragged upstairs to see a sickly child, or to look at an ailing servant, or down to the kitchen to see one of the staff's relatives. Jones, Bright's valet, was careful to point out to them how fortunate they were to have the services of a 'true physician' instead of an apothecary. Poor Bright – in such a family circle medical advice was bound to be sought. Eliza was often to be exasperated by the way he never resented such claims on his attention.

Richard Bright's arrival was eagerly awaited by all. But Phoebe had written to say that it had been hard even to fix a date for setting off: 'he says he cannot tell the day.' As painters and carpenters were to take possession of Ham Green in their absence, they planned in any case to go to Malvern; from there it was Phoebe's intention to go to Worcester and choose a tea-set as a wedding present for Sam. As for their father's gift, Sam would have to wait for 'the platter and plate since they had yet to be engraved' with the combined coat of arms of Bright and Jones. Bright was not surprised to learn from his sister of his father's reluctance to attend the wedding. He felt he could not bear to see all Sarah's relations, all the people and places that had meant so much to her. He had not the energy nor the heart for such an occasion, though for the sake of the young couple he knew he had to go.

But on 10 September he arrived, looking for Bright to tell him that his book had reached Bristol Infirmary, 'creating a stir.' Receiving the love and congratulations of innumerable friends, his kindliness on that day was much talked about by Sam and Bessy on their honeymoon:

Indeed we have a great deal to thank you for in every way and although you may have some distant idea . . . it is quite impossible you could be fully aware of the very great pleasure and satisfaction with which we regarded your having been present with my sisters at our marriage – it must always make the remembrance of that happy day much more delightful. Mrs Jones has expressed herself in the strongest way and my dearest is continually talking of the manner in which you had all received her.

On their journey south Bright and Eliza spent a few days in Worcestershire. Instead of Welland House they chose to stay in Lowbridge's compact and comfortable house, Brand Lodge. Eliza, 'enchanted with its warren of small rooms', watched with some amazement at the change in Bright: she was always to be surprised by his two sides. Now he was like a 'vagabond', eagerly pulling her with him up the bare slopes of the Malvern Hills, or dragging her down, shouting out poetry, or hurrying her along to seek rare flowers hidden in the copse of Brockley Manor. He made her ride on horseback along the Beacon to Malvern Wells, and there he brought her 'macaroons and took a long while choosing a toy for Willie'.

On their return from Worcestershire, Eliza, accompanied by her brother Spencer, went straight to Devon to collect the children. Bright, back once more in the wards at Guy's, found such demands made upon his time that he was almost glad, he told his father, not to have Eliza and the children to consider. Yet there were other demands to face. Mrs Follett wrote to him for a 'poor man's plaster' and Mr Follett for a grey horsehair cap, since he suffered 'terribly from the heat of his cloth cap'. Bob Morehead wrote to ask whether his father could get a cadetship for one of his sons in the East India Company, and whether Bright could get his son Charles a place at Guy's. Sir George Mackenzie wrote, anxious that Bright should be kind to a Scottish sculptor, Mr E. MacDonald, whose works were to be exhibited in the 'great city . . . and the best thing you can do for him is to mention him and his works to your friends'. Dr Laird wrote wistfully; now suddenly confined to an armchair in a Bognor boarding house, he enquired for news of Willie and promised to send his 'small friend a fossil of a lamprey and some shells'.

The old aunts wrote to lament at not having consulted him. Surely he could have prevented their brother's untimely death. 'They would very much like you to come to your uncle Benjamin Arthur's funeral,' wrote his father, 'but I do not think there is any absolute occasion for your doing it . . . your affairs should prevent you. Ben I hope will make his appearance and I hope Henry will come.'

By the second week in December 1828 Eliza had returned with the children. Taking up her pen she wrote to her mother to tell her of her safe arrival, and how Bright 'is never failing in his attention towards me and my thoughts and feelings of this time are not mine, they are his which become mine, coming into my life again to light it up.'

*

Six children were born to Eliza and Bright, their names and dates of birth being faithfully recorded at the end of the Apocrypha in Bright's large Bible. The children were brought up in the loving atmosphere of a Georgian nursery, with none of the strictness and rigour typical of the Victorian age. Twice a year Eliza took them out of London to more beneficial climes. They went often to Topsham and Ham Green, and sometimes to seaside resorts. Both Eliza and Bright felt these separations acutely.

There is little to tell us what Bright himself felt about married life. He wrote to his father when he could – 'a few lines will at any time suffice but I shall wish for them often,' his father had told him – and when apart from Eliza he wrote to her daily. But few of these letters survive – as he kept telling Eliza to burn his letters it is not surprising. If she did not herself commit them to the flames then they went the same way as many of his notebooks and sketches which, a generation later, were thrown on to a great bonfire by his daughter's son-in-law, Frank Newbolt, the strange brother of the poet. (We know he kept notebooks: 'Put it down in your notebook and then you will remember it,' Eliza would often say.) Bright left nothing autobiographical either. When many of his medical contemporaries like Brodie, Pettigrew, Holland, Christison and Bateman wrote their life stories, both Addison and Bright refused to resort to such 'puffery', as Addison called it.

It is from Eliza's letters that we learn almost everything we know of their life together. They are difficult to decipher, since her neat and steady hand sprawls not only down, but across the same page, one word covering another. Paper was expensive; perhaps this was one of her economies. Her pen took the place of the ordinary daily conversations indulged in by most married couples; naïve and chatty, always concerned with the passing day, every matter was worth the telling. Bright was spared few details. As a doting mother, she reported every sign of a baby's progress, every gesture, every new tooth, every new word. She wrote about Anna lying content in the Topsham nursery, cooing at the nurse; Anna crying at the voice of her aunt, making dismal faces at her uncle; Willie scrambling for wild orchids in the fields round Tunbridge Wells – in trousers too big for him, though smart and with a white speck in the weave. Every pimple was noted, every spot magnified, every cough described. She fussed over the effect of a rhubarb purge; she was apprehensive about the preparations for the children's sea-bathing. She fretted over their lack of sleep, the loss of Willie's cap, the price of a dress or the texture of Anna's linings to her drawers. She grieved that he was not there to admonish the children over their temperamental tendencies, for she left Bright to deal with their morals – 'his lofty ethical world was far beyond her reach', she once said to her mother. 'He is so truthful and so pure in mind . . . never once does he offend or shock . . . or say a word out of place . . . '

As a wife she wrote about her own health, her headaches, her insomnia, her bowels. Sometimes it seems that he was not convinced by her complaints – about the inconveniences of the various boarding houses, for instance. Daily she exaggerated, hoping to lure him to her side; in every letter she reminded him that pleasures had no relish unless they were shared, that without him there was no charm in anything – 'though I see how beautiful everything around me is, I feel sometimes despair . . . how long must it be before we can enjoy the delights of the country together again?' She was always complaining about the painful partings, always resentful of the need to keep in touch with both families. Nor could she ever reconcile herself to those times when he was detained, and for some reason or other had to postpone that longed-for day when they would be together. His duty to Guy's, or to a colleague, patient or graduate, always outweighed all personal considerations, but she could not dismiss 'all those disagreeables as you do by saying "I cannot help it" '.

Eliza felt deeply the need of his support: 'my companion and help. . . nobody helps me or thinks of all my little comforts as you do . . . How I wish you were here and how I should be quite happy, but there is always something wanting.' Once she had to stop in the middle of writing a letter; her misery and longing for him overwhelmed her and she had to lay her pen down quickly, put on her coat and walk out in the garden, and 'like a person in a dream I tried to join in the games of the children'. Even though she was surrounded by those whom she loved best, as on Christmas Day at Topsham in 1829, she could hardly bear to eat her dinner for thinking of him. All she could do was to feel the ring on her finger (which he had sent to her by her brother Bob) and 'turn it round, round and round'. It was often worse at Ham Green for there she would watch the other couples together – Bessy and Sam, Benjamin and Mary – and she would become ill with self-pity as 'my eyes follow them into the woods or the greenhouses'. And as for the sound of carriage wheels in the drive, why they made 'her heart beat fast – and then I would remember how very far you are away from me'.

He was never out of her thoughts; she worried continually that he might be lonely in the evening, that he stayed at home when he had been asked out – 'Do pray go and hear Paganinni, it will be so much better than moping at home', and why had he not discovered before that the Athenaeum had a pleasant dining room? On the occasion of his being ill, with only a blue pill to take for his pain and her not there to comfort and nurse him, she was distraught; with Jones the valet away at the same time, how on earth was he managing? 'I know how much you always want him . . . you must indeed be having a comfortless time.' That was the time when, with his head clanging like a bell and the earth swaying under his feet, he had to get out of bed to see the Brunels at Bridge House, Blackfriars. Both the young Isambard Brunel and his father had suffered internal injuries as the result of an accident in the Thames tunnel they were constructing at the time. When Bright was better, she worried about him still: 'you will I am afraid make yourself ill again . . . do pray go to bed at 12 midnight.'

Eliza's letters were also full of exacting demands, and he often had to go out of his way to fulfil them. But he never complained, and one gets the impression that on the whole they amused him and he found shopping relaxing. Preoccupied as mostly he was, he could be the most absent-minded and forgetful of men, but with the help of Jones and the faithful Anna, he managed to get the things she asked for: 'Buy a book for little Willie and buy a pair of trousers for him which can be bought in Oxford Street for 1/6.' 'I want to send Bessy's baby threadbare gloves. They can only be found in the Arcade or King Street in Covent Garden.' 'Please tell Jones to go to Mrs Plume; she promised faithfully to send my stays by the 7 o'clock morning coach or the day before.' 'Change Willie's old shabby bonnet for one to fit his head.' 'You have not sent baby's cap in the parcel, I hope it was that you forgot it and not that it could not be found.'

When the time came for Bright to join them on holiday, there were more instructions and reminders; whether it was to Ham Green, Topsham, Worcestershire, Tunbridge Wells, Brighton, or some other seaside place, there was always an extra bag to be added to his own luggage. 'Tell Jones to put Follett's new flannel petticoats into your bag.' 'Those geological transactions which are always lying about the house, bring them when you come.' Her father would enjoy looking at them. 'Your sister Sally desires you to bring her a shawl with plain middles and silky fringes. I think you can get them at Lewis' or Compton's and Swan & Edgar.' 'Please bring the walking stool, the stick is in the study. I do not know where the seat is, I suppose Jones does.' 'Bring goffered crepe enough to trim a cape . . . some black silk elastic stocking for mother . . . they cannot be obtained in Exeter.' And so on.

His family, too, used him thoughtlessly. However pressed for time, he somehow found it possible to buy a specific gravity gauge for one of the Ham Green gardeners, a hot air apparatus for Sam's new house in Orchard Street, Liverpool; and for his father often some unwieldy thing like a steam bath with a long pipe or a good-sized box with holes pierced in it for the herbs. He liked shopping for his children, buying them confectionery and sharing their rapture over Perry's ice cream. Eliza was continually being surprised by the unexpected and appropriate things he bought for all of them, like the coloured rakes and forks for the hay fields at Brand Lodge – 'I do not know that they were ever so much pleased with anything of the kind before and though rather large, they manage them famously.' He liked particularly to choose some delicacy for the small evening parties he gave to his colleagues. This was usually when Eliza was away. The lonely hours were then filled by a symposium on some medical topic, or perhaps natural history or geology. Perry's was the best cook shop in Oxford Street and it was from there that the succulent veal, *vol au vent* and nut *mille fruit* came. And he never forgot to order Dr Bostock's favourite oysters, were he to be there for dinner.

13
Recognition
1829–1833

Slowly Eliza was beginning to realize that life with Bright could never take a fixed shape; that working as a doctor and sacrificing himself for others was what his life was really about. She attributed immense importance to his intellectual interests, but failed to understand the reason for the long hours spent in his study when he got home.

There now occurred in Bright another spurt of creative energy. The next four years, 1829–32, he devoted to a second volume of his book, *Reports on Medical Cases*, another brilliant series of observations. In the introduction to the first volume he makes the point that 'his work would not be complete until every disease which influences the natural structure or originates in its derangement has been connected with the corresponding organic lesion'. What he had done with nephritis – correlating the abnormal changes seen in the kidney at autopsy with the symptoms of dropsy during life – he would now attempt to do with other diseases. And, what was even more important, he slowly began to influence both Addison and Hodgkin, and to teach his students to observe and examine in the same way.

Bright had once remarked that 'want of experience is the greatest sin in a physician for which nothing can compensate'. So, seeking experience once more, he now pursued his object, spending hours in the tiny post-mortem room, amassing a wealth of observations at the bedside, carrying out clinical examinations on all his patients and on some belonging to other doctors, and using chemical analysis as a routine procedure. Then he would disappear into his work-room nearby, or return to his study at home, to draw his pictures and write up his findings.

It was at this time that he pondered long over a baby with hydrocephalus which he thought had been caused by falling off a table; but after that autopsy and another similar case he recognized that a blow could be the starting point of tuberculous meningitis. He paid frequent visits to Mr Cardinal, the celebrated hydrocephalic, whose condition was now deteriorating. He was carrying seven pints of water on his brain:

> if a candle was held behind his head or the sun happened to be behind it the cranium appeared semi-transparent and this was more or less evident till he attained his 14th year. Fits of an epileptic character came on at about the age of twenty-three and since then his health has suffered . . . he read and wrote well . . . his memory was tolerable but it did not retain dates and periods of time and it was stated of him that he was never known to dream.

At his death Bright found himself 'dowered with interest'. He came across many people suffering with rheumatic fever, and many were the times he placed a painful, red-hot, swollen joint in a more comfortable position. Chorea linked with rheumatic complex interested him. What was it that caused the hideous grimaces, the jerky, rapid, purposeless movements of the limbs. He was the first to describe a mitral murmur in this childhood complaint, and he always said that intelligent management on the part of a physician could do much to prevent the patient from becoming a cardiac invalid.

By 1831 Bright had filled 700 pages. These four years must have been among the happiest and most rewarding of his life. This second volume of *Medical Cases* was in two parts, and it was dedicated with sentiments of the 'most heartfelt esteem' to 'his faithful friend, James Franck, Inspector General of His Majesty's Forces and Fellow of the Royal Society'. The relationship between these two appears to have been a close one (Bright named one of his sons after him), but little is known about Franck as a person. He appears on fishing expeditions and was Dr Babington's companion on one or two trips to Scotland. He figures around the Boardroom table at Guy's and in the Council Meetings of the Royal Medico-Chirurgical Society. He acted as Bright's adviser on more than one occasion. In fact his younger brothers are mentioned more often in the family correspondence.

Once again in the Preface to the book the author acknowledges his debt to Guy's – 'the sumptuous hospital'; to his medical and surgical colleagues who had, as usual, shown him 'nothing but kindness and co-operation'; and to Dr Bostock and Dr Benjamin Babington, his two 'most able and assiduous friends'.

His descriptions in this second volume remain marvellously simple and colourful, and there are forty or so beautiful illustrations – not all done by him, but certainly personally supervised. The descriptions and drawings reflect each other with microscopic accuracy: the damaged brain looks just like the Parmesan cheese he says it does; the vesicle *is* the consistency of a half-cooled blancmange. He describes what he saw at the bedside, what he found in the post-mortem room, with no exaggerations. He clears away doubts and difficulties, yet at the same time raises questions which are still not answered today.

This time he describes over 400 case histories. He deals with diseases of the brain and the nervous system. Neurology fascinated him. He had never forgotten his own hallucinatory experience when ill with typhus fever, and it made him particularly sympathetic towards those suffering from the weird illusions of an irritable brain. Where many of his contemporaries advocated restraint for 'lunatics' and used straps and corsets, he felt that the deranged mind needed no added fears, besotted with terrors as it was already.

He describes aphasia, headaches, hysteria, fits and epilepsy, and forty different cases of cerebral haemorrhage. Here, he unravelled much that was still mysterious and was a pioneer in the subject of cerebral localization. It was he who worked out that an obstruction on the left side of the brain would cause paralysis on the right side of the body; that deficient circulation and lack of nourishment to the brain was 'a powerful cause of odd behaviour'. He pointed out that cerebral haemorrhage was commonest in males over forty, often over fifty, and that there were many small seizures before the one that was final. He was interested in diaphragmatic hernia and heart-block, and the pathological studies of jaundice and hydatic cysts are penetrating and valuable. There is a masterly quality in the first ever description of acute yellow atrophy. He was the first to describe Addison's disease, pointing out the mahogany skin and other symptoms, though he did not connect these with the diseased renal capsules he found at autopsy, as Addison was later to do. He also dealt with cirrhosis of the liver and glycosuria.

His accounts of hydrophobia and diseases of the pancreas are astonishingly readable. And his tale of the epileptic 'whose somnambulism took him about the streets without hat or coat, walking in a complete unconsciousness from Clapham Common to Shoreditch', is totally gripping, as is the moving account of the little girl ill with whooping cough. As she was the daughter of a colleague, Bright spent long anxious hours by her bedside. But with her death, Bright was able to prove that condensation of the lung was present in cases of 'Chin cough', as some of his poorer patients liked to call it. It is a wonderful description of broncho-pneumonia and pulmonary collapse.

*

In Spring 1832, in the drawing rooms of the Duke of Sussex, Bright learned from Sir Henry Halford that his professional worth was at last to be properly recognized: he had been nominated to become a Fellow of the Royal College of Physicians. Sir Henry hoped Bright would accept this 'as a mark of the very high esteem' in which all held him for his professional labours. Before he went to bed that night Bright wrote to tell his father how the honour had answered all his hopes: 'Indeed I do not know anything of the kind which could give me greater pleasure, not for any immediate good it will do for me in practice, but as showing the goodwill of the better part of the profession towards me and placing me amongst them on a still more comfortable footing.'

It was on 25 June 1832, 'the only day when such an election can take place in the year', following Dr Tattersall's Harvean oration, that he was solemnly admitted as a Fellow. He had to shake hands with the President and all the assembled Fellows of the Royal College, and having paid the necessary fee he was welcomed without a dissenting voice into that ancient and learned body. After the ceremony he slipped into the Athenaeum, where he wrote once more to his father: 'I feel much pleasure at my new dignity and the more because I am quite sure that the feeling is unanimous as was the vote.'

The honour had little or no influence on the course of Bright's life; his name was already widely known. Medical men in the provinces had begun to study his case histories, and young family doctors who had not seen a particular case before often wrote to him for advice. 'The writings of Bright put Edinburgh on the alert,' wrote an Edinburgh doctor faced for the first time with a case of enteric typhus. Other doctors wrote offering him material, and referring to cases they had under observation which they thought might be of interest to him. He received many letters from abroad, too, including letters from his friends in Vienna, trying to lure him into the post-mortem rooms there.

A new public was creeping into existence, with new demands. Bright was surprised to find he was being consulted more often, as people wanted to be properly examined. But he remained totally committed to Guy's and he tells us little of his private work. It is from Eliza's letters again that we get the vignettes:

'How is your Mr Barry?'

'Did Miss Wagstaffe die?'

'How goes your troublesome lady?'

'Poor Mr Hinstanton what a bad accident it was!'

'I hope you found poor Sir Poultney better?'

'How is Lady Williams?'

In 1833 Bright was chosen to give the Goulstonian Lectures at the Royal College of Physicians. It was a formidable occasion. The lectures took three days. Two of them were centred round a dead body, upon which he had to demonstrate his facts. He was, he said, extremely nervous, as he always was when confronting senior members of his profession. Eliza told him how absurd this was, since he was going to provide the first instruction most of them had ever had on the kidney; they were surely fortunate to hear him reveal so many things that 'they should all perhaps have discovered for themselves'.

As a lecturer Bright was gentle yet dominating; with his half-cynical, half-humorous look, and his rich engaging voice, he could hold an audience easily.[1] If he did not sparkle, it was the quality of his observations that gained him silent and acute attention, while he had personality and technique enough to enliven the dullest subject.

He talked with strength and confidence 'on the development of those morbid growths which we call malignant', and gave many clinical and post-mortem reports. The last lecture of the three was devoted to the renal origins of dropsy. Two hundred and ninety-six urine samples had been analysed with the aid of students for the occasion. He described in detail the four varieties of nephritis that he had found in the post-mortem room and told them how the urea found in the blood by Dr Bostock could cause convulsions. He told them how struck he was by the function of the skin, and the frequency with which the heart was diseased, especially with hypertrophy on the left side; he told them all about 'the various evidence of cerebral disturbances' which followed. And then he reached his conclusion: 'My conviction is complete as to the existence of some decided connection between the three facts – anasarca, coagulable urine and diseased function going on to diseased structure of the kidney.' When he stepped down from the rostrum, he received a standing ovation.

After that, Eliza's pleasure seems tame: 'I am delighted to hear that your lecture was so good and received much admiration. I am anxious to know if you have been asked to print it. I did not know in those cases that the patron so honoured was to pay the expenses of printing. Is it always so?' The lectures were subsequently printed in the *London Medical Gazette*.

When he began his lecture on renal disease, Bright referred to the help and support he got from his students: 'I have lately had great assistance from the intelligent and zealous co-operation of three of my pupils, Mr Barlow, Mr Tweedie and Mr Rees.' These three young men were to become the nucleus of 'his team'.

In Bright's day, the physician had no registrar, no house physician, no one like the ward sister of today; he worked alone and so had to depend much upon his pupils. It was his persistent concern to see that there was always someone he could trust in attendance on the wards. He gave up as much time as he could to train his pupils and teach them how to care for the patients, and he made them participate in research. Bright had been slowly gaining in credit and popularity with the students, and the numbers attending his lectures increased all the time.

He had none of Addison's flowering eloquence, none of Aston Key's power to inflame the passions of his hearers, but he spoke simply, with no ceremony and no irrelevancies, and was never dull, always opening out new fields of enquiry. His ardour in investigation had once provoked resentment, but now it commanded an enthusiastic response. Those who got to know him became devoted to him, giving him a kind of affectionate gratitude for the knowledge he imparted, and for his attentiveness to their own enquiries and endeavours.

While Bright was sympathetic to the young, he was also strict and penetrating. His students had to become good, sensitive doctors with a delicate sense of touch – 'the touch of a blind man is your duty to acquire'.[2] 'Undoubtedly the more a man sees disease, provided he looks at it with the eye of intelligence, the better: but think not that it is enough simply to let the eye or the hand wander upon the patient: and do not flatter yourself that you possess, by intuition, the power of discerning and discriminating disease.' They had to learn the homely magic of the nose and recognize 'the putrid exhalation which hangs about the bed of the patient labouring under gangrenous abscess of the lungs, the heavy odour of eczema, the foetor which marks mercurial action even before it shows itself in the gums, and ulcerative condition found in the intestines'. He taught them how to examine patients, to diagnose and to treat. They had to learn the insidious tricks of the kidney: 'for its first approaches you must look with all the same solicitude and care felt on discovering the first suspicious signs and symptoms of tuberculosis'. And if there was no cure they were to learn all the available remedies which could cause recession and relieve discomforts.

Soon after the Goulstonian Lectures Bright was astonished to find himself face to face with a youthful deputation. The introductory address he had given to his students on Practical Medicine at the beginning of the first October session of 1832 had been such a success and had made such an impact that they demanded it should be printed. He wrote a letter to thank the students:

> I should be wanting in sincerity were I to deny or even to disguise the satisfaction I experienced from your earnest request that the accompanying address might be printed for use: and although I am well aware that it derived its chief interest from the excitement of the moment and, therefore, fully anticipate that you will be disappointed in its perusal, I have complied with your wish under the confident belief that the little which it does contain will, at all events, have no unfavourable influence on your present studies or your future welfare.

Bright's 'Introductory Address' was a small booklet of several pages written to encourage the medical student as he took his first step on the long, hard road of commitment. In it, he poured out words of cheer, and warned them with humour of all the pitfalls to be met in hospital life. He shows an insight born of his exceeding love for his subject – the human body. 'What machinery,' he asks, 'could compare with the human body? . . . What is the coarse contrivance of the furnace and its fuel compared to the subtle process by which animal heat is engendered?'

The first page of Bright's booklet, headed 'An Exacting Vocation', has been quoted many times by other lecturers seeking inspiration:

> To you – affectionate children will look for the welfare of their parents; to you – the anxious parent will turn for the rescue of his child; and on you – the fond husband will depend for all that is dear to him in the hour of danger; to you – perhaps, may be confided the

lives of numerous men led to the field of battle, or marched through unwholesome countries; to you – the health and efficiency of crews destined to long and perilous navigation may be entrusted; on you – the public eye is to be bent in days of plague and pestilence, for who shall now say that from such visitations even our happy climate may be free? And under all these circumstances you must be ready to give an account of what has been done, not only to those who are eagerly collected around you, but to a much more troublesome inquiry within, who will accompany you to the retirement of your closet, and with its inquisitorial voice not only ask you whether you have done your best upon the present occasion, but whether from the time you commenced your professional studies you used your utmost exertions to acquire that knowledge, which would fit you for the discharge of your duties; for it is this consciousness alone which can enable you to lie down with comfort when harassed by the occasional unsuccessful issue even of your best endeavours.

14
Savile Row
1831–1834

In the spring of 1831 Bright had told his father that he would date the second volume of his *Medical Cases* from his new residence in September. It was a forecast faithfully kept, and the quarto volume went into production as the family moved into 11 Savile Row: Jones, Anna the cook, Susan, another nursemaid and two housemaids; into the mews at the back went Mr Wilkinson, the coachman, and his wife, who helped in the house when necessary.

Earlier that year (1831), the Brights **had** gone house-hunting, having decided at last that they would **have to** live somewhere more fashionable. Reluctantly, Bright had to recognize the fact that there were now many more demands made upon him outside the Hospital; he was being consulted by many and, whether he liked it or not, was increasingly being inveigled into a private practice. This was of some comfort to his father, who thought private work could be the foundation of a permanent provision for his family. Indeed, he had even suggested that whatever stood in the way of this would be far better given up:

> It does appear to me from what I have accidentally been informed, that the constant pressures of engagement at the hospital cannot but have that effect. The advantage in experience and credit which your duties of lecturer were designed to produce, have been realised . . . if the emolument is not likely better to repay your terms and you can obtain assistance as you seem to expect, which will enable you to relinquish part of your hospital engagements without injury to the good feeling between you and the Treasurer and the Governors, I do not think you will act unwisely by so doing.

In April they had found a house in Savile Row, already favoured by leading members of the medical profession; this was long before the tailors had made this their domain. Bright wrote to his father about it:

> The street is narrow . . . It is respectable, if not fashionable. The

Hon. H. B. Simpson, Lady Maryborough, Lady Tryg, Lady Cunningham, Sir. J. Newpath, are the first names I see there now. In medical men it has been somewhat celebrated of late. At No. 16 is Brodie, the first surgeon: at No. 8 lives Dr. Hooper who has retired and Mr. Pettigrew who is a surgeon. Our home is No. 11. As far as I can form a judgement the situation is fitted for me, because it does not remove me too far from my old residence and yet puts me decidedly in the west. On the whole, therefore, though the undertaking fills me with anxiety I suppose it is right.

His father lent him the money needed to buy the house – £600; Eliza, always more concerned about money and security, was glad Bright did not have to sell out stock. When he received his uncle Ben Arthur's legacy, it was she who suggested that it should be saved for their sons. 'I hope you will not be tempted in any way to spend this money,' she wrote. 'We have lived in happiness and comfort on what we have and can continue to do so, do you not think it would be advisable to put it somewhere to get the most interest for it to leave to our dear children?'

Although comfortably off and in want of nothing, money was an ever-pressing problem. They lived simply, but with an increasing family and ever-growing responsibilities and appearances to maintain, they were always in need of it. A doctor who wished to make his work a success had often to draw on his own bank account. The monthly salary of £10 the Hospital gave him in addition to his fees as a lecturer had to go a long way, and he was continually paying out. Sometimes he used his own money to keep a patient in hospital or to pay for his extra nourishment, he had to buy drugs, specimens were expensive, and if a case detained him then he had to pay someone else to do an autopsy. Getting repairs done, buying books and equipment, and printers all put further strains on his purse. Sometimes, too, he had to travel considerable distances.

The Brights had not been in any particular hurry to move, as there was a good deal of work to be done before they could occupy the house. The water closets had to be put in good working order; the basement and the kitchen area had to be whitewashed and painted, as well as the staircase, hall and bedroom; the drawing room ceiling was in a bad state, though the paper and paint of the walls could wait for a year or two. Bright's study had to be fitted up with bookcases, so the bulk of his collection could be housed there. He thought that they had sufficient furniture in general, but would buy if there was anything going cheaply in the owner's sale.

So that last summer in the Bloomsbury house had been spent in a state of flux, with the maids sorting out and packing while at the same time trying to maintain a smooth-running routine. In May, Bright and Eliza spent a few days at Ham Green, while Phoebe and Sally joined the throng crowding into the exotic brilliance of the Horticultural Show in Ranelagh Gardens, Chelsea. At Ham Green Bright turned all his attention to his father, who was sick. Under his care his father got better. For relaxation he turned to horticulture in the greenhouses. In the evening the library door was continually opening to his father's friends, who liked to look in to see 'Dick' and talk – and always left his father comforted and recovered. After they had returned to London, Bright and Eliza received grateful letters from the two sisters, thanking them both for the loving care and attention they had given to their father. A few weeks after this Phoebe wrote that she was much by the side of Mrs Randolph, for the Canon was sick, and then Bright received from Dr Estlin a report of the prebendary's autopsy, dated 25 June 1831:

'Though your sister disapproved, Mrs Randolph consented to my examining the body. The Doctor's symptoms were varied: pneumonia, and the heart was small and very flabby . . . Finding so much disease in the cavities I did not examine the head, it would have taken me a much longer time and Mrs Randolph being in the adjoining room, could, I feared, have heard us.'

The first son of their marriage, Follett, was born on 11 June 1831 and christened in July at St James's, Piccadilly, which was to be their parish church. Eliza and the three children spent August on the Isle of Wight, in a lodging house 'with an unpleasant smell'. Mr Follett joined them there, but was annoyed at being so far from the sea, while Webb, on circuit, arrived one evening when there was nothing in the larder to give him, 'no fish or fowl, no meat or game'. In September they moved in to No. 11.

They were proud of their house – 'this house which you have made so very dear to me', Eliza wrote to her husband. It had a long upstairs drawing room, where they put the cabinet with its display of porcelain and the high rosewood piano. Eliza was pleased with the new rugs, the iron hob grates, and the small wrought iron balcony railings. The two inverted cones by the entrance door, which served to extinguish the link-bearer's torches, matched the other houses in the street. They were pleased with their new 'patent kitchener', a cast-iron oven instead of the old open spit, and their water heating system. For light they clung to candles, neither of them liking the glare of gaseliers. Produce like the apples and pears sent from Ham Green 'were arranged on the shelves of our laundry'.

There was a certain sadness about the month of December that year. It was to be their first Christmas in Savile Row, and the fog kept close to the windows, seeping into the nursery where the two children and the baby lay ill. Eliza was once more pregnant and was low in spirits. Bright told his father he was busy with winter diseases,

> 'and in addition all our children [Willie, Anna and baby Follett] have taken it into their heads to select this time for being ill so that our hands are pretty full. Dr. Babington has, at my request, seen Willie and Anna today. Willie wrote two sides of a sheet to his aunt Sally yesterday intending to finish his letter today, and when I told him he must lie in bed all day, this was his first difficulty, how was he to finish his letter to thank you for all his lovely presents. He cuts out the Duke of Wellington and Bonaparte in cardboard . . . '

The intermittent fever left Anna with a bad chest, and both parents tried hard to ignore the rasping sound that came from it. She was a lovable child, fair and dimpled, with an enormous capacity for amusing herself. She floats into Eliza's letters, playing with her dolls, dancing and singing. That long winter she had breath for none of these things. On 4 April 1834, in a letter to congratulate his brother Sam on the birth of a daughter, Bright wrote that 'for my own part I do not feel desirous of being further instrumental as I am almost sufficiently provided . . . Amongst us we shall abundantly perpetuate the name for this generation at least'.

The fog continued and the spring was long in coming. Bright realized the dangers he was exposing Anna to in London, but not until April did he consider her strong enough to travel. When spring came he sent them away to Dawlish in Devon. Once more, Eliza resigned herself to the separation, writing from Salisbury to tell him how glad she was to think that he had a dinner party to go to that evening, since it would help him to forget their departure for a time.

All July Eliza awaited him at Dawlish. Bright had hoped to join his family there; he loved Devon, and always looked forward to visiting the places of their courtship. But it is, of course, from Eliza that we hear about the whole current of recollections which ran back to those days so crammed with emotion. To her Dawlish was always a 'sweet dear place'; and as she sat in the same pew in the church they had both occupied that first Sunday of their engagement 'the memory of having been surrounded by almost all she had ever loved on earth and in health' had so overwhelmed her that she had to restrain herself from crying out. 'Shall we ever visit it again in such happiness? I fear, never.'

Bright's days that summer were full enough with his ordinary daily duties as a hospital physician, but there were also signs that an epidemic of cholera might break out. To Eliza he belittled its seriousness, giving her other reasons for not being able to join her. Sadly, she left Dawlish, one of her brothers taking Bright's place and arranging all the travelling details and seeing her and the children safely to Somerset. In fact it turned out to be one of the most enjoyable times she had ever spent at Ham Green without him. The weather was warm and fine; Anna was coughing less, and the children were all well, spending much of the day with their nursemaids in their secret retreat by the riverside at Chapel Pill. Willie was riding a great deal, in the company of his cousins from Abbot's Leigh. 'Onesipherus and Robert are both four feet giants and burnt copper colour – Willie looks like a dwarf. He gets most terribly laughed and sneered at by them, but he doesn't seem to mind.' The Harfords of Blaise Castle were giving a dance, the Napiers a dinner party at King's Weston, 'so you see I am getting all that I hate most'. To one dinner party came Dr John Estlin. 'I told him about my pains. I fancied he thought me very ill, talking about myself. Indeed, I cannot say I admire him as a doctor.'

As August progressed, Eliza's letters were filled with the fear of cholera. It was beginning to dominate the nursemaids' conversation. Good hygienic practices were the essence of prevention, but in most places there were open drains and in the cities cesspools often seeped into the drinking wells; in places of poverty, squalor and overcrowding it bred quickly. Eliza heard terrible reports: in Exeter, one of the servants told her, 400 lives had been lost in four months, and the people had died so fast that it was hardly possible to bury them. Whatever people said about the risks being small if reasonable precautions were taken, Eliza was terrified; she was afraid, too, for her parents, who were in a vulnerable position, being surrounded by such 'dirty poor houses'. Should they not move to Exmouth where the meadows were at a greater height? Could not the doctor command them to do so? She was beside herself. As for her brothers, *'always* mention Bob and Spencer when you write'. For Webb her prayers were constant.

This cholera had arisen in Asia; spreading by way of central India to the Crimea and Persia, it was now in Europe. Bright himself had written to his father, and to Sam in Liverpool, as early at November 1831, telling them how serious he thought it was going to be, even though there were then only two cases reported in Scotland.

It's impossible not to look upon its unknown nature and laws with considerable dread . . . I am fairly convinced that it is a very contagious disease . . . With regard to Pill, every means of cleaning the street and the courts and the houses which can be enforced will be useful in giving persons attacked a better chance and in prevention – but the question too, is how you can prevent its attacking Ham Green. If it appears in Pill, I should exact the most complete quarantine possible and if you prepare yourselves, you need have very few things brought to the house except meat – and I should strictly prevent any of the Pill people from coming for medicines and if anything of the kind was to be done it should be done at one of the cottages on the Green or some further distance.

Bright's training at the Fever Hospital had taught him the importance of preventive measures. He gave the public advice – and many in the end took part in nursing the sick, cleansing the houses and streets and clearing the fouled gutters. Along with other concerned doctors he called on the authorities to make the drinking water purer, appealing to those whose influence would add weight. He did not mind where he went or when, and like everybody else risked his life many times a day. There were too many victims for him to look after alone, so he saw the acute cases himself, and left much to the clinical clerks he had trained.

In February 1833, the death of Bright's father-in-law, Mr Follett, dominates the letters. Eliza left London for Topsham immediately; he had suffered from an affection of the heart for some years, but it was still a shock for Mrs Follett to find him in the morning, lying against the pillows dead. 'My poor mother seems so much disappointed that you did not come,' she wrote to Bright,

and besides she has an idea preying on her mind that if you had been here my dear father would not have been dead – that your opinions would have been the greatest possible comfort to her. We have determined to beg you to come down immediately – the funeral takes place early on Saturday and she wishes you to be here as one of those of whom my dear father was very fond. You must set off immediately. Ask Dr. Locock to call to see the children every day.

To have to leave town at such a time must have been hard for Bright. Following the uneasy months of cholera there had appeared a particularly severe form of influenza, which was causing concern amongst the profession. Hitherto it had affected mostly people in the outer districts, but now it was launching itself in the business centre of the city. People knocked at any doctor's door. But Bright did manage to go to Topsham for a few days, where discussions over leaving Mrs Follett alone in the house delayed him. Thrown off her balance by bereavement the widow longed to be left alone to decide the future for herself, and every attempt her children made to raise the subject was sternly swept aside.

Back in a London gripped with icy cold, Bright submitted once more to the routine and the extra work influenza entailed. Lacking the necessary peace of mind and too busy to write his customary weekly letter to his father, he left it to Eliza to tell Richard Bright of the happenings that follow. Apparently, Dr Babington at the age of seventy-seven was not sparing of himself either; and though his wife was always telling him not to neglect himself over the epidemic, he worked harder than ever. But one day 'he ached from head to foot' and by suppertime of 24 April 1833 he was bound to admit, on returning from his rounds, that the only place he really wanted to go to was his bed. But that very evening certain members of the Royal College of Physicians were coming to his house to discuss a new Medical Pharmacopoeia for the College, the old one being considered long out of date. For a man with an aching head and great difficulty in breathing, the proceedings must have seemed interminable. It was not until after eleven that Dr Babington could at last go up to his room, followed anxiously by his wife. She was never able to exchange words with him again, for the following morning he was found delirious with double pneumonia, and two days later he was dead.

It was one of the greatest shocks of Bright's life. Babington had always had a profound influence on Bright. He had been his tutor, his friend and his trusted adviser as well as his father-in-law; no other man could ever be what William Babington had been to him. The event upset the whole of the medical profession, for the character of this benevolent man was 'probably as nearly without fault as is consistent with human nature.'[1] It was said that Sir Astley Cooper never really recovered from the loss; Benjamin Harrison was not seen to smile for weeks. Everyone wanted to pay him homage; everyone wanted to talk about him; many eulogies were spoken and written. Bright himself, with a swelling heart, preceded one of his own lectures at the Royal College of Physicians with a panegyric on the man's character:

Would that I were able to depict the virtues of our departed friend! Scarcely do I feel myself worthy to attempt the task; because I *know* that my words are inadequate to *express*, and I *fear* lest my mind should be unable to *grasp*, one half his excellence.

His was a *sweet simplicity of manner*, which gave a moral grace to every action of his life – his a *profound humility* of mind . . .

His was a *power of self-control* the most praiseworthy . . .

His was a judgment the most correct. His was a *benevolence of heart*, such as few have witnessed . . .

His was a *patient, pious resignation*, to the will of God.

His was *parental affection*, most deep, most ardent, most judicious, most enduring . . .

His was a *strong perception and an accurate appreciation of virtue and of vice* . . .

His was a *cheerful mind* and a most *delightful converse* . . .

Add to all this an *admirable skill in his profession* . . .

*

That summer Anna, Bright's small daughter, became more ill. Broadstairs was chosen as the place to give her the benefit of the sea air; but, as Eliza said, 'the place does not improve on acquaintance . . . the children, I am afraid, will tire of pottering down to the bare sands. I have ordered donkeys this afternoon . . . Franckie [born in May 1832] is frightened by the noise of the wind and sea . . . Anna coughs and coughs.' A doctor had to be called to treat Eliza for palpitations: 'I would rather have been cured by you.'

That autumn (1833) Anna's condition worsened; the nearer one got to the children's landing the louder was the sound of her breathing. Why should a child have to fight for her breath, Eliza kept asking Bright. No child should suffer like that. And so Eliza took little interest in events outside the room and Bright tried to organize his work so that he could spend more time helping to nurse his daughter. And she lay coughing, wearing herself down, or sat against the pillows, unable to speak; sometimes she tried to smile, but she always seemed to look offended – and solemn. She looked at Bright sideways and he could hardly bear it: it was as though she could not have believed it of her father, with all his contraptions set up to give herb-filled oxygen.

As Eliza needed her sleep, it was Bright who more often than not cared for his daughter through the night. By the time breakfast was on the table he had to pull himself together to meet the routine of the day, leaving her to Eliza and Dr Locock. But she died suddenly in November, at the age of five. From that time on 'she haunted them'. Bright refused to speak of it but Eliza, in her letters, referred often to the gap left by the lost child; she saw her bounding along with her brother on the heath at Tunbridge Wells; she saw her at Malvern, riding on a donkey, up the Pig's Path; and once the sight of the Heywoods' little girl running into the drawing room at Brand Lodge, 'the same size and the same shape', seriously upset her. 'But then you will be angry if I write to you about her, who loved her so dearly.'

In March 1834, Eliza took the three boys to Tunbridge Wells. It was one of her favourite places; being near London it was easily accessible for a Sunday visit from her husband. Since Anna's death she had grown wary at the thought of what could happen to others whom she loved and, feeling insecure, she begged him to 'spend even one day' with her. But as soon as she had written it, she regretted it, realizing how miserable his departure would be: 'when you left me again it would be worse than the short enjoyment would be worth – besides the whole time I know you would be most uncomfortable and restless for fear of what mischief was being done amongst your patients'.

But Bright did manage to spend one magical day with his family. Eliza tells us how they sauntered across the heath, Willie always running ahead, picking violets and primroses, Franck and Follett toddling on either side of him. Bright and Eliza talked about a drugget for the dining-room carpet and of Jones, the valet's, love of his comforts, Eliza trying all the time to forget the little figure of Anna. They had much to talk about.

By this time, Bright was taking Eliza more into his confidence. His private practice was growing. Many general practitioners were calling him in in consultation. His telling her something about them made her feel she was more part of his world. Even so she remained a little jealous of his preoccupation with the lives of others and always complained that he never told her enough. He was always careful about what he divulged, and he was by nature reticent. Several years later, Eliza was to discover that he had been in attendance on Queen Adelaide and on Queen Victoria's very young children while no one at home was even aware of his visits to Bushey Park and Buckingham Palace.

Staying with Eliza at Tunbridge Wells this time was her mother; when Bright appeared Mrs Follett tactfully kept to her room. She was absorbedly interested in all their thoughts and doings, but she rarely interfered, and showed always her gratitude for Bright's kind and affectionate attentions. Whenever she took leave of him, he pressed her to return for another visit. According to letters, she tried often to tell him of her feelings, but always found it 'quite impossible to venture to express it'.

All too soon, the visit was over and Eliza had to watch the coach to London disappear up the hill. As soon as she returned to the house, she wrote him a long letter. She had thought him looking 'quite worn out . . . I do not think it worth while to have so much trouble and fatigue, for so few hours of pleasure . . . unless the illness of any of our party should make it necessary, you should not come again . . . Now, my beloved husband, receive all my love and may every year we live find us as happy in each other's love, as we are now and blest with our children . . . '

In July she wrote to him in answer to a letter of his: 'You tell me to burn your last letter but I cannot for it is one of the sweetest I have had lately, full of affection. Tomorrow, my dearest husband, is our wedding day anniversary. Eight years we have spent together but except for those painful periods of separation and till the last they have been years of perfect happiness.'

15
Scotland
1834–1835

Bright always looked forward to holidays. This is revealed in many of the letters he wrote in the winter referring to places where he proposed to take Eliza and his family in August. He loved to make plans, and it was on a particularly bleak day in February 1834 that he brightened 'a dreary hour' by hinting to his father in a letter that they might make a trip to Scotland. This was the year the British Association was going to hold its general meeting in Edinburgh, the fourth since its conception.[1] He had heard that many of his friends from the Continent were thinking of attending. It would be a good opportunity to introduce Eliza to the place and the people and relive again those arcadian days of his youth. He wanted to show her the Trossachs, and was already planning the route and the hotels. But of this he told her nothing, biding his time until such an opportunity occurred when she was 'feeling at her lowest'.

In June Bright suddenly decided to escort Eliza to the Malvern Hills. He was now being pursued by patients to such an extent that he thought it wise to leave no address behind. The children and the nursemaids travelled in one coach and he and Eliza followed in another. Again they stayed at Brand Lodge – now ringed with honeysuckle and cherries – Eliza preferring it to Welland House, which was too big, she said, and when he was not there, too lonely. Bright called the small house 'the warren', but he gives us no account of the visit other than mentioning that Follett, now three years old, was smitten with a butterfly net; so he took the two small boys to where the dragon-flies, 'like long darning needles of shimmering blue', skimmed over a mere, and the moorhens nested among the tall bullrushes, with their stout heads of brown plush – just like a jacket 'worn by one of his old aunts'. One night, Eliza tells us, when the children were in bed, he placed some glow-worms on the mantelshelf of the darkened room 'to show how the luminous tail segments of the female shine like so many living lanterns'.

He left Eliza looking forward to a visit from her brother Spencer.

But it was not long before complaining letters began to arrive at Savile Row. 'I have been here so long that I do not remember last Sunday at all,' she wrote. When he was there – there was a 'stillness and beauty', but now there was nothing to 'please or amuse – nothing in the world but hills and trees and sheep'. Even her brother's company had made no difference to the dozing quietness of the place, nor had Bright's sister Elizabeth's coming dispelled her fears that should any of the children fall ill, Worcestershire was 'a dreadfully remote place' in which to seek medical help. On top of all this 'Follie's bowels are upset and Franckie's gums are sore'. It was after a great deal of trouble that she managed to find a Dr Addison, who had been at Guy's – though no relation to Dr Thomas Addison – and was 'no disgrace to you'. He had been recommended by Mrs Tom Heywood at Hope End near Ledbury, 'who was, incidentally, desirous to know when you are coming here for she is extremely anxious that you should see James'. To cheer her up Bright unfolded his holiday plans in the very next letter he wrote to her: the week in Edinburgh would be followed by some days together in the Lowland lakes. 'Understand, it is to be our excursion.'

'What do they say at Ham Green of your idea of going to Edinburgh?' Eliza wanted to know. Unbeknown to her, there had in fact been quite an exchange of letters. Phoebe had seized the chance to interfere. Why did they not include Elizabeth in their visit to Scotland? It was an opportunity her sister might never have again. 'I should think that when you are attending the functions and private meetings', wrote Phoebe to her brother, 'Eliza would be very glad of a friend and you would be more at ease when you thought that she had a companion. I have for some time hesitated to mention my idea. I know that you are so good-natured to me that you would put yourself to inconvenience to do what I wish, but as the idea originated in me and Eliza has no idea of anything of the kind I trust to your love of truth to tell me if you have any objection to the plan'. Bright, on thinking it over, considered it to be quite a good idea.

When Bright mentioned the suggestion to Eliza she was shattered. It was a proposition that would in every way mar the pleasure of their being together and alone; since the time of Sam's wedding, they had never gone anywhere together without a retinue trailing behind them. She had so looked forward to being free from constraint and having her husband to herself. Her disappointment was intense, and it took several days to go and filled several letters. Bright seems to have been completely taken aback by her protests. Like Phoebe, he had thought she would appreciate his sister's company, and as for the three visiting the Trossachs together, there were always ways and means by which they could contrive to be alone together. He wanted and needed his wife: 'I hunger for your close companionship.' Surely the candour they shared could never be any the less for the presence of a third person?

Slowly, Eliza softened to the idea, though she kept telling him she could not see any of the advantages in the plan. Indeed, she thought it would increase the difficulties – such as getting places in public coaches, and finding beds for three instead of two – and friends arranging dinner parties would hesitate to ask them with a third person. Besides, there would be more bags and boxes for him to look after. 'However, it is of no use to think of the disagreeables and I must try to think of the pleasures we shall be giving Elizabeth and by this means I trust please your father.' And though she could not help but feel sorry that it had even been proposed, she did admit that it would not lessen their plans at all and 'we shall feel comfortable and get satisfaction in the idea that we are doing right and giving your sisters both pleasure'. Moreover, 'Elizabeth is so extremely kind and good-natured that I should like to give her some amusement in return for so kindly shutting herself up here with me . . . So, you see, my dearest husband, I have reasoned myself into looking upon it in a more pleasing light than when I first had your letter proposing this plan.' The matter was thus closed.

Bright longed to leave the noise of London that hot August. On the first weekend of the month he had intended to return to Worcester-shire to collect his whole family and escort them to Ham Green. But he was having a particularly trying time, and because of several worrying cases he had to put Malvern out of his mind. Reluctantly, he picked up his pen to tell Eliza. He got the expected protest by return:

You can imagine how much disappointment I felt when I had your letter yesterday. I got it as I came out of Little Malvern church and read it walking up the hill. I have so freely expected you on Saturday, that the days and nights I have counted. But I feel with you that it would be quite impossible, worried as you are to leave town, indeed I hope you do not think of it till your attendances are quite done . . . Therefore, my dearest husband, make yourself comfortable about me for I will bear my disappointment like a heroine and go on looking forward to a more distant time for I know you will come to me as soon as you can with propriety.

But she remained concerned about Willie. 'If Benjamin is going to Ham Green, would it not be wise to send Willie with him and he could stay there till our arrival. It is distressing to think how little the children have of Willie's company. I fear that they might forget him altogether.' If Willie did have to spend the beginning of his school holidays in London, then he should not be shut up in the house, for he needed both fresh air and exercise. Perhaps Bright could take him on his rounds? If so, then Jones would have to see he was neatly dressed in his light trousers and clean stockings. If a new ribbon for his collar was necessary then one should be bought. 'His brown hat can be found in a box in the rocking horse room and if a bit of crepe is put on it then it will do quite well for the country as well.' Bright was used to fitting Willie up with clothes. It was more often than not left to him to get the boy ready for school at the end of his holidays. He took him to Mr Stevens, the tailor, who made for him a black coat and waistcoat, not of the best cloth, but good looking and 'fit for a gentleman'. He took him to Mr Hooker in Little Brook Street, 'the best hatter in town', and there he got him a cap; the neat ready-made shoes were obtained from Wilkinsons – Grundy's being too dear. He saw to his gloves, too, and his books, and always bought some fruit for his tuck box.

So at the beginning of that August, Willie was his father's shadow. Bright loved children, and he valued this chance to have his oldest child, now aged eleven, to himself for a while. He was a sensitive, quick-witted, peace-loving boy, always talking about planets and stars, seeming to be aware only of what was good and blind to anything evil. Willie knew little of his father's world but soon began to understand the nature of his work. He enjoyed doing the rounds. The weather was warm, and there being no hood to the carriage he was allowed to stand. It was a new carriage, which had been considered necessary because of Bright's growing eminence. The question of its lining had been discussed at length, but Bright and Eliza had agreed that it was more important to have a lock on the inside of the door for the sake of the children than to have extra adornments. Bright had had it painted red, so that he could spot it easily when in a hurry, for sometimes in the more crowded areas Wilkinson had difficulty in finding a stand in which to wait.

Getting about London during Willie's holidays Bright's progress was often slow. There were diversions: he took Willie to see where they had laid his grandfather's body under the floor of St Mary-the-Virgin, and on to St Paul's to see the handsome monument to him erected by public subscription. Behnes had portrayed the tall figure of Dr Babington in an academic gown, and it stood astonishingly white. Bright took him also to the Adelaide Museum, where he left him to hear a lecture on the scientific successes of the day. Even when there were no diversions, there were other delays. Sometimes a former patient would recognize him and stop the carriage. There was a youth of fourteen whom he had once treated for a fever, who always thrust his fat and beaming face, 'full of health and gratitude', through the carriage window as he went by – and another youth, who sold fish about the streets, 'in which occupation I frequently saw him'. Then there was Sam Long, the watchman, who leapt out of his private yard to salute him, and the little ballet dancer from Astley's Theatre, barely fourteen, already on the streets and hopelessly 'drifting' to total destruction with tubercular lungs. Often at posting houses or other halting places, on the outskirts of Knightsbridge or Southwark, beggars appeared from nowhere, many of whom he had tried to treat or helped to wean from drink. As he approached Guy's there was always the poor man crouching beside the horse trough at the foot of St Saviour's, who possessed nothing but a 'three-legged dog that nobody else wanted'; Bright never passed without throwing him a penny. He was often waylaid by old ladies, elderly tramps and the odd gypsy, who had perhaps known him as a graduate on horseback going to and from Guy's and still gave him an apple or a spray of wild roses. Little boy chimney sweeps were Bright's particular favourites. They ran in haste to greet him and he never failed to send a donation to the Smithfield Market by Jones on the first of May for the sweeps' 'special day'.

On 17 August, Eliza and Elizabeth left Malvern with the children; they arrived at Ham Green in heavy rain. Eliza was weary. She did not know whether it was the long exposure to the cold and damp of the journey or whether it was seeing so many visitors in the house, but on the night of her arrival she got no sleep at all. 'I did not forget myself for one moment till 5 a.m. and awoke again at 6.00 a.m., and as you may suppose how very far from well I feel today – my heart beats and throbs so terribly you cannot think my dear, dear husband, how I wish for you.' She began to relinquish the hope of any Scottish holiday and was consumed by a fear that she was destined not to see him again. Apparently Bright had not had the time to write to her and his silence plunged her into a morbid melancholy. Her father-in-law comforted her, 'Phoebe gives me vinaigrettes, and Sally, who looks thin and old, puts herself out to help me'. Benjamin was there, having escorted Willie from London. He had given Willie his first pony and was now the object of the boy's rapturous affection. By now Willie was a competent rider.

The weather improved, Eliza heard from Bright, and in the balmy days of sunshine her fears slowly melted. 'Ham Green is full of children,' she wrote to Bright, 'Benjamin's three . . . my name sake, Phoebe Eliza, is so like her mother . . . Sam's two toddlers . . . and Robert's sons ride over nearly every day, besides the orphans of Charles Tyndall . . . and they are all merry and happy, running without shoes across the lawns which are cut now by one of your father's odd contraptions . . . it mows down as it goes.' In the heat the children dispersed about the woods, until one of the aunts or uncles gathered them together under the cedars with a book or a magnifying glass and a specimen – 'none disappear into the laboratory as they say you used to do . . . '

Eliza was able to tell Bright how well his father was, and how a dull room was still brightened by his presence; the children were often seen in his company, especially Willie who was reading *Ivanhoe* to him and sharing his spyglass to watch the distant Portishead Regatta. 'Your father has done well in this year's flower show . . . we all went into Bristol to see him win prizes for currants, plums and black Hambourg grapes and everybody admired the new wistaria from China and those newly discovered dahlias and petunias . . . they all got honourable mention.' 'Franckie is, I think, more admired than Follie,' she went on, 'but as you know I always said he would be, as your sisters like to think differently from other people.' She had had to call in Dr Estlin to see Franckie's swollen gum. It was lanced and 'he did not squeal nor make the least objection'. 'He [Dr Estlin] spent the whole of Tuesday evening here and amused the whole party by showing things through a microscope. I was much pleased with the exhibition and wished that you kept one at home and would sometimes amuse me and instruct me by showing me things in it. Mr Estlin has a new pocket one which he brought to show your father because it is remarkably good.'

*

The time of departure for Scotland was fast approaching; both Eliza and Elizabeth were greatly looking forward to it. Bright wrote to say that he was tying up all the loose ends of his work; that his many professional friends had promised to do what they could for those of his private patients who remained in London, while at Guy's there were Addison and Hodgkin and his pupils, Owen Rees and Barlow, to look after his parish patients. When Eliza replied, she told him that their carriage had gone to the coachmakers 'for all sorts of things to be done – and you need not be uneasy about it', and then she turned her attention to the matter of his clothes: 'You had better have flannel drawers put into your bag for fear you should wish to have them to put on at any time. Order Jones to see that your best shirts are those that are taken . . . Perhaps you would find a black neckhandkerchief useful – at any rate it will be better than that ugly yellow one which you wear at night sometimes.' Now September was approaching it would be cooler, and no doubt almost cold in Scotland, so he must certainly consider getting a new warm cloak. '. . . the old one would do for any other person, I do not think we can have too many travelling ones.' She seemed to remember him having said to her once that he would like a new evening cloak as his own was so very shabby. 'I should think for £5 5s. you could get a very good one like Bob's or your brother Ben's . . . ' According to Eliza Bright liked good clothes, but disliked shopping for himself and so tended to hang on to his old ones. Susan was always complaining that his clothes were too tattered to mend, his large shoes were kept well repaired by Jones, and his 'black cotton stockings were much darned'. He appeared to be particularly attached to a white cambrian stock without tie or ornament of any description and worn high on the neck, curving round the chin.

On their departure from Ham Green for London, Elizabeth saw to the packages and Eliza laid down the last imperative orders for the welfare of her children, who were being left behind in the care of nursemaids and aunts. Sad as she was to leave them, as soon as she entered her own front door again at Savile Row 'I forgot them for my husband'.

On their way to Edinburgh an incident occurred which shook Bright not a little. They had intended to break their journey by stopping overnight with Sam and Bessy in Liverpool; but, much as all three would have enjoyed looking at the new house, they were in the end too pressed for time. Instead, they stopped at Warrington to rest and change their horses. There, as Bright wrote to Sam, 'we had the misfortune to run over a little child – or rather, as all the people said – the child ran under our horses'. The child was taken into a shop, and Bright himself made sure he would be well cared for.

> A gentleman in the shop assured me the child would be under very good care – I saw him examine the child and he had no bones broken . . . I introduced myself to the surgeon, gave him my name which he said was familiar to him, and then desired him to do his best for the child and I would be glad to repay any expense of professional care.
>
> I then gave my address and also yours to a gentleman who was endlessly kind about the business and who I believe to be the owner of the shop and hoped that he would drop you a line to say what became of the child and I gave him a sovereign to give to the mother of the child.
>
> What then I want with respect to this matter is that should you hear anything about it you would act for me as you would wish to act for yourself and that you will send the substance of any communication to me at Dr. Alison's, 43 Hériots Row, Edinburgh . . .

As they neared Edinburgh, Eliza was 'in a happy frame of mind', but Bright was apprehensive and full of uncertainty. Indeed it seems that it was with something like dismay that Bright watched for the walls of the city. In a letter to Webb Eliza tells us how 'at the sight of its spires, my dear husband sat pale and silent, having only just a moment before delighted Elizabeth and me with descriptions of its beauties, so well remembered and loved by him . . .' Once again there is this hint of diffidence and a lack of self-confidence. He was uneasy at the idea of facing some of his friends in Edinburgh for the first time after such a long absence. Later his children would often tease him about this, lovingly reassuring him that he never did acquit himself badly whatever the occasion or situation.

They arrived on Saturday, 7 September, and were immediately engulfed in the growing excitement of a city determined to make the fourth meeting of the British Association for the Advancement of Science the most memorable yet. The following week Earl Grey, the Prime Minister, who was about to retire from public affairs, was to be given the Freedom of the City, so the preparations for this added to the excitement. That very first evening there was one of the most magnificent aurorae boreales ever seen. The light lured many learned men from their dinner tables to gather on Arthur's Seat, where they talked about it through half the night. Dr Dalton of Manchester 'calculated that the arch was a distance of forty miles from the earth'. It was followed, apparently, by a Sunday of exceptional beauty. But by noon on Monday came the expected storm, which heralded three days of incessant rainfall, the like of which 'Dr Alison tells us has not been seen in the north for over thirty years'.

It is from the pen of Elizabeth that we get this information. In the same letter to her father she told him how much they were enjoying their stay with the Alisons. No. 43 was a busy household, for Dr Alison was a physician of some standing at the Infirmary, with a large private practice. Now the house was full of visitors; besides the Brights there were the Moreheads (now living in Yorkshire) and Professor Sedgwick, the geologist, who was retiring as President of the British Association, and his wife. There were 'people coming and going all the time . . . though most leave the house during the day to partake of the various activities offered by the Association . . . there are more often extra places set for breakfast than for any other meal . . . tell Phoebe that the charm and hospitality here almost surpasses that of Ham Green.' Mrs Alison herself took Eliza round the sights of the city, followed by Elizabeth, enraptured with everything and savouring all to tell her father. In daily contact with her brother for the first time in her adult life, she noticed with pride how distinguished men went out of their way to congratulate 'Dick on his admirable inquiries into the kidney . . . many of your friends come to shake him by the hand . . . Dr Buckland, Boase, Sir David Brewster, and there are always many doctors at his side.' At the same time she witnessed at close range some of her brother's probing search for truth amongst this learned body of men. 'Dick tells me that, though he attaches little importance to his own opinions, the fact that all the doubts and mis-representations which he has encountered over his work on dropsy are now all dispelled, makes him very content . . . He says that even Sir George Mackenzie had had a look at his medical tome.'

Except for this one letter of Elizabeth's there is little material for a confident picture of this Edinburgh visit, but the daily newspapers of the day give us some idea of what their programme must have been like. All that first weekend the influx of people was continuous. Never had Edinburgh seen such a distinguished gathering of scientists, both British and foreign. Six hundred or so Association members had been expected, but the numbers had swollen to nearly twelve hundred.

Like everybody else that first Monday morning, the Brights would have collected their tickets from the Royal Institution for the various sessions. Then there were the soirées, the general meetings and the public dinners. Each afternoon projects were laid informally before the assembled company, and there was something to meet every taste. The botanists might go to the botanical gardens, the artists to picture galleries so 'graciously opened'; the curious might be lured to the Panorama on Calton Hill where was depicted Captain Rosse's exploration of the Antarctic; and everybody was advised to see the fossil of a tree found complete in the quarries of Craigleith.

The Brights certainly would have attended the first dinner, when the whole proceeding was opened by Sir Thomas MacDougal Brisbane, President elect; they would also have attended the last great gathering at the Assembly Hall. What else they did and which of the sessions Bright attended we do not know. There was much of interest to claim him: Professor Rennie's talk on hydraulics, Dr Babbage and his calculating machine, Dr Buckland's lectures on fossils, Professor Sedgwick on minerals, Dr Powell on the formation of ice and hail, Mr Whewell on the phenomenon of tides.

Revisiting the scenes of his youth; sitting in the college classrooms; telling Eliza something of his boyish hopes and fears, and something of the great men of those days – Sir Walter Scott, Burns, Playfair and Dugald Stewart, in whose honour memorials now stood on Calton Hill; meeting on equal terms the men he had once looked up to with reverence – all these things moved and delighted him. He said as much to Willie in the letter he wrote describing Craigrook, 'the turreted house of towers with multitudes of windows of all shapes and sizes where lives my friend Jeffrey'. Edinburgh had lost none of 'its spontaneity', he said. Jeffrey was now Lord Advocate and earlier that year, 1834, he had been made a Scottish Law Lord. It is not clear from Bright's letter to Willie how long they stayed there. It might have been several hours, or it could have been a day or so. But there was time enough anyway to sit in Jeffrey's 'little gilded closet' and discuss at length an itinerary for the trip to the Trossachs, to see the improvements done to the sloping garden, and to lavish affection on all the household pets – for 'there is no living without these things', the Judge told Bright. 'After we talked to old Poll, the parrot, measured the pet thrush, examined a lamb which was lame and watched the swallows teaching their young to fly, we three left for Callander.'

It proved a delightful holiday, according to Elizabeth's recollections. Their itinerary was very limited, but the holiday was spent in the solitude of the hills which Bright always so enjoyed. By this time a considerable intimacy had developed between Eliza and Elizabeth, which added to Bright's pleasure. His invariable curiosity took them from Callander to Loch Vernacher, up the Glen of Fingas to Ben Venue and Ben A'an. 'A Mr Stewart of the Glen offered us good fare, a but and ben,' he told Willie, and though hill ponies were put at their disposal, his small boat was the more favoured attraction. They enjoyed some peaceful hours on Loch Katrine, sometimes fishing, sometimes rowing from one spot to another, sometimes under rowan trees whose 'coral-tinted berries startled the eye' while Elizabeth read out loud *The Lady of the Lake*; then, always conscious of Walter Scott's 'silver strand and Ellen's wooded isle', they travelled south-west to dawdle around Loch Lomond, until it was time to return to England. When they reached Bristol, Richard Bright thought that the children should remain at Ham Green for the winter. But Bright, unwilling to be parted from them any longer, hurried them all back to Savile Row, and Willie on to his last term at Hampton.

It made their homecoming all the more agreeable to hear of Webb Follett's successes. Wherever Eliza was, she thought constantly of her brother. When he visited them she was always quick to see the changes in his attractive, somewhat delicate frame, but this time she was 'too happy and too proud' to note any physical frailties. He stood before her now as MP for Exeter and the youngest lawyer ever to be made a King's Counsel. 'There never was such a man in more amiable situation,' Bright wrote to his father, 'never a man so universally liked and admired even by those who in the ordinary course of man's feelings, might be expected to envy or speak lightly of him . . . the solid fruits of his short career are amazing.' Eliza's happiness was infectious and lightened their concern over Franck and Follett, 'both prisoners this Spring from an illness which we have not and never shall completely discover'. When the children got better they were fed on the 'many good things which keep arriving from Ham Green. Pork chops, fruit and vegetable . . .' There is no mention of the customary holiday in August 1835 – perhaps because 'there was such a serious intimation of all not going well with Eliza's confinement', so that Bright 'thought it right to have Dr Locock at times in attendance'.

But on 16 September Bright wrote to Ham Green: 'You will I am sure join with us in rejoicing that a fine and healthy little girl was this morning safely added to our party. We disturbed the doctors about one o'clock and by quarter past six she was born.' At first there was alarm for baby Emily, who 'seemed to be going all the wrong way', and many were the nights when Bright crept to the cotside to make sure she was still breathing. But at last a good wet nurse was found and he was able to turn his full attention to his hospital work.

16
Bright's Team
1835–1841

Bright needed that comparatively quiet August, for he was deep in his work. How much his colleagues were aware of his industry cannot be gauged. Only his friend Dr Charles Locock ever wrote about it:

> It is curious and instructive to us all, to note how closely and entirely he works out his own investigations: how absorbed he is solely in making out their value without apparently wishing to make a brilliant hit, but quietly and gradually clearing away doubts and difficulties, and ending in axioms which have been universally recognized because he felt them to be genuine and true.[1]

He was labouring to finish a paper on twenty-nine cases where tumours were affecting the spleen, and at the same time studying abdominal tumours, throwing himself with delight 'into those beautiful, complex and skilfully devised organs contained within the abdomen on which our being and comfort so completely depends'. Annotating fresh cases, sorting out details of others long amassed, and illustrating each terrible tumour in exquisite detail – all absorbed him. There were four other papers in preparation, all bearing on abnormal growths, all original work. There is the one on abdominal hydatic disease; another on tumours involving the kidney; another on thirty-three cases where a tumour had invaded the liver. In the fourth remarkable paper he describes how twenty-nine of his patients were weighted down with ovarian tumours. No surgeon in those days removed growths and so all increased in size to grotesque proportions. These six papers were to be considered so valuable that two years after his death in 1860 they were collected together and published in one volume by the New Sydenham Society – the council all agreeing that the task of editing was to be restricted so that 'nothing could deprive them of their greatest merit – namely of being clinical portraits fresh from the hand of a master'. Only where the drawings were concerned was there re-arrangement. In the original papers most of the illustrations were on stone and 'appended at the end of the paper; in the present reprint they have been reproduced in wood and are incorporated with the text, so as to facilitate reference'.

Bright's achievements at this time of his life were prodigious. Besides all this writing, there was his clinical work, his teaching and his lectures, he had also taken on more private patients. In October 1835 he was busy over a case of considerable interest. On 14 October a young girl of nineteen was admitted into Guy's under him. She was very ill and kept vomiting, and Bright found himself going to see her many times a day. She had been delicate and breathless all her life, her mother told Bright, and she had often noticed a strange gurgling in the girl's chest. On examining her, he found that her heart was on the right side of the chest, and that there was little respiratory action in the lower lobes of the lungs. He spent many hours at her side trying various remedies 'that would sit easily on the stomach', but she died a few days after admission, exhausted by excessive vomiting. At autopsy he was fascinated by the misplaced stomach which passed through the diaphragm and by the large tumour which had divided into two, causing the disarrangement of all the viscera in the chest. He devoted several pages to the account of what would today be described as a complicated diaphragmatic hernia.

It was the general interest this case aroused that inspired yet another project. Why not resurrect *Guy's Hospital Reports*? They had been started by Babington, Astley Cooper and Haighton but abandoned in 1798. Any experience gathered from the bedside, any outstanding work or original observation, any article devoted to a special field, could then be preserved for ever and form part of Guy's heritage. It would be a way of encouraging the student to identify the unusual, to get into the habit of noting down, observing and describing accurately the results of autopsies and operations; the most trifling thing could be reported, and even if at the time it was not perceived as important another person at some future time might discover a significance.

With his usual enthusiasm, Bright put his plan before the Treasurer. Harrison, always sympathetic to his ideas, supported him now and re-established *Guy's Hospital Reports*. This was but the latest in a series of valuable innovations Harrison had already carried out at Guy's. He had extended the hospital premises: he had opened special wards – one for the study of diseases of the eye, one for gynaecological cases and lying-in, and one for children, a provision hitherto unknown in Britain; he had persuaded people to give him money to modernize the water closets, for he considered good sanitation more important for health than any rare drug or expensive gadget.

The first volume of *Guy's Hospital Reports* was published in 1836 under the editorship of Bright's pupil Barlow, and to this day a new volume is published each year. In the years to follow Bright was to contribute many important papers, all beautifully written, all original in conception and execution. His descriptions of nephritis are always so accurate that it has often been pointed out that modern writers would have done well to transcribe his words rather than write their own account of the disease.[2] In that first volume, there is no more superb classical description to be found anywhere than Bright's own slowly unfolding story of the disease he discovered. As we have seen, his work on the kidney was first described in the two volumes of his famous book of *Medical Cases* published in 1827 and 1832; he elaborated further on the subject in his Goulstonian Lectures of 1833, and now we find his last extensive work on the kidney described in two chapters of that first volume of *Guy's Hospital Reports*.

In the first chapter he summarizes his renal discoveries and clarifies several points (see Appendix II); it is this paper which includes his famous description of nephritis, which is wholly quoted in all the outstanding modern books of pathology (see Appendix III). In the second chapter he adds new observations to substantiate the old ones; this chapter is famous for his comments upon the conditions of the heart in relation to a diseased kidney. In it he gives also a 'Tabular view of the morbid appearance in a hundred cases connected with Albuminous Urine'. These hundred cases are neatly set out in columns: each story is told in one or two simple words, every organ at autopsy is described in less than a sentence (see Appendix IV). Each case is so brief that the impact is all the more vivid.

*

In 1837, when Dr Cholmeley retired, no one was more pleased than Bright to have Addison take his place as full physician, but feelings ran high over the choice of his replacement as assistant physician. There were two main candidates for the post, and both Thomas Hodgkin and Benjamin Babington were friends of Bright. It is quite possible that now Sir Astley Cooper's influence was on the wane, Mr Harrison may have consulted Bright. And though the final decision would rest with the Governing General Court of the Hospital, Bright himself must have felt painfully divided on the question. Babington was Martha's brother and an intimate friend of his, but he was also fond of Hodgkin. It was he who did most of the autopsies for Bright, always hoping for the triumphant exposure of that particular motley-light-coloured kidney which 'thou and I have now so often had the opportunity of noticing together'. He had the highest opinion of Hodgkin's work, but was somewhat puzzled by his own ambivalent feelings towards him as a person. He was a droll and delightful companion, peppering his conversations with Latin and French, the two languages Bright himself most enjoyed using. But, like everybody else, Bright found him unpredictable: he was often absent from work through malaise; he was impulsive and rash in his views, throwing himself into strange causes, embracing aboriginals, 'infidels', Jews, and even the new controversial University of London Hospital. He was attracted by its free, non-sectarian attitude – something which attracted Bright just as much – but as the new hospital was fast becoming a serious rival to Guy's it was perhaps this question of loyalty that worried people. His tactless attacks on the colonialism of the Hudson Bay Company must also have annoyed Harrison, dependent as he was on its finance for his building projects. Yet Hodgkin displayed no disloyalty; for twelve years he had worked devotedly for Guy's, and he saw his promotion as a certainty. Still, he did lack the clinical experience of the older man, and Babington was a good all-round physician. Like his father, he was amusing, able and popular: it was these traits that finally won for him the position.[3]

Everybody hoped that Hodgkin would stay on as pathologist, but he felt obliged to resign and sadly left his beloved museum. He went as pathologist to St Thomas's but there again something went wrong and he soon left. He then withdrew from medical work altogether, he became interested in philology and travelled to the Middle East with Sir Moses Montefiore. The work he did at Guy's on the spleen and lymphatic glands was not fully recognized for twenty years. It was Sir Samuel Wilks in 1865 who, anxious to perpetuate the fame of this great man, gave the name Hodgkin to the disease he had first diagnosed.

It would have been easy to retain his services by increasing the number of assistant physicians: only three years later the Governors were to appoint both Barlow and Hughes as assistant physicians.

7. A sketch of Budapest by Richard Bright.

From Travels from Vienna through Lower Hungary by Richard Bright M.D., Edinburgh, 1818.

8. Guy's Hospital. A view of the front square, c. 1810.
By courtesy of the Guildhall Library, City of London.

One can only wonder at their stupidity in being prepared to lose such a man. Besides, the overburdened Addison and Bright could well have done with an assistant each, rather than having to share the aid of Babington, hard worker though he was.

With Dr Cholmeley gone Bright and Addison must both have been conscious of a certain lightening of the atmosphere. As far as clinical teaching was concerned they were at last freed from his criticism, and his restrictive old-fashioned practices. It was with extraordinary diligence that they now applied themselves to raising the standard of training in the fast-growing medical school. One of the first things they did together was to write a textbook, *The Elements of the Practice of Medicine*, eventually published in 1839, to help and advise the student in practical work. They both remembered vividly the lack of such help in their own training, when the theory learned in class was of little use once at the bedside, where the problems confronted were never anything like those that were hinted at by professors.

Bright had always been extremely concerned about patient care, and considered that a doctor's training should include nursing. Doctoring, he said in his textbook, did not only mean learning diagnosis, observing the signs and symptoms of disease and recognizing complications; it included treatment and care, learning how to give comfort, anticipate wants, urge recovery or render peace at the end. It included learning how to take pressure off protruding bones by rubbing in lead or applying plaster, by positioning cushions and using Dr Arnott's water-pillows; learning how to treat a bedsore; knowing how diluted brandy or laudanum would stimulate healing, how nitric acid with distilled water would clear pus, how linseed poultices would remove scabs. 'We have all of us senses,' he told his readers, senses which had to be trained and cultivated. 'By the eye you will learn much; many diseases have the most distinct physiognomy' – for instance, 'the pallid face of haemorrhage – the dingy whiteness of malignant disease – the vacant lassitude of fever, the bright flush of phthisis, the contracted features and corrugated brow of tetanus'. 'You must acquire the sense of touch,' he said, and

you must watch the progress of disease . . . it is quite impossible otherwise for any man to gain information . . . the lapse of a few hours will so change the face of disease, that where, but the day before nothing but knee or hand was swollen, today the heart should be beating its laborious stroke in a thick crust of coagulable lymph . . . or, the restless activity of the inflamed brain shall be changed into the death-like coma . . .

The way the book is written tells us something of Bright's relationship with his students at the bedside. He did all that was possible to encourage, to arouse interest and enthusiasm, to mould his pupils into caring and knowledgeable doctors. His simplicity and lack of egoism, which come over in this book, must have made him the most attractive of teachers. And his own lack of confidence, his fear that sooner or later something in his own work might reveal shortcomings, must have made him an easy man to follow. He never contradicted or pretended to be an authority on anything; he was always pleasant and considerate, and, as Benjamin tells us, 'would join heartily in a laugh against himself'.

The Elements of the Practice of Medicine consisted of three 'fasiculi' written at different times between 1837 and 1839. These were put together to form a first volume and dedicated to Benjamin Harrison. It was popular, for there was no other book like it for the students. It was written because the authors felt 'the want of a work at once elementary and practical to which they might refer their pupils as a companion and assistant during the period of their studies'. It was a good reference book with a variety of excellent clinical pictures and anatomical descriptions. The advice on care and treatment was based on observable facts and actual experiences. It contains the first accurate description of appendicitis, the 'history of this affection' being attributed more to Addison than Bright.

Apparently the authors themselves were not entirely satisfied with it, feeling it was badly put together. A second volume was intended but it never appeared; in spite of the pressure of friends, nothing would induce Addison to complete the work after his colleague's death.

There were some good reviews, but *The Lancet* attacked it at once, for its lack of arrangement, for its 'fine-spun theories palmed off on its readers' in 'confusion and dis-order'. As editor Thomas Wakley accused both the authors of being muddleheaded and lazy teachers 'whom students would do well to avoid'. He also suggested that they must have paid for their hospital positions, for otherwise men of such poor calibre would never have been appointed.

It was Wakley's habit to attack the medical profession and its hospitals, but from the moment of *The Lancet*'s conception in 1823, when Wakley had the effrontery to publish Astley Cooper's lectures without his knowledge, Wakley took every opportunity to attack Guy's Medical School. As its reputation grew he wrote with increasing venom of its nepotism and its 'careless surgeons'. Both Bright and Addison must have known Wakley as a fellow student at the United Borough Hospitals. He was athletic, good-looking and popular despite his ruthless and aggressive ways. He grew up to be a strange mixture of a man; though scurrilous and shrewish he bore no personal malice and never wished to humiliate an enemy. He hated injustice and was jealous of the privileged classes, yet he was always ready to fill his own pockets.

Bright, like others, felt that the standard of the profession should be raised and all the nepotism, manipulation and malpractices ended, but the methods Wakley used to attain these ends were distasteful. His reporters were spies, infiltrating the hospitals of the metropolis to seek out incompetence, shadowing medical lectures, mischievously misrepresenting what they said. *The Lancet* became a duelling ground for a series of fierce encounters between himself and the more distinguished members of the medical profession.

On one occasion he attacked Bransby Cooper for supposed negligence, when a patient coming from the country to have a lithotomy done by Sir 'Arstly' died under the hand of his 'nevey'. And no sooner had this libel case been won by Guy's than Wakley leapt upon Aston Key and attacked him viciously for not honouring some promise to his students. *The Lancet* contained a malevolent criticism of Bright's article in the first volume of *Guy's Hospital Reports*, and further spite was directed at Addison and Bright's newly published textbook.

Week after week the dirge of distortions, lies and insults continued. Puns were made on the doctors' names: 'the door was opened by a Key; the treatment of fractures was incompetently performed by a Cooper; the teeth were seen to by a Bell, the disorders of the intellect were reflected by Bright, the spinal column by Back, while electricity was used for aching limbs by Aikin.' Led by Harrison, Guy's refused to be flustered and boycotted the paper. Active, busy, and absorbed in its own reform, Guy's tradition and reputation gave it strength. Bright's discoveries alone had given the Hospital a prominent position in every country in the world. The name of Dr Bostock was remembered by a grateful public for his and Dr Addison's investigation into the phenomenon of general poisoning. The publication of Hodgkin's lectures on 'The morbid Anatomy of the Serous and Mucus Membranes' had been widely noticed. Dr

Addison's brilliant teaching was attracting more and more students to the school; and Harrison's progressive attitude was becoming well-known – and though he failed to persuade the Governors that residential accommodation for students was necessary, he did manage to improve their lot in other ways.

*

At forty-eight years of age Bright was still the indefatigable worker he had always been. Now that demands were being made upon his time outside the Hospital, he initiated an all-embracing system whereby the services of all students were made use of in the work of the Hospital. He insisted that facilities such as benches, flat surfaces, a laboratory and clinical rooms should be provided for the students and for the purpose of instruction. He managed slowly to include senior students in his own research work. Here again he was before his time. To gather up a team of young men entirely devoted to clinical investigation was a totally new conception.

Bright's team of 'young friends and pupils' included his four clinical clerks who helped him care for his patients; they wrote their observations in a record book and their reports 'formed the subject of conversation between the physician and pupils in the room where they assembled before and after visiting the patient'. George Johnson was most probably his favourite. He was always at Bright's heels and was later to do experimental work on the kidneys of cats. Anderson, Gorham and Tweedie assisted him in turn, discriminating between the renal patients and others. Behind the assistant physician Babington, who helped in the research work, and Dr Bostock, the chemist, hovered the young, retiring Barlow and the unpredictable Hughes, a victim of eczema, both senior pupils. Robinson, Toynbee and Owen Rees were all to attain positions of eminence in renal research. The dandified, pernickety Rees shied away from every terrible 'sight and smell', but his squeamishness was often forgotten, so inspired was he by Bright, and he was to devote most of his working life to minute studies of renal tissue. When he wrote his book on the chemical analysis of the blood and urine, he dedicated it to Bright in gratitude for 'the kind encouragement received from you when as a mere boy I first entered upon the study of pathological chemistry'.

Bostock, too, dedicated a book to Bright. When Bright wrote to his father in March 1837 at the birth of his daughter, Clara, he said: 'this very moment in comes a "History of Medicine" with a compliment to me far beyond my merit – a dedication by Bostock to me. It makes me quite as proud as the event of a daughter.'

Bright's team appreciated his unappeasable sense of personal responsibility for his patients; they were proud of his achievements, and pleased that his books and other publications created a stir abroad and brought visitors to the wards. They valued the long stimulating discussions which then occurred and were almost more keen than Bright himself to reward the foreigners with a view of the famous granular kidney; they enjoyed above all the evenings at Savile Row.

Dinner parties, considered by Bright as 'so disagreeable a thing', were a different matter when he entertained his young scientific friends. He took tremendous trouble to see that all went well, that the wines were to their taste, and that the food included some extravagant delicacy. Other doctors who were concerned with renal disease were drawn by Bright's originality and came to these dinners. These occasions grew almost into an association without a name, where Bright kept interested colleagues up to date with his researches, while he in turn liked to hear of the experiences of others.

Bright never forgot the 'back-room boys' at Guy's, and he taught the members of his team to value their work too. There was the fatherly figure of Manson Hill, the 'surgery-man' or 'cupper', the friend of every nervous dresser and every brash pupil. There was Canton, the official draughtsman, 'the idlest and untidiest'[4] man most people had ever met. He would sneak away, leaving his boudoir chaotic, 'rabbit bones, viscera, cheese rinds, pelts, stale cake and matted wax all piled on his table'. His brushes caught on his clothes, and his paints collected upon his face and covered his person. But he was famous for the beauty of his illustrations, for however well the spirits of wine in which the specimens were kept retained their characteristic appearance, it was still felt necessary to have drawings made.

Then there was Joseph Towne, who recorded in wax most things a medical student had to recognize. His amazing gift had been accidently discovered by his father, who had found him one night making wax models with great skill. One in particular had caught his eye – it was a skeleton of a man, thirty inches high, modelled from drawings the boy had taken out of a book and from bones of local birds and animals. Encouraged by his father to seek his fortune in London, Towne had been recommended to Astley Cooper. Harrison at once recognized how invaluable his work would be to the museum of the Hospital, and gave him a basement room, no bigger than a cupboard. There he remained behind locked doors for fifty years practising his remarkable art, ignoring all the praise and astonishment that his work was to produce – for he received gold medals from the Royal Society of Arts, and patronage from Queen Victoria for the exquisite statue he made of her father, the Duke of Kent. This private man took with him at his death all the secrets of his techniques, all the processes by which he worked in wax, all the methods he used to procure the colours, which remain as fresh today as at the moment of his moulding them.

Towne was hardly ever seen about the Hospital, but although few people knew what he looked like, everybody knew about him, and all were affectionately solicitous of his welfare. John Hilton was a particular friend. As the Demonstrator of Anatomy, he took his own beautifully dissected specimens in to Joseph Towne to be copied and modelled in their entirety: and though known as a blunt, rude and sarcastic man, he treated Towne with gentle and loving respect.

Bright was much attached to Joseph Towne, and was often seen hovering over the littered workbench, helping him to position the melting wax, shaping an eye or a liver, or watching some diseased portion of interlocking nerve threads and blood vessels being perfectly copied. Addison, too, was much indebted to him. For him Towne faithfully simulated the skins of 560 patients, with all the spots and acnes, rashes and pimples, blisters and sores, and they can still be seen today in all their awesome beauty. The work of such an artist as Towne compensated much for the lack of other teaching material.

*

Although criticisms were rare Bright's youthful followers were always ready to argue with anyone who belittled him in any way. But never were champions so fervent as on the occasion when the 'grub street' rogue Wakley attacked him yet again.

This time the venom concerned another and younger Dr Richard Bright, a surgeon of Ely Place. It could have been little fun for Bright to have had a weak, plausible and adventurous inebriate dogging his name. The man had attended lectures at Guy's but was never the dresser he claimed to have been. When challenged he was able to produce references written by Astley Cooper and others. Always short of money, he published books, exploiting Bright's fame by writing on female diseases and the treatment of dropsy. He was in the pay of a quack, a pompous gentleman calling himself 'Professor' Holloway, who advertised his ointments and patent medicines claiming miraculous results. On picturesque handbills and in cheap periodicals blazed the name of Holloway, glowing with promises, but it was a letter to *The Times*, signed by the Mayor of London, in which he claimed that 'Dr Richard Bright of Ely Place, the celebrated physician at Guy's' had completely cured an ulcerous arm, that set Wakley off into impotent fury. He loathed quacks and was particularly suspicious of Holloway and his boasts.

In *The Lancet* of 14 March 1846 he wrote the full story:

An extraordinary case of a cure abandoned at Guy's Hospital, where '*Sir*' Bransby Cooper and other surgeons told the patient that the only chance of saving his life was by losing his arm. He therefore called in Dr Bright, of Ely Place, chief physician at Guy's, who, on viewing his condition kindly and liberally said: 'I am utterly at a loss what to do for you; but here is half a sovereign. Go to Mr Holloway and try what effect his pills and ointment will have, as I have frequently witnessed the wonderful effects they have in desperate cases'. This unprejudiced advice was followed, and a perfect cure effected in three weeks . . . after four hospitals had failed. When Dr Bright was shown the result of his advice and charity, he said, 'I am both astonished and delighted, for I thought if ever I saw you again, it would be without your arm. I can only compare this cure to a charm.' . . . To say he is Dr Bright of Ely Place instead of Savile Row is a trick which passes muster and does its work for no one takes the trouble to enquire if there be any celebrated physician named Dr Richard Bright of Ely Place (which we need hardly say there is *not*); no one thinks indeed of any other Dr Richard Bright than the chief physician at Guy's.

Wakley was worried to think that such an eminent physician as Bright should be associated with a quack; on the other hand, if Bright was not in league with Holloway, he could not understand why he did not take legal steps to defend himself and his reputation – and, worse still, did not take this opportunity to attack all charlatans, all humbugs. 'Let Dr Bright proceed', he wrote, 'a little longer in his untoward course, and his brethren instead of seeking him as a consulting physician, may avoid him as the ally or willing victim of the Quack. We promise Dr Bright that we shall follow the matter so closely and doggedly that unless he alters his line of conduct he shall be more remembered as the utensil of Holloway the quack than as a distinguished physician.'

Time after time he tried to lure Bright into issuing a public statement of denial and denouncement. But Bright maintained his amazing serenity. One or two daily papers took it up, but only in a half-hearted way, for they seem to have been reluctant even to give Wakley the benefit of publicity, for it seemed to them that Bright's good character and position of eminence should have protected him from such treatment by Wakley. It was a Dublin reporter who expressed the general feeling of indignation and astonishment at the temerity of *The Lancet* in daring to impugn the conduct of such a man.

In *The Lancet*, in May, Wakley asked again why Bright did not 'disavow and denounce the impudent quack'. Why could he not copy Dr Locock's example, who had 'at once expressed his deep regret at his name being branded with pulmonic wafers'. How unsatisfactory is the conduct of 'the hero of Holloway's handbill and how Dr Locock rises in the estimation of the profession by contrast'. In June Wakley wondered how Bright would be received by the 'general body of Professors at the Royal College of Physicians' dinner . . . such a man who dishonours the profession and who gives consent of silence?'

Wakley's campaign continued for two years. For two years Wakley abhorred 'Dr Bright's sullen and contemptible behaviour for allowing the prostitution of his name . . . when a doctor takes no steps to disconnect his name from such enormities, he in effect becomes incriminated, the punishment will follow his silence.' In the end Wakley had to recant when it was discovered that it was after all, the obscure surgeon of Ely Place who had been the culprit. But he gave no apology – probably because he felt that Bright should in any case have taken steps to defend himself. Some of Bright's acquaintances had found it hard to understand his silence on the matter, but, indignant as he must have been, Bright did nothing, telling his friends privately that the advertisement was beneath his notice.

17
Changes
1838–1840

The spring of 1838 found Bright with many different things to preoccupy him. In the Hospital, he was trying to reassure some particularly frightened patients who were suffering from heart failure. In his private practice there was a Lady Williams occupying a good deal of time. He was at the same time dealing with Willie's broken wrist and trying to convince his brother Benjamin – obviously afflicted with cancer of the throat – that though Dr Brodie was good where broken bones were concerned, he was doing little for his hoarseness and loss of weight; it would therefore be better for him to return to Dr Estlin in Bristol, 'whom I count for a good deal'. Eliza, staying at Tunbridge Wells with the children, was wanting advice over whether Follett would have a gentleman's saddle or a Portuguese one, whether Clara's 'watery dejections could mean she had worms', and whether or not they should take the holiday governess with them to Brighton later that year. She had had to abandon French verbs, she said, 'the high spirits of her charges being too difficult to curb. . . They are being so happy and you cannot think how well.'

Meanwhile, Bright wrote to Eliza, he found himself at night 'almost too weary to drag himself to the desk' to write the lecture on 'Cases of Spasmodic disease accompanying affections of the Pericardium', which had to be ready for a meeting of the Medico-Chirurgical Society. And, as he was to chair the Library Committee, he had to think how to word his reproof to Dr Copland, who kept failing to return his library books.

At Easter he did manage to spend a few days with his family at Tunbridge Wells. When the time came for him to return to London, barely refreshed, he left his children to spend an afternoon in the brilliant sunshine under the spreading oaks of the anatomist John Hilton's garden – 'Hilton dressed in pale buckskin and presided over the teapot himself.'

Grateful patients of Bright's would often rally round to help his children. At Tunbridge Wells Lord Abergavenny sent his carriage with orders that the coachman should take them to the rabbit warrens on his estate. At Brighton the Duke of Devonshire invited them to an evening display of fireworks. 'It was a warm evening and we took the children and the ostler in case we wanted a second man. It was the pleasantest thing of the kind I had ever done.' And in her letters Eliza often mentions the visit of a local doctor, communicating his 'respect for you' and going out of his way to entertain the children.

When August came Eliza was once more writing that she and the children were 'most comfortably settled at Ham Green in the bustle that generally goes on here'. This time it was Brunel's steamship, the *Great Western* that was occupying all minds. Richard Bright could not keep his eyes away from that 'huge thing of life with its four masts, emitting volumes of smoke'. Eliza refused to be moved by the sight, she said, but the ship had an exciting effect on William, as he was now called, caught they all thought from his Uncle Robert, who had a passion for its engines – and there he was now 'waving to us from the deck as she glided by, with two other steamers and a tug accompanying her'. As usual Eliza wrote to Bright about everything:

> Your father is quite well. I read him some parts of your letters, he says he has never heard of Dr Bright and Addison's book, perhaps you had better bring one as he likes to see everything . . . The gowns arrived safely but Jones is no packer. Tell him that my bonnet should be wrapped up in clean paper and well covered both inside and out and please tell him to be careful and not bruise the flowers nor stick pins into it . . . Willie is coughing too much, Follett is out of spirits and Franck's eyes are full and reddish . . . Emily is very light not half as heavy to carry as she used to be. Thomas [the old family coachman] was complaining bitterly that he had not seen 'the doctor' for so long . . . He thought you could give him something for the pain in his knee . . . I have little more to say but how much I miss you and how lonely my heart feels without you but I know you don't like me to tell you and therefore I must keep it to myself.

On 20 August we find Eliza writing to Bright again, this time in real despair: 'Does it ever cross your mind to pay us a visit? Everybody gets some weeks of pleasure with their husbands . . . Caroline and Robert have a month together, Sam and Bessy are never apart – other doctors take holidays, why is it I am more lost than most wives at this time of year?'

William's letters, too, were full of how much they all missed him and longed for his company:

We need you to tell us, Papa, what the flowers are in the hedges . . .
I have never seen their like before . . . Grandpapa sends his love to
you and wishes you to come here if you can but not to leave any
business undone . . . Aunt Phoebe took me to see the Bristol
Institution. It is fine, is it not? We saw some of the fossils given by
Grandpapa . . . the little boys are generally out most of the day and
Emily keeps asking for you and wants to go home . . . My dear Papa
I am just going to bed . . . Mama has just finished a beautiful cat for
baby.

Bright had intended to join his family at the beginning of
September but an urgent summons to Hatfield delayed him. 'I grieve
to hear such an uncomfortable account of you . . . I had foolishly made
up my mind that you would be here this Saturday . . . Sally got your
drawing board out of the attic for you . . . How is Lady Williams?'
Bright himself felt wretched, and wrote to Eliza to assure her that he
was only waiting now for Lady Williams to die to bring 'himself and
the expected new nursemaid for a three weeks holiday'.

It must have been a rushed few days before Jones was finally able to
pack for him. He had to see a Mrs Gilbert, who insisted on a
consultation; and a Mr Rosacre, who lived a few miles out of town,
needed to see him. Then, 'ordering him to resume all my
precautions', he went on to a Mr 'X', but he was already dying with
gross dropsy. Bright was anxious to be at the autopsy, where the
'kidney was found to be large and white, and double the natural size',
and this delayed him further. Then he found himself at the bedside of
a 'good friend'. This was Mr Ryan, the young editor of a periodical
called the *Medical and Surgical Journal*. He was 'suffering with cancer
and needed full attention'. So it was not until the second week of
September that Eliza had him at last by her side.

How quickly he seems to have added a merry tone to that holiday.
He was seen much in the company of his sons, going for rides with
William (now fourteen), striding beside Follett (seven) and Franck
(six) 'with fishing gear clutched in moist hands', wrote Eliza to her
brother Webb, 'and so excited that they could hardly seem to feel
their feet under them, as they jumped and ran beside him'.

Bright also found time to walk over to Abbot's Leigh to discuss
Rugby School with Robert. He had already decided to send his sons

there, but as his two nephews Richard Bright and Robert Onesipherus were already experiencing life with Dr Arnold, he wanted to satisfy himself yet again, to be reassured that Robert was pleased with their progress under his 'system of liberal and humane education'.

Like his father, Bright considered education to be of the utmost importance. There are two letters from Mr Mills, the headmaster of the preparatory school at Hampton, and both suggest that Bright was an extremely anxious parent. The first one concerns William. Bright must have written saying he was worried about his son's progress and 'was he not', he asked, 'somewhat unmanly'? This produced an indignant reply:

Willie has the highest character that could possibly be ascribed to anyone. In the eleven years of teaching I have never seen his equal. He is honest, his upstanding manners are highly pleasing . . . he is anything but childish, and though other schoolboys are certainly more self-sufficient, they are blockheads, impotent, flippant, needing to be scourged and reduced to reasonable modesty . . . Mrs Mills is pleased also to inform you that 'Willie is the best and soundest man in the school'. He has excellent academic abilities and these will gain him a place in the lower fifth at Rugby but to maintain that standard he needs all encouragement and kindness.

The other letter is Mr Mills' reply to Bright's letter asking him to accept Follett as a pupil.

Hampton. October 3, 1838.

I am naturally tempted to wish for your second son as a pupil. I should expect to find him a good clean child, but at the same time I am fearful to enter into connection again with a Parent so painfully anxious as yourself.

The best of my energies are unceasingly devoted to my pupils and anxious parents can push me no further. I am only paralyzed thereby. A father who would act a wise parent both for the child and himself must show his confidence over a wide space and not contemplate the end and the result in such a manner as to fret all the period between. If you are disposed to be calmly confiding in us and our system, we shall on our part be most happy and desirous to receive your second son in due time under our care.

His brief holiday reunions with his children always saddened Bright, and, as he said to Eliza, they made him all the more determined to be there at perhaps the more crucial moments of their lives. So, he himself accompanied William to Rugby. There was never time for family prayers in the morning, so it was at sundown that the 'great family Bible and the large prayer book, bound in red leather' were placed before Bright: on the eve of departure a special prayer was said for William.

There seems to have been an immediate accord between him and the housemaster, C. T. Arnold (cousin of the famous headmaster). This extremely intelligent and kindly man was to become greatly attached to each of the Bright brothers in succession, and Clara was to marry his son. Nevertheless, Bright found it a wrench leaving William. He remarked to Eliza on his face drained of blood and wondered sadly whether 'his quiet piety would ever give him the friends he craved for'.

The first letter from William did not take long to come. In it he assures his parents that he is 'very comfortable' and that 'Merivale's house contains as nice boys as any in the school'. All the boys had 'little sitting rooms or studies, one between two boys', where they had 'a complete establishment of our own. There are generally two chairs, two tables and a fireplace put in them, and we have to buy a tea and sugar caddy and a set of tea things, a candlebox, candle stick, snuffer etc. and we have a weekly supply of tea, sugar, candles, etc.' He also describes the school routine:

When we get up in the morning the first thing we do is to walk over to the school and into the large schoolroom a few minutes before 7. When the clock strikes seven Dr Arnold and Mr Paulett one of the masters go up into a desk and there reads prayers. When prayers are over the first Praepositor or Head boy in the school calls over the names and we go out as we answer into the different schoolrooms belonging to our forms where we say the lesson which we have prepared the night before. We then go home to breakfast and at a quarter past ten we go back to school again . . . My companions are ENGLEHEART, PERRY and BROOKS.

*

At this time Bright's life suddenly began to change. In 1837, on the accession of the young Queen Victoria, he had been appointed

Physician Extraordinary to Her Majesty. This, of course, had given him enormous pleasure, but he had not taken too much notice of it. He knew how many eminent doctors, who had no official position at Court, had been consulted by William IV, while Henry Holland had told him that there had been so many doctors round the bedside of George IV that nobody had even troubled to take their names.

But his name was beginning to be recognized. Richard Bright wrote to say how proud he was of him. Cousin John Heywood, returning from a visit to London, had been able to tell them at Claremont how he had overheard two men in a public place talking about the doctor Bright in words of praise. And, what was more, a member of his club had actually talked to him of Bright without realizing that John Heywood was his cousin. Old Aunt Phoebe had listened to this story with a full heart and promptly repeated it in a letter to Ham Green.

His private practice was growing rapidly. Other doctors, attracted by his fame and troubled by the continuing symptoms of their patients, called him in for his opinion. Well-to-do people began to seek him out, and often strangers would approach him in preference to their own doctors, whom they knew intimately. His attitude to all this was largely one of dismay. For one thing he had to do more travelling. He had always done a certain amount, and his return home was often unpredictable, but Eliza hated him to be out late, unless it was on a call to the house of a patient of 'an enemy or rival', and then she looked on it with triumphant glee. A late summons always meant a dark ride through treacherous lanes, and sometimes, rather than disturb a coachman, he would take his horse and trot across the squalid acres of the East End. She worried continually about his safety. Many of the mail coaches, like 'The Celebrity' or 'The Defiance', were unreliable and dangerous in the hands of careless drivers.

It is interesting to read from Bright's letters how comparatively easy it was to travel then, before the railways, now in their infancy, had acquired their dominant position. Some people, like Bright's old Lancashire aunts, never travelled at all, hardly walking beyond the village dairy. Bright's brother Benjamin went everywhere on horseback, while Thomas Addison, like Robert Southey, walked, preferring to use his legs rather than 'stew in a box'. But professional people, provided they had the money, could cover a great deal of ground.

It seemed nothing to Bright to travel to Suffolk on Monday and to be back at Guy's on Wednesday, having spent the Tuesday in between at Reigate, where some merchant had suffered a stroke. He had patients in Guildford and Leicester, and one weekend he had to go to Cheltenham, to support a colleague's sick daughter. If there happened to be a former patient living on the way to Tunbridge Wells, Rugby or Brighton, or wherever his family happened to be, he was sure to knock at the door; and more than once he seems to have gone to Scotland. 'You are indeed travelling about or rather flying. I do not understand how you manage it,' Eliza once wrote to Bright. He travelled fast. The post-boys on the roads got to know him, and on the long journeys fresh horses were ready for him at houses where he changed. He tipped well at toll gates and gave drivers extra if they found a quicker way round or chose better roads.

He was summoned one Christmas Day by a Dr Prout to a youth of seventeen shaken by uncontrollable fits; on Boxing Day we find him staying in a house where a Sir Poultney lay ill. Then he was off again to see a Mrs Papworth, whose urgent summons was to tell him 'how pleased she was to see him before she died'. One unnamed patient called him in just to say she had recovered.

Sitting in his carriage he selected the next appropriate destination from the wad of notes in his hand. 'Dear Doctor . . . my wife says she is in excruciating pain from the gathering . . . that she must have some relief. She has washed off Mr L . . .'s powder and is bathing it in iron water and says you will see her and do something for her.' So off he went to Lambeth. Sometimes he travelled on the roof of a coach, sometimes in a carrier's cart; sometimes he paid the driver of a post-chaise to drop him at a point where he could cross a field or common; sometimes he travelled in a conveyance sent to fetch him.

He wasted no time; he had a good supply of books in his roomy carriage and wrote many of his papers during these journeys: among them the Lumleian Lecture for the Royal College of Physicians on 'Disorders of the Brain', and his studies on circulatory disturbances, dependent upon pulmonary changes – he was the first physician ever to associate clubbed fingers with these complaints. And on 5 October 1839, at the Guy's Physical Society, he put these cases forward for discussion: 'The fact . . . that capillaries generally and those of the finger ends especially took on a change of action and enlarged . . . is worthy of note but its application must be left to a more extended accumulation of experience.'

From the letters written to the family at the time of Bright's death, it is possible to piece together some sort of picture of him as a practitioner. Wherever he went he was welcomed for his tact, his skill and his kindly intelligence. Fatigue forgotten, he was always sympathetic to both relatives and patients; however harassed or busy, however many visits he had yet to make, he refused to appear hurried. If Eliza told him he was 'careless in his dress', he was meticulous in his habits, and was careful to obliterate every trace of his temporary occupation. He always put the soap back in the right place, folded the towel, returned the borrowed book to his patient's library, replaced the bandage or spirit lamp on its rightful shelf.

Though his private patients lived in very different surroundings from his parish patients, his attitude and manner were the same to all. He attended to the needs of Mr Holt in Luke ward, who had fallen into a vessel of boiling glue, quite as long as he stayed at the bedside of Lord Truro. And if on occasion he could hardly endure the callous isolation of the prosperous and complacent, we learn from Eliza that his influence was such that he often left them thinking about the scandalous inequalities everywhere around them, and having stirred up their consciences many a name was added to various donation lists.

Today, Bright would have been consulted solely as an authority on renal disease, for it is said that modern medicine is too vast for one individual to grasp, and that specialization is therefore inevitable. But even when Bright was consulted by patients with obvious kidney trouble, he did not confine himself to that one subject. They consulted him because they were ill, and his observations covered the whole range.

*

Following a holiday spent with his family at Dawlish, when 'he had been surprised by the size of Franck's stockings and William's knowledge of the Bible', he paid a hurried visit to his father. At the age of eighty-four Richard Bright was fretting from the effects of a stroke; though paralysed on the left side, it had affected neither his mind nor his memory. 'His apprehension indeed seems perfect, and just now he has asked what cows they were lowing in the field,' wrote Bright to Eliza. 'Many of his old friends come to see him . . . the young curator from the Bristol museum has just paid him a visit having heard of his decision to donate his valuable geological collection to Bristol . . . I might add some of my own. . . . Dr Buckland wants to write his obituary for the Geological Association and has been questioning me.'

Dr Estlin had stayed two nights by his side, and Dr Lovell had applied a blister to the nape of his neck and a plaster to his useless arm. Both were glad of the respite Bright's presence gave, so it was left to his son to 'render further services'. These, as Phoebe pointed out, would seem totally inadequate compared to those rendered by their father to them, his children. 'He could have been a great man in the world of science had it not been for all of us.'

The following January, 1840, Richard Bright died. There were few obituary notices for he had never allowed himself to become a public figure. They buried him in the manner of his asking. The coffin was to be followed only by his sons, his two executors and his trustees. There was to be 'no pomp, no show and with as much regard to secrecy as was proper'. They put him to rest beside Sarah, and 'beside her', Henry remarked, 'he wanted no other paradise'.

18
The Pattern of Life
1840

By the spring of 1840 William was sixteen. And, amazingly still under the care of Susan, were Follett, aged eight; Franck, aged seven; 'a pink-faced Emily' aged four; Clara, a 'fat little girl' of three, and Henry Eustace, nearly two and still swaddled in flannel. Eliza was pregnant again, and by September Charles George was to arrive and occupy the bassinet. There was great interest in the children, and Eliza always thought herself fortunate 'to have such nice neighbours'. Lady MacGrigor lived round the corner – she had a big family of her own and was always taking the boys off Eliza's hands; while Mrs Grote, who lived in the house next door, would invite them in to hear her at the piano. Lady Brodie, always kind, was amused 'to see such a large family occupying a smallish house'. 'She is always telling me how youthful I look and asks how my dear husband manages to look so fresh.'

Indeed by the fourteenth anniversary of their engagement – an occasion which had found Bright in an apologetic state – the Doctor had changed little. A portrait of this time shows that he still retained the animation that constituted his charm, still that keen, quizzical, amused look. And if his features were more defined, his face less round and the lines on his face more marked, then his hair was still as thick as ever and quite as curly and brown, and his expression quite as serene. Much to his chagrin he had grown a little stouter, and he wondered much how his brother Robert had managed to keep so slim. 'I ask him how does he contrive it? He does nothing to produce it, where I have been hard at work travelling one of the roughest lanes in England, fourteen miles a day without being able in the course of two months to make any impression on my too solid frame.'

Eliza was still slim and attractive – though there was added the look of an over-anxious mother. She herself felt that she had changed. She was more matronly and less agile and was quite appalled when she remembered how many miles she used to walk in one day. She had been much gratified by a Mr Taunton – 'When I bowed to him, he asked your brother who it was and then apologized to me by saying that he expected to see a pale and sickly picture and instead he saw Aurora'.

She did in fact find the house rather cramped, and was always telling Bright that they should move to the country, but they never got round to it. Her mother, Mrs Follett, and her maid now occupied the two upper rooms, and there was only one decent-sized room left to put up a visitor of any importance. An easy-going relative was tucked up in any room vacated by one of the children. William's little attic room was intermittently used by Benjamin, now trying to ignore his illness, who entertained them with a lively and amusing rendering in 'whispers and gesticulations' of all 'the goings on' at some soirée or dinner party he had attended at Holland House. He was, he told his brother, *determined*, like everyone else to share in the happiness of the young queen on the eve of her wedding. London was agog with expectancy. According to her daughter, Mrs Follett had been 'prattling on for a long time about Queen Victoria's happy day', and asking if it would not be possible for the children to see the procession from the windows of the Athenaeum. But whether they did or not goes unrecorded.

The front door of No. 11 Savile Row had to be answered almost continuously these days and more and more letters were arriving. This was always a source of worry to Eliza, for she was afraid that in her absence something important would be overlooked, and some letters even left unopened. Jones was still careful to bring the patients' appeals to the doctor's notice, but Bright was not always there. He had got into the habit of putting odd bits of paper, invitations and tickets on the mantelshelf of his dressing room, leaving her the responsibility of passing them on. This was once cuttingly criticized by Phoebe, who on one of her visits failed to find the tickets for a picture exhibition, for she had 'certainly never thought to look there'.

'Most celebrated fellow,' Dr Schon of Vienna had written, echoing the congratulations from Germany, Paris and Holland on his receiving the Monthyon Medal in July 1838 from the celebrated Institute of Science in Paris. It was a kind of Nobel Prize of that day. Baron de Monthyon (1733–1820) had done much towards the relief of human suffering and after his death a gold medal and a sum of money were to go to anyone accomplishing some practical and virtuous action. Bright, as a scientist, was the first Englishman to be thus honoured for his 'ingenious work on the kidney'.

Bright said himself that he scorned public honours, and he accepted those that came his way reluctantly since they added to his already immense burden of work. In the period 1838–43 this was certainly so. He was President of the Medico-Chirurgical Society, Consilarius and Censor of the Royal College of Physicians and Fellow of the Royal Society. He was lecturer to the Royal Veterinary College and acted as examiner in the students' finals. He was an honorary member of most medical societies in Europe, including the Turkish one. Other societies approached him, but he refused them since they were not related to his work. He had little time now even for the Geological Society, and as his fame grew more and more requests for public addresses were politely turned down. 'You are still refusing to dine out, I fear,' wrote Eliza more than once. He did attend the Apothecaries' Dinner given in his honour, however, and in an amusing speech he told them of the struggles he had had in his youth to learn their 'Pharmacopera Londinimus'. He was inevitably pestered for favours, and many working models of 'magnetic power for the benefit of the human frame', baths, crude syringes and other instruments found their way into his room. Charities like the London Society for the Protection of Females asked to be allowed to put his name on their list as honorary physician. The Institutes for the Promotion of Science in Manchester, Bristol, Edinburgh and others did the same. He was a Member of the National Institute, Washington, DC.

In spite of his growing fame life for Bright still centred round the wards at Guy's. Not even Eliza, after years of marriage, could have said what the daily round meant to him. That spring (1840) there was an increasing number of cases of scarlet fever. The first child he saw in the outpatients department was dropsical, but as albumen and blood had long been known to accompany or follow scarlatina he was just interested. But when child after child appeared 'in the wards, in the private field in London and its neighbourhood', with the same added symptoms this 'almost epidemic prevalence of that anasarca with albuminous urine' seemed 'quite unprecedented within the limits of my experience'. Bright went to Shoreditch, Greenwich and Epsom, and he saw case after case: little Fanny Gummer, Mary Whittaker and Jemima Seaforth, a waif of twelve in Charity ward; Jimmy Evans, puffy and flushed of face, with small bolsters for legs. Bob – nobody had bothered to give him a surname – came from the Naval Victualling Yard at Deptford, where ill-nourished and with a high temperature he had continued to pack the salted meat into barrels until he had collapsed.

Studying each case in detail, he now set aside the very full programme he had planned for that spring in order to write a paper for the next edition of *Guy's Hospital Reports*. He was glad of the opportunity to affirm the fact – which he had maintained all along and yet was still misapprehended by some of the medical profession – that even though one of the complications of scarlet fever was albuminuria the kidney need not be permanently damaged. With the right treatment – diet, complete bed-rest, medicines to make the skin act freely, mineral aids to improve the tone of the kidney and an infusion of gentian as a tonic in convalescence – recovery would be complete and permanent. Only those who were exposed to adverse conditions too soon, or got a chill, would succumb to nephritis – an hour of exposure in a shower of rain was enough. In the case of the poor little pot-boy, Johnnie Wiseman, the scarlet fever was ignored and he went on working in a cold damp cellar at the White Hart Inn. By the time he was admitted to hospital he was dropsical, dying after three days, and there at the autopsy was the by now familiar granular kidney.

John Davy reappeared in London at about this time. Still an army surgeon, he had just returned from abroad and lost no time in getting in touch with Bright. He had earlier lost two of his own children from scarlet fever, so he showed considerable interest in Bright's investigations. But now he was in high spirits, and succeeded in instilling some cheerfulness into Bright. He was hard to resist once a new project had fired his imagination: now he was talking of boosting the country's economic resources by breeding the eggs of the salmonidae commercially. He had plans, too, of settling down in the Lakes, with visions of Bright 'visiting them to renew his acquaintance with Mrs Fletcher', his mother-in-law, 'as social as ever'. They arranged a special evening for Davy to renew his acquaintance with Hodgkin; he had met him once before in Bright's rooms in Bloomsbury Square. Now, on the eve of his departure for Constantinople, Davy was anxious to hear Hodgkin's opinion of the Turkish character. To Davy's disappointment the meeting never happened, as Bright was summoned urgently to Paris. (On Bright's death, John Davy asked the secretary of the Royal Medical Society of Edinburgh that his portrait should be hung next to Bright's. 'His love for him was great.'[1])

I can find no reason for the summons. There is only a letter from Bright to Jones, with directions that his mail should be deposited at the Foreign Office in Day Street and addressed to Lord Granville, the British Ambassador in Paris. As Eliza's brother Webb was staying there at this time, we can only assume that he had had a relapse and sent for Bright. The dates coincide with the presentation of the Monthyon Medal, but it is known that the French Consul gave it to him personally at a small ceremony in London. Besides, it is doubtful whether Bright would have left his patients in order to have a fuss made over him, neither would he willingly have crossed the Channel. He hated the sea, his youthful experience of it having left too deep an impression upon him ever to be forgotten: 'But the sea is at all times so little trustworthy that I am one of those who avoid it with all my best endeavours when anything but business or health enters into the account. To look across the sea is delightful – to be upon the sea is hateful.'

It was just after this visit to Paris that he began his daily visits to that hospitable, generous, cultured and lovable host, Lord Holland. It was a pleasant drive through the open fields of Hyde Park to the village of Kensington and up Holland Lane, to the great old Jacobean manor house, the cynosure of many society hearts. At night it was ablaze with brilliant lights, and it was always warm inside, for there was a new heating system, which, though noisy, Lord Holland was immensely proud of, for it gave off no fumes or vapours.

Sometimes Bright found Lord Holland sitting in the Long Gallery which stretched from the back to the front of the house, a vast, rich room, lined with rare books. Sometimes he was escorted to Lord Holland's own apartments – to a golden boudoir of cedarwood, bronze and stucco, through the mullioned windows of which could be seen the Italian garden and an orangery studded with shining leaves. There he examined the troublesome stomach and the gouty limbs. Illness was then set aside and some other topic would be discussed. They valued each other's company and Bright was always prepared to give up some of his time to conversation – though in general he kept his home visits short: social intercourse was not only tiring to the patient but an effort and time-consuming to him.

It was always with a certain dread that he left Lord Holland's room; the house was never empty of visitors, and it was almost impossible to slip out of the front door unnoticed. Invariably he was waylaid by a Member of Parliament or a writer, Charles Dickens perhaps or George Moore, and whether he knew them or not all were keen to learn about the condition of their dearest friend. Amongst the others he met there were little Lord John Russell, the idol of the people, now fighting for the cause of education; Lord Ashby, the Whig, now asking for better conditions for workers and restricted hours for children; Mr Macaulay, the historian, who admired Lord Holland more than any man in England, and his own childhood friend, Henry Holland. And Lady Holland, devoted to her husband and full of anxious concern, pestered him continually with the most acute questions about Lord Holland's progress.

The doctor of the household, Dr Allen, had a difficult time; Bright was often to see him chivvied and chased by Lady Holland, always unpredictable and liable to be irritable, who followed him with a torrent of abuse as he sped to do her bidding. During Dr Allen's lifelong service to the family, there were many who believed that they were witnessing the final phase of his reign, so ill and frayed did he appear; his friends had long abandoned their efforts to induce him to leave before complete enslavement. Only at his death in 1843 did Lady Holland show, too late, her appreciation of her 'companion, friend and protector'.

Lady Holland was interested in the medical world, and she said many hard words about some of Bright's colleagues. Amongst his intimate medical friends he may well have enjoyed a bit of gossip, but not outside this circle. But many were the times he found himself forced to listen to her, remaining silent while she discussed the gaffes of Sir James Clark. Such effrontery to tell Lady Flora Hastings that she was enceinte (pregnant) when she had a malignant tumour; it was all very well for Sir William Webb Follett to proclaim that defamation was too expensive to bring to court, but it had made her position as lady-in-waiting most uncomfortable. And what about Sir James Clark's other bloomer? Telling the young queen, on the eve of her marriage, that she was getting measles, when all the time it was a form of hysteria that was producing the fever, the blotchy face and the running eyes. And how was it that such a prominent man as Sir Matthew Tierney could not even recognize a case of cholera?

In October 1840 Lord Holland died; he got up much as usual, only to collapse in the arms of his valet, and it was Thomas Wakley, as coroner, who decided there was no need for an inquest, as he had died in the presence of four doctors. After the funeral, which was private and very secret, Holland House lost its life, and though the lower rooms were redecorated for entertaining Lady Holland's 'terrible sorrow' kept her much in town.

In widowhood, Bright must have found her more endearing, as everybody else did. Though displaying still all the dash and courage of the past, she seemed older and less intimidating. Many notes found their way to Savile Row from 9 Stanhope Street; notes suggesting that she should call upon him, or pressing him 'to come any evening that might suit', or scolding him for not eating at her supper table. 'I am sorry to have missed your visit,' she would write, 'could you call again . . . my kidney complaint is more troublesome.' She looked forward to his visits, took her medicines eagerly, and asked pertinent questions about his domestic life. When writing to him she never failed to hope that his family was well, including 'the little strange personage who appeared at my gate about whom I feel a present interest'.

Many of their mutual friends were already Bright's patients, but she was always recommending him to others. 'I am happy to think that Mrs Elphinstone of the Albany is now under your care.' And no one was more delighted when George Anson, the Keeper of the Privy Seal, deserted his own doctor for Bright and was already saying that he felt much improved.

Throughout the summer Bright had been intermittently visiting Sir Astley Cooper, who was suffering from emphysema (a disease of the lung). The respect each had for the other amounted now to real affection and it distressed Bright to see him suffer. It was Astley Cooper's wish that at his death an autopsy should be done, and that it should be written up for the *Guy's Hospital Reports*. They were to look not only for any evidence of tuberculosis in his lungs, which had so sapped the strength of his immediate kin, but also for anything that could explain why he could never sleep while lying on his left side (this was never explained). So it was late on a damp February evening in 1841 that the examination was performed by Hilton, the anatomist, in the presence of the two surgeons, Key and Cock, and the two physicians, Bright and Chambers. The diagnosis of emphysema was confirmed when his chest was opened, and an inguinal hernia was noted. But it was the sight of an ingenious readymade gadget, which they found maintained an umbilical hernia in position, that really touched them. Not one of these present had ever seen Astley Cooper other than tall and elegant, dignified in bearing and beautifully clothed in well-cut coat and black silken hose; so the sight of a piece of cork neatly cut to the size of the umbilicus and kept in position with adhesive plaster came as a slight shock.

Another friend who consulted Bright at this time was Lord Jeffrey, in spite of the fact that Henry Holland was his London doctor. He was drawn by Bright's diagnostic ability and commonsense. Both he and Lady Jeffrey consulted him regularly, preferring his blunt decisions to Holland's pose as the society doctor. This time he was worried about his trachea, 'that had taken half his voice away'.

Jeffrey himself at sixty-eight was at the zenith of his popularity. He had given up the editorship of the *Edinburgh Review*, but, always a brilliant talker, he was much in demand everywhere.

Ever since Jeffrey had tossed the boy Bright into a haystack at Ham Green, Bright had been captivated by the older man. Above all else, he was such fun. He was the same age as Bright's two older brothers, and the drawing room at Ham Green used to echo with laughter and the inflexions of his marvellous voice. Even Phoebe had not objected to his turning the routine of the house upside down. After evening prayers, they were accustomed to return to their rooms but he liked to remain talking until two in the morning, and to lie in bed till ten, when it was pointed out to him by an indulgent Richard Bright that when he did finally sit down to breakfast most of the family had already been at work for several hours.

Bright had many patients like Jeffrey who stayed faithful to their own doctors while at the same time consulting Bright about their ailments. And with his remarkable memory one letter seems always to have been enough to keep the patient's complaint and personality fresh in Bright's mind. When Bright found himself too busy to follow up cases which other doctors had asked him to see and examine, or to ascertain that their improvement was in fact being maintained, he would send Jones to their homes with a note of enquiry. In this way his patients knew that they had not been forgotten.

Bright could spare his family barely a week that August (1840). Once more Eliza was left disconsolate, this time on the Isle of Wight. With the 'Atlantic wind beating rain against the windows', she wrote to him, 'the candles blown out on the table and . . . the roar of tremendous seas . . . I cannot bear the thought of separating the children so completely from you for I am afraid they will never love you as I would have them love you . . . Surely now they are growing up we can end these impossible situations . . . I think we must try and get a bigger house . . .'

On 3 September she wrote to Bright again:

My dreaded journey is all arranged, the coach takes me up at the door. I shall have the port manteau and one small box which is more spacious than the carpet bag. The children and servants go in the other carriage. It is very windy today and James [her brother] says that if it lasts old Major cannot draw the carriage . . . I am grieved to hear of Webb's cold, do please cure him soon. I have not told my mother. I feel embarrassed about the kindness of Dr Thompson here, he has not sent an account, what shall I do? A rabbit belonging to Webb's children is going up with ours and must be put the same night into Duke's Street.

Two other letters arrived at about this time. One was from Phoebe, begging him to visit Bristol and see Mrs Carpenter. 'She had just received the small poignant parcel of the doctor's belongings and Mary [their daughter] is equally stunned.' Three months before on 4 April Dr Lant Carpenter had disappeared without trace in the Mediterranean. He had spent the winter in Italy, accompanied by a young doctor to care for him. He was on his way home when the ship ran into bad weather, and it was thought that he had fallen overboard, though as he was sometimes a victim of depression suicide was considered.

The second letter came from Abbot's Leigh, from his brother Robert. In August Robert had sought his help in unravelling their father's long and complicated will. But Bright under stress of work had refused. He had not even managed to accompany his family for his customary holiday, he said; his profession now left him with little time for family matters. Nevertheless, Robert may well have found it difficult to comprehend his brother's unhelpfulness. Extremely busy himself, he was now faced with a will consisting of fifty-three closely written pages and several added codicils. The family assets amounted to a small fortune, but little of it was in cash. There were the extensive family estates and stocks held in sugar, canals, steamships and railways, and most of the rest was tied up in the Bright, Gibbs and Co. business. All was to be divided between the sons, with adequate provision made for the daughters.

It looks as if none of the brothers was particularly helpful over the will, yet they were all asking for money. Robert was left having to make decisions for all of them, which often brought protest. To Bright Robert now wrote: ' . . . in all these matters I have been unavoidably the scapegoat – each of you are angry with me in turn and if anyone of you be content with me at last I must think myself in luck.'

Much of the wealth contributed by Richard Bright of Ham Green was diminishing yearly, and much of the remainder was complicated by mortgages. Robert sympathized with all his brothers' concern over money matters. Knowing himself what an expensive business it was to educate sons well, his own worries were similar. 'But', he wrote to Bright, 'why should any of us be irritable in the family difficulties I do not see. We cannot help them – we are all trying to do what is best and right and we are all getting on through life better than millions of men.'

Shamed by his younger brother's admonishments, Bright must have worded a loving reply. We now find him making one of his lightning journeys to Ham Green, regardless of Eliza's expected return. On 8 September he wrote to Henry, telling his brother about the few things of his father's that Phoebe had put aside for him. There was a miniature of his mother, an agate snuff box and sundial, a silver time-piece and puzzle-cock, and 'two black medallions and several West Indian shells'. She packed them carefully with migonette, heliotrope and roses, which Eliza later arranged in bright nosegays about his rooms. The contents of Richard Bright's considerable cellar were not divided up until 1844, when the brothers drew lots. The geological collection which Benjamin inherited went at his death (1843) to Henry, who had gone to live at Crawley Manor, near Winchester.[2] Its removal created problems as it filled over fifty cabinets and cases and weighed three tons.

19
The Last Years at Guy's
1841–1844

The more absorbed Bright and his team became in the pursuit of information, the more obvious became the difficulties under which they were all working. Keeping the renal patients under close observation when they were scattered in every corner of the hospital presented considerable problems. There was no telephone or warning system then, no quick way to summon a doctor in an emergency, or to call the researcher to witness an ureamic fit.

We do not know whether Bright suggested to Harrison that all renal patients might be together in one place, or whether Harrison himself took the initiative, perhaps wanting to reward Bright for the valuable contributions he had made to Guy's. Perhaps one of the Governors of the Hospital, having read Bright's latest paper on nephritis – 'Observations on Renal disease', published in Vol. 5 of *Guy's Reports* in 1840 – was jerked into action and insisted that Bright be given all the support and help he wanted. All we do know is that some time in 1842, for 'the first time in the History of Medicine, two wards were set aside for a year for the intensive study of the disease which Bright had made his own'.[1]

> Our establishment [explained Bright] then consisted of a female ward with 18 beds; a male ward with 24 beds and a room between the two wards for the meeting of Physicians and pupils, for the registering of cases and a small laboratory communicating with the middle room, fitted up and decorated entirely to our purposes . . . The objects which we proposed to ourselves were to examine, as far as it was possible, the changes which accompanied the secretion of albuminous urine in the various functions and secretions of the body; whilst at the same time we registered the various circumstances connected with the origin, progress, and treatment of the disease – a disease than which there is none which offers a more extended field for careful and well-directed observation.[2]

In this organized and disciplined environment Bright now gave his team a thorough training in the basic art of physical exploration, imprinting on them indelibly his own qualities – caution, patience, honesty, and pertinacity. He put the young doctors Barlow, Owen Rees and Pavy to work in the laboratory, to study albuminous urine. The students he kept in the post-mortem room, he himself working beside George Robinson studying kidney tissue under the microscope – tissue taken from the diseased organs preserved in alcohol over the years. Unfortunately this work was continually interrupted, and if it ever was finished it was never published. It is assumed that he allowed Robinson to use most of the material for his paper on the same subject published that year, 1843. Bright was not one to forget his other patients and, pressed for time, he had to leave more and more of the work to others. But the specimens were put aside for him to see, and the preparation upon which he was working himself was always left in such a condition that he could at any time return to it.

Mechanical tools the team had virtually none; with few instruments of precision or other aids Bright collaborated with his colleagues outside Guy's to develop new techniques in order to help his pupils study the pathology of the kidney. He had himself invented a small mechanical figure, which took pride of place in the clinical room. It was supposed to help students put organs in their right positions in the abdomen, and it was then possible to stencil in the position of tumours in a few minutes.

The question which probably concerned Bright most was the relation between the functions of the kidney and the cardiovascular system. Had there been an efficient sphygmomanometer instead of the glass tube sometimes inserted into the carotid to measure the force and rate of the pulse, then no doubt Bright and his team would have done more work on hypertension. As it was, he sought enlightenment by making his team go over the same ground again and again, with all the different cases.

With all the old enthusiasm of his student days, often abandoning other tasks and excusing himself from meetings, Bright threw himself into the work of his unit. It was here too that he brought his students for their clinical teaching, and held regular discussions with the post-graduates that flocked to see him. The rest of Guy's knew little of what went on in these wards, and very few realized the vast extent of Bright's researches.

*

Eliza's life changed considerably – and for the better – at about this time. For now, except for going away for the summer holidays, we find her staying at Bright's side, taking more part in his plans, acting as his secretary and confidante. With the two eldest boys at Rugby, Franck at Mr Mills, the girls sharing a governess with the Folletts at Hampton, and only Charles and Henry left in the nursery, she was able at last to be a more permanent housekeeper.

Many a weekend was spent in Webb's comfortable home. He lived with his growing and attractive family in a large, solid, red-brick house at Hampton. He had risen quickly to fame; his good looks, his consumptive delicacy and charm, were irresistible. Nobody could quite make out the exact qualities which had given him his knighthood, and made him the most successful lawyer of his day, but he was certainly immensely persuasive, matchless in perception, logical and clear-headed, and possessed of a remarkable memory. His own family made a good deal of fun of his pomposity and his obsession with grandeur; it was suspected that getting rich was his primary concern.

The rambling old garden, in which Webb took so much interest, was wonderful for the Bright children, accustomed as they were to the narrow surroundings of Piccadilly. They all enjoyed the wider horizons, the unimpeded views, the river Thames at the bottom of the garden. In the garden was a stone mounting block, where Clara and Emily and their cousins Rita and Annie would measure the height of their jumps, and behind the walled garden was a round dovecote empty of pigeons. It was there that Franck and Follett shared secrets with Webb's two sons of about the same age. It is possible that they, like Franck, were pupils at Mr Mills' school nearby.

Bright was often to be found in the schoolroom on a Sunday afternoon, preferring to watch his children acting than listen to politics in the drawing room. He was often amazed by the way his children remembered so accurately those vivid memories which he himself had, at one time or another, described to them. When one of them dressed up as an Icelandic fisherman or a Hungarian gypsy, the dress would be meticulously correct in every detail; every gesture and mannerism was exactly remembered. It was William who surprised him most on these occasions. Quiet and aloof as he ordinarily was, he was a master at stage directing and improvising, while his way with the two toddlers, Charles and Henry, was most endearing.

William had none of his mother's sparkle, none of the Babington wit; but with so much of his grandfather's sweetness of nature, and his goodness and patience, so suited to a medical career, Bright had quite set his mind on his becoming a doctor. It was partly with this in mind that he had taken him to scientific lectures at the Adelaide Museum, taken him on his rounds, told him something about his work. There was no reason why he should not achieve distinction in the profession. He was taken aback then when William, now beginning at Balliol College, Oxford, wrote to him (18 November 1841) saying that he wished to be ordained. From every point of view it disappointed Bright.

Religion was very much the centre of Rugby School, and William, a young man now and of exemplary habits, was strongly influenced by the religious side of his education. By the time he reached the sixth form he had acquired an amazing knowledge of theology. He read and re-read the Bible. He sought out all religious books, developing a profound interest in other faiths, and was known to spend much of his allowance on accounts of the lives and peregrinations of the saints. How much all this fervour was due to the Headmaster's personal attention cannot be told. One can only assume that as a sixth-form boy he was much in contact with Dr Arnold, who undoubtedly would have encouraged and advised him.

William's letter made Bright realize to what extent his son's struggles of conscience had gone unnoticed by him. At the beginning of each holiday he had given William an opportunity to talk about events at Rugby, had even waited for a word of illumination as to his ideas of the future. But William, knowing his father's feelings, had lacked the courage to broach the subject of a career and allowed opportune moments to talk slip away. The habit of obeying his father was strong, and wanting to go into the Church as he did, he felt he could not withstand him to his face. The letter had taken a long time to write.

'Upon this most serious subject . . . ' he began, 'I have before been strongly inclined to mention it but a few words in your last letter confirmed my resolution. I hope that God has suggested the thoughts to me and that He will bring good out of it.' After telling him what a 'most kind good father' he was to him, he begged him to forgive him for the 'pain caused by opposing his wishes'. He was full of gratitude, he said, for the moral example he had set for all his children. Then he tried to define his underlying reasons for wanting to enter the Church, but his feelings were too personal and he was incapable of interpreting them. 'I think I had better not write more at present, but send this in hopes it may induce you to ask me to explain myself more. You have treated me with full confidence in other things, why should we not open our hearts and minds together on this subject too, as far the weightiest of all?' Though disappointed, Bright was a devoted father and saw immediately, as he admitted to Eliza, that what William had done to him he himself had once done to his own father. He recalled how long it had taken his father to acquiesce in his determination, and how much Dr Carpenter had helped to persuade his father. As far as we know, Bright never again reverted to his former hopes for William.

*

It seemed to Eliza that Bright felt an absolute need to overwhelm himself with work, but if ever she appeared worried about him he assured her that it was all necessary. There could be no carelessness when dealing with illness, as he tried to say to the students when he gave out prizes at the Medical School on 10 May 1842. At this same occasion he also unveiled Townes' bust of Sir Astley Cooper, shown to the public for the first time.

The summer of 1842 was a warm one, and it seems that Bright was worried about his work and his own flagging energy. 'He needs all the comfort I can give him, which he won't take,' Eliza complained to Phoebe. In the same letter she mentions alterations to their summer plans, and Bright having to curtail his holiday. Apart from this there are no letters until the spring of 1843, when Eliza started to fuss because he never seemed to be giving more than half his attention to what he was eating. 'But he brushed this aside.'

Then, to his own surprise, he actually found himself 'considering cutting down on some of his teaching work' as his fatigue became more extreme. It must have occurred to him then that the increasing nausea was certainly a harbinger of illness, but he ignored it and only when he became feverish, Eliza tells us, did he put himself to bed. He 'starves and drinks a lot of water, and says his pulse is fast'. He also suffered bouts of terrible pain. He got interested in the colour of his eyes, the darkness of his urine and the paleness of his stools, and when he became jaundiced all the terrors of the diseases he had so often observed and described must now have dangled before him. He didn't want to see a doctor, but had in the end to allow Eliza to call Dr Chambers to look at him.

Famous contemporaries of Richard Bright at Guy's Hospital.

9. Thomas Addison (1793–1860).
Oil painting, artist unknown.

10. Thomas Hodgkin (1798–1866).
Oil painting, artist unknown.

By courtesy of the Special Trustees, Guy's Hospital.

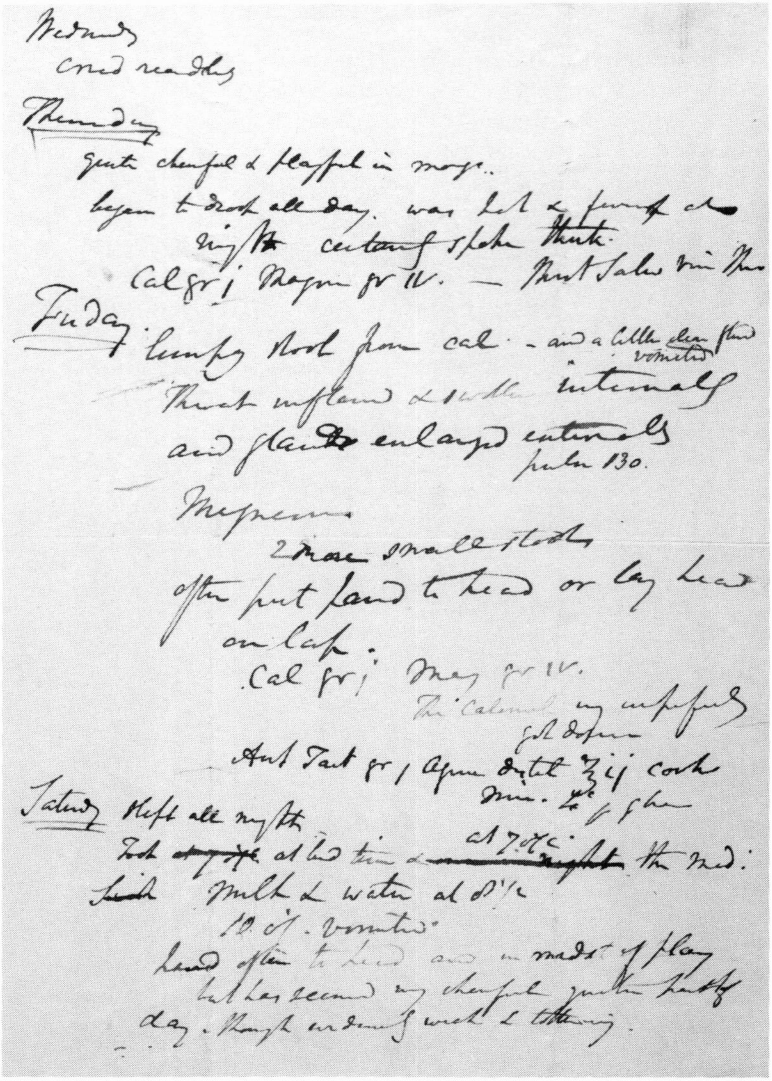

Wednesday
Cried readily
Thursday
Quite cheerful & playful in morng..
began to droop all day; was hot & feverish at night. certainly spoke thick.
Cal gr i Magn gr iv. — [illegible]
Friday lumpy stool from cal — and a little clear fluid vomited
Throat inflamed & swollen internally
and glands enlarged externally
pulse 130.
[illegible]
2 more small stools
often put hand to head or lay head
on lap.
Cal gr i Mag gr iv.
The Calomel very unpleasantly got down
Ant Tart gr i Aquae distil ℥ij [illegible]
Saturday slept all night
Took [illegible] at bed time & at 7 o'c [illegible] the med:
Milk & water at 8 o'c
10 o'c vomited
hand often to head and in midst of play
but has seemed very cheerful quite happy
day. though evidently weak & tottering.

11. Facsimile of medical notes by Richard Bright.

The rigmarole of illness that hit the master of the house upset the whole household. There were endless enquiries, ceaseless comings and goings, ever more gifts. Owen Rees and George Johnson offered to nurse him, but we do not know who did it in the end. Barlow's name is mentioned also. We can but guess – and marvel at the complete cure. Acute cholelithiasis means more often than not having to remove the stones from the gall-bladder, but somehow the blockage resolved itself and the gall-stones caused no further trouble.

Then came the problem of convalescence. There were many houses where Bright would have been welcome, but neither he nor Eliza would have dreamt of inviting themselves anywhere as privileged guests. In the end it was the Hon. John Wilson Croker who offered them his house by the sea. It was an unforeseen gesture. When first married, Eliza had often talked to him about Croker's kindness to her brother Webb, who, as a law student with a small allowance, had practically lived with him and his wife. Webb had fallen in love with Croker's niece, Jane Mary Giffard, and eventually married her.

Croker had been an extremely efficient Secretary to the Admiralty, and a writer and critic in the *Quarterly Review*. He had many enemies – Macaulay called him that 'bad, very bad man' – but his love for his relatives, after he had lost his only son, transcended all.

To the Brights he had always shown the greatest courtesy and consideration, and he was never hurt over the number of times his invitations were refused. Croker's own weak heart and his fear of over-exertion, as well as his love for Webb and concern for his fluctuating health, kept them in touch. So it was with alacrity and pleasure that Bright sat down to accept the invitation. 'I cannot sufficiently express to you and Mrs Croker', he wrote, 'my thankfulness for your kind offer. As far as I am absolutely obliged to abstain from practice, it is my great wish to get away from London as soon as I am pronounced capable of undertaking a journey and how to find a suitable and comfortable retreat has been a source of real anxiety to Mrs Bright and me . . . and as our children are on the whole very well conducted we have no fear of doing you any material mischief.'

Alverstoke, a small village in old St Swithin's Manor, near Gosport, consisted then of a few old houses built round a triangular common of gorse. Bright was pleased with 'Alverbank'. It was, he said to Croker, writing to tell him of their safe arrival, made 'to form an impregnable fortress against all apothecaries and I trust they may never be able to make the slightest impression upon its appointments'. The house was isolated on a small plateau, higher than the gorse-covered verges that led to the beach, higher than the ilex trees which edged the salt-water moat half surrounding the house. It was further imprisoned by a mass of trees – ilex, willowy ash, stunted beech and Scots firs – shaped and slanted umbrella-like by the prevailing south-westerly winds. While dressing Bright could see the Solent, the curve of Stoke Bay and his children playing at the water's edge. Below, on the terrace, was his favourite spot, with its white Florentine vases and trailing geraniums and the scent of firs rising about them. There he could gaze at the ships and watch the shores of the Isle of Wight changing colours, but the beach was hidden by the tops of trees.

John Croker had chosen his architect carefully. Every room was in proportion, every wall solid, every fireplace simple and beautifully arched. The light-filled breakfast room, with its octagonal ceiling and wide doors leading on to the southern side of the terrace, was considered by Queen Victoria to be too small and so, to please her, Croker had had another room built out, adjoining the kitchen. It was customary for the royal couple to rest here and take refreshment before crossing the Solent to Osborne, and Lord Palmerston, a frequent visitor to Osborne, would also partake of Croker's hospitality. Writing to the Crokers on 24 July (1843), Bright assured them that he was 'making decided, I might even say, rapid progress, under the A.B. cure'.

'We have been enlivened by the visits of both Mrs Bright's brothers and my own . . .' he went on to say, 'so that we have been surrounded by a kind of family circle.' On 4 August he wrote again:

> I regret exceedingly that the last hour of our very pleasant residence at Alverbank is now come and I cannot leave your home without again thanking you for your hospitality . . . The degree in which I have re-created my strength since I have resided here is such as to increase, if possible, my sense of obligation for your very well timed act of friendship . . . I hope we have not made more confusion in the house than may be reasonably expected with children . . .

The Brights then travelled to Dorset and stayed for the next few weeks in Swanage in 'an abode already prepared for them'. He felt so fortified by his stay at Croker's seaside home that he was able, he told him, to bear 'the imperfections of lodging house arrangements' all that much better. Here, at last, he felt strong enough to join in most of the family activities and was even able to enjoy books of a philosophical nature. Soon afterwards he heard of his brother Benjamin's death on 7 August at Colwall, but Eliza managed to persuade him that it would not be a good idea for him to attend the funeral. So it was not until early September that he was able to join his sisters at Ham Green.

There were many discussions between them all over the future of their home. Their father's will had suggested that Ham Green and Lowbridge's house in Great George Street should be sold and the proceeds go into the residual estate, but each son in turn was to have an option on Ham Green. Benjamin had bought it, adding land to the garden and building extensions to the house. Much of Benjamin's life was spent in debt, as he was irresponsible when it came to buying rare books. Realizing this, his father had left him £16,000 in cash and £600 a year in land. Now his wonderful library, including an original Shakespearean Folio, was to be auctioned at Sotheby's, a sale which was to take ten days. This was to be Bright's last visit to Ham Green as a home. There is nothing in writing about his feelings, only a mention of what such a garden would mean to his children.

Once more in Savile Row, with greatly improved health, 'attendant upon the change of air', Bright settled down to his old duties and occupations. In a letter dated 30 October, he acquainted Croker of his uninterrupted improvement; though he felt he could not confidently state that 'this favourable continuation will be lasting, yet I hope that I will be able to maintain my post with tolerable firmness . . . '

In spite of his good recovery, Bright, now fifty-four, felt he should cut down his work. It was better to leave Guy's now than be forced to admit later that he could not manage the pace. There were, too, the increasing claims of an ever more demanding practice, and it would soon be impossible to give sufficient attention both to this and to the beloved Guy's. Besides, there was his family to consider. Convalescence had made him realize what he was missing in his own home and how much his children needed him.

It must have been somewhere around the beginning of 1844 that Bright finally asked Harrison to release him. We know nothing of his feelings at the moment of departure, and can only imagine that in his usual unassuming way he must have made an unobtrusive exit. But we do know that the break was not complete. He was asked to remain on in an honorary capacity as medical consultant for Guy's. There were to be the regular 'get-togethers' of his renal team at Savile Row, when opinions were exchanged and old patients remembered and discussed. Then there were, when time permitted, the intermittent meetings of various societies and informal talks on medical matters in the rooms of old colleagues. Bright could never turn his back completely on what had meant so much.

20
Webb
1844–1845

Bright had once expressed his astonishment to Eliza at his substantial success in the world of private practice; he had taken so little trouble to win it and no pains to retain it. The confidence shown in him by his professional brethren had much to do with it; they knew that if they consulted him he would bestow the most minute attention upon every case. If they themselves missed some detail then he would certainly find it. His old friend Henry Holland got him many cases, and he had an excellent professional relationship with Dr Chambers, one of the finest physicians of the day.

Webb, his brother-in-law, was one of the patients Bright shared with Dr Chambers at this time. This was an exceptionally difficult case for him. Eliza hovered round miserably, never able to accustom herself to his illness, always fearing the worst, never really believing the inevitable would happen, but the conduct of his sister-in-law, Lady Jane, never failed to impress him. However bitter her distress, however heavy her heart, she smiled and talked as if they were all about to go off on a holiday together. Webb himself, always on the defensive, had the fluctuating temperament typical of the consumptive, and a strong fighting spirit. He belittled his febrile periods and thought up fresh jokes about doctors; he said anyone would do to look after a consumptive, so long as he wasn't a foreigner or a man who was obliged to use a dictionary before he wrote up prescriptions. In fact he was well satisfied with Dr Chambers, and when he wanted he could get advice from his brother-in-law, Bright, with whom he was very intimate. Bright watched, with concern, Webb's slow deterioration. He had first seen Webb when the disease in his lung was minimal, when the arrested lesion was calcified; since then the disease had advanced, and at a later examination he noted sadly the activity of the lesion which had spread into the lower part of the upper lobe of the lung. Now, once more, the picture had changed: palpitation produced a small rub, percussion disclosed dullness, listening a sound like a 'cracking pot'. The right side of his lung 'was doing its duty very imperfectly'; it was something like an old vest full of holes, which at a stretch could give completely. This time (March 1844) Bright advised him to rest properly, to go to bed and nurse his cold, to leave his town house in Duke Street and go to Hampton. Croker urged Bright to send him abroad. For some time Bright was too busy to reply, but on 29 April at last he had time to write a long, confidential letter. He begged Croker to be reticent, telling him how he 'liked Follett's condition at this moment much worse than I did before'. He felt that 'a sea-voyage would not necessarily be beneficial as it is more important to rest the lung, it should not be irritated by taking on any kind of excitement . . . for my part I shall confine him more strictly than he had hitherto been and have applied a blister which has offered some relief'.

That spring Webb was reappointed Attorney-General under Peel's second administration. He went to the House of Lords to attend Daniel O'Connell's appeal, where his friends were saddened to see him trying to walk across the floor, having refused the offered assistance, and then, perhaps because of some paralysis of the lower limbs or perhaps because his congenitally weak spine failed to support him, accepting the proffered chair and addressing the assembly sitting down. And yet there he was in June, with all his vitality, making a triumphant speech on the Dissenters' Bill.

With the August migration into the country, London began to empty and Bright was able to contemplate a holiday. The Folletts thought of introducing their children to the Continent and suggested that the Brights should do the tour with them. Eliza leapt at the idea. For weeks she had been dreading the coming holiday period, more loath than ever to be parted from her husband now that she had the added and insidious worry of her brother's frailty and the feelings of insecurity which went with it. Accompanying Webb in a precarious state of health might help solve Bright's conscience about leaving his other patients. Then, it seemed to Eliza, in a moment it was settled. The thought of going abroad and having her husband's company in comparative privacy; of being with Webb, and knowing that if he or any of the children got ill there would be somebody in attendance able to cope, filled her with extraordinary joy.

There followed two weeks of preparations. Bright rummaged in cupboards for maps and walking hats; cleaned paint-boxes and bought new brushes. He put his patients, one by one, under the care of Dr Chambers. He had to gain leave of absence from Rugby for his two sons, Follett and Franck. It was to be Franck's first term. His housemaster, C. T. Arnold, had to agree with Bright that it was an 'advantageous opportunity of him seeing for the first time the land of our neighbours', and that geography could certainly then be acquired as a reality – but, even so, he did think that at thirteen Franck was too young to profit entirely by such a journey.

Three specially heavy coaches had been hired for the journey, each drawn by four horses. The Folletts occupied one and, with the exception of William and the two baby sons, who were being left behind, the Bright family went in another. The servants occupied the third, it having been decided that, rather than have the maids, valets and running footmen sitting outside their carriages, perching uncomfortably on the imperials or travelling trunks, it would be better to accommodate them separately. Such an impressive entourage would very likely attract attention and procure quicker service than they might otherwise have had; besides, by going on ahead they could prepare the accommodation for the night, which was particularly important where a sick man and children had to be considered. It amused Bright to see the amount of fuss his brother-in-law made over the whole trip. He had to be assured of the best inns, the best cabin in the ship, and the place of honour at the Captain's side. Lady Jane also liked to see that their importance – by way of the best rooms, the best closets and the assiduous attention of hotel housekeepers – should be recognized. In this way they travelled through Holland, Switzerland and Germany, the two families remaining always in reach of each other. On one occasion the children of the two families actually changed places with each other.

Had it not been for Rita Follett keeping a journal of the trip, little would have been known about it; as it is, the account is sketchy enough, and being written under the formal gaze of a governess there are more geographical and historical details than personal reactions. All the same, we do get some vivid impressions. They received much hospitality in Holland, and loitered by wayside crucifixes in the Simplon Pass; they gathered wild strawberries in Germany, and alpine flowers in the Alps; there was a thunderstorm, and anxieties over Webb's uncovered head and lost hat; they spent hot nights in Geneva, and in Genoa the couples had, reluctantly, to dress for a special dinner. Webb was too fatigued and breathless to join the party on their visit to St Maria delle Grazie in Milan, where they saw

Leonardo da Vinci's 'Last Supper' and were distressed to see the paint dropping off in tiny flakes.

Once the Italian lakes were reached they settled for a while. The Brights' spirits rose as they found themselves amongst such beauty, but the Folletts had preferred the scenery of Switzerland. Webb spent most of his days quietly, stretched limp on a sofa, quoting furiously from obsolete guidebooks, while Bright, paintbox in hand, wandered off into the mountains. Before leaving the hotel he would hand money over to 'Aunt Lizzie', as Eliza was known to the Folletts, warning the children against excessive quantities of pastries and the brittleness of foreign toys. He advised Webb against too much sun, and suggested that breathing hot steam would relieve his cough.

One learns little more from Rita; but between the lines of her diary one can sense how much the Follett children adored their father and how they suffered at seeing him so white and frail. Bright noted that Spencer, the oldest son, was the most observant and the most frightened. The burden that Bright bore as a doctor must have been immense; sometimes, we are told, he slept in Webb's bedroom, and changed the drenched sheets.

By October the hoped-for improvement in Webb's condition was at last being maintained. They were able to leave him behind in the care of Lady Jane, both by now filled with a new confidence. Bright besought him to rest, pledging himself to do anything for his household in London and to see the necessary people concerning the adjustment of his working schedule; at the same time his honesty and caution compelled him to warn Lady Jane not to expect too much.

One surviving letter written by Eliza to William at Oxford gives touching proof of the estimation in which Bright was held abroad. When they rested in towns along the homeward route, the news of his arrival soon passed from mouth to mouth. Former pupils lost no time getting in touch with him; professors came to see him; humbler practitioners, their patients in tow, begged him for advice. Bright, though reminding himself that he was in fact on holiday, reluctantly saw patients. He knew, too, that many professors would have been offended had he not stopped to talk to them. He saw it as quite natural that they should want to hear from *him* how far his own subsequent experiences had borne out his first discoveries, and to discuss with him their own observations.

Back in London at last, he felt fit and was absurdly gratified by the pleasure his reappearance gave when he visited the houses of his patients, many 'up from the country' now that the season had begun and London hummed with activity again. From time to time Webb wrote. 'I hope he stays in Italy all winter; he will benefit more than from his sea voyage return,' Bright told Croker, whose overpowering anxiety always kept him in touch with the Doctor. But apparently Webb, falling into one of his moods of melancholy and overwhelmed with homesickness, decided for himself on an earlier return. 'A foreign air breathes no pleasure for me,' he wrote. He was too attached to his own home and professional pursuits to remain away any longer. He returned in the middle of winter, and Bright watched him anxiously. All through that spring Webb was supported by the belief that he might after all recover, never realizing that each relapse saw the unfolding course of his fatal disease; he blamed his weakness on the colds he kept getting. But another bronchial infection brought him to his bed, and this time he was nursed by the Pennells at No. 9, Cumberland Terrace, Regent's Park. Once more Bright had to plan his day so that it was possible to call frequently on the dying man.

In John Lowe, who had replaced the faithful Jones, Bright seems to have had a good servant. When he was particularly occupied with a case, Lowe made it his business to keep himself informed about the other patients. He knew them by name, he knew where they lived and, with the help of the footmen, grooms and coachmen, he was able to keep them under close surveillance; he would then inform his master of any change in their condition. He was always tactful and discreet. Eliza certainly appreciated his resourcefulness, and the way he fulfilled his obligations to his master. She could always depend on him to tell her where Bright was, and it was through him that she was able one day to summon Bright instantly to Webb's bedside.

Webb had long given up the struggle; he was too weary, he told his sister Eliza, discovering that now he could face a better existence. Thus neither Dr Chambers nor Dr Bright needed to tell him that all further treatment was indeed futile. Lady Jane never left his side, while Eliza fainted with emotion each time she visited him. Webb was given the Holy Sacrament on the Thursday; on Saturday he died. According to *The Times* it was his two brothers, 'J. W. Croker, Dr and Mrs Bright, several members of the Pennell family and Williams his servant (who sobbed like a child) that watched the easy transition when the moment of death was scarcely perceptible'.

There was a public funeral, an ordeal which Lady Jane would have preferred not to have to suffer. But, as she said, Webb, who had enjoyed the trappings of the Temple so much, would have wished to be laid at rest in the Crypt beside the Knights Templar. On 4 July 1845, at 11 a.m., the funeral took place with all pomp. The press of the day stated that the burial of 'this distinguished ornament to the Bar', which took place in the forty-seventh year of his life, was 'impressive for the efficient way it was conducted and of great contrast to the untidy shambles of many a Royal Funeral to which the public had become accustomed'. The occasion drew a large crowd of people, who stood in watchful silence as the cortège passed. Six of Webb's most distinguished friends were pall-bearers, – including two of Bright's patients, Sir James Graham, First Lord of the Admiralty, and Lord Lyndhurst, the Chancellor of the Exchequer. Five thousand people were present at the service, which ended fittingly, at the vault, with the singing of Handel's 'His body is buried within the grave but His name shall live for ever'.

Webb had been a greatly loved man, and amongst his friends much sorrow was felt. Family history, repeated by hearsay down the years, said that her overwhelming grief made Eliza a little odd for a while after the event. Her speech was melancholy and her voice low. Bright seemed unable to give her any comfort, he told Franck, and even the beguiling presence of Henry and Charles only seemed to increase her weeping, since her mind then turned instantly to her six fatherless nieces and nephews – the youngest, with Webb's grey eyes, being only sixteen months old. Where Bright was grateful for the many letters they received at this time, she dreaded them, declaring that no compliments about her brother could assuage her agony. Even Franck's first letters from Rugby, telling her of his love for football, failed to rouse her interest.

When September came, one of Bright's patients offered him the use of an old farmhouse in the Lakes; it just suited their needs. 'Here we are as peaceably and in a manner as consonant to our present feeling as we could possibly descry.'

At first Eliza was slow to participate in the activities Bright thought up for his children, but gradually she felt something of the healing influence of the countryside. Wherever she had gone in London she had expected at every turn to catch sight of her beloved brother, but here there was no lurking ghost. No one was more relieved than Bright to see Eliza gradually return to normality. The children became a source of joy to her once more, and, instead of excusing herself from the evening stroll, as she had done at first, she walked out with Bright, holding his arm and allowing him to enliven the walk with talk about all the great events of the day.

But Lady Jane Follett never recovered from the shock of her husband's death. Bright worried about his inability to help her. He was not her doctor and she had changed to a new one, whose name was not even familiar to him. He could only have the occasional look at her and see how the nourishment she was taking failed to support her strength. She was a consumptive, too, and looked to all as if she wanted to die. It was no wonder, her friends said, that 'the widow of such a man might well droop and wish to follow him'. She survived Webb for two years, dying with 'a sensation of instant death'.

21
William
1846–1848

We know little about the patients Bright looked after in the last fifteen years of his life. We have to be content with the odd letter of gratitude from a patient, a short note from a relieved relative. Some scrawled prescriptions have survived, but most are nameless and undated. The names of many important people he visited appear in family letters, and the places mentioned and the presents he received also give clues about his work. His name does crop up in some biographies of the period, but he is not included in the lives of many others, nor mentioned in their diaries, where we know for a fact that he was consulted. But from the little material there is, we learn how, until the very end of his life, he remained acutely observant, with a wonderful photographic memory. Only once did he make a serious misjudgement – and it never ceased to shame him: he was consulted by a physician of forty-five, who had a pronounced and persistent albuminuria. Bright is said to have expressed the opinion that he would die within two years, whereupon the physician abandoned his practice and betook himself to the country to enjoy all those things working people have not the time to do. There he lived comfortably, dying of cerebral haemorrhage at the age of eighty-eight, thirty years after Bright. Otherwise he was an extraordinarily good doctor.

There was something about Bright that got his patients better, as the little rotund Revd Storrey whom he visited at the time of Webb's death repeatedly told him. Storrey brought out his cash from a tobacco jar and happily counted it in piles before an embarrassed Bright. An epigastric pain had taken all his courage and a Colchester doctor his strength. He had, he said, carefully studied doctors and now considered that in Bright he had discovered the man who could do most for him. Minute care seems to have been given to his symptoms; the treatment included the use of 'a nice portable vessel, holding about two quarts which I take up with both hands and hold over my head, only I gain the centre of the head, as the coldness hurts my hearing . . .' Eventually a letter reached Bright telling him how remarkably well all his friends said he was looking. It came with two barrels of Colchester oysters and a warm invitation now that the railroad was functioning to stay whensoever he felt thus inclined 'to break away from the harassing time of your profession'.

At the same time he was seeing Jeffrey again about his indigestion, reminding him that with advancing years he could not expect his stomach to do as much work as it had when he was younger. Both of them, he said, should eat less, 'for the diminished powers of digestion should be in proportion to our own naturally diminishing energy'. He was also attending his old friend Dr Franck, who was simply dying of old age. And when Croker wrote to him from The Grove, Moseley, inviting him and his children to see his new irregular, angular drawing room and the Duke of Wellington's cloak which he had just had given to him by the old warrior himself, Bright had to refuse: Henry Holland had called him in to see Sydney Smith, and 'although the horses might bring my body to Moseley and my inclination might retain it there in all tranquillity, yet my unquiet and perturbed spirit would be tormented with the thought of duties neglected and after I should not get my quiet day at Moseley'.

John Morgan, from Guy's, was a sad case. Bright would visit him early in the morning at Broad Street Buildings, where in the backyard he kept his tame female kangaroos. He was devoted to this skilful surgeon, the first to remove a diseased ovary, the first to perform section of the cornea. As a child Morgan had collected animals, birds and birds' eggs; his superb collection of stuffed birds can be seen to this day in Cambridge University museum. He had spent many hours with Bright, Addison and Hodgkin, discussing the possibility of experimenting with Indian poisons to still the terrible convulsive spasms of tetanus and hydrophobia. Like Bright and Addison, he was interested in mercury and venereal disease, and he often accompanied Bright to a meeting at the Veterinary College, sometimes watching there an operation on an animal before attempting to do the same on a human being. He had not been all that strong, often complaining of bilious headaches, and while Bright was discovering the symptoms of nephritis, Morgan unbeknown was watching the approach of the very same symptoms in his own body. With the courage natural to him he said nothing about it, and it was already too late when Morgan told Bright his troubles.

With all these demands upon him Bright found that leaving Guy's gave him none of the extra free time he had thought it would. As for

Eliza, still threatened by melancholy over Webb's loss, she seized at
all household activities as solace. Spring 1846 brought her many
perplexities. Since Anna had left to get married there had been a
temporary cook, then another permanent one, 'a horrid woman',
who, Eliza now realized, would have to go. As a result she had to
spend many an hour contemplating 'all the unpleasant people that
come to offer'. When, finally, one came that suited, there followed a
further change of other servants. The housemaid, sent from the
country by her sister Agnes Synge, was foolish, with a flat chest which
worried Bright and a supreme ignorance of what her duties entailed
which worried them all. So she had to be replaced. Then the young
boy Edward was returning from hospital: he had spent some time in
Guy's with a fever and glandular lumps, a case which had caught the
interest of Dr Hodgkin. He had always been a favourite of theirs ever
since, as a red-faced boy, he had first come to Bloomsbury Square to
look after the fires. Finally, there was a new footman to be considered,
and it took some time before Lowe approved of the proffered references.

That Lent she also had William in bed. He had been sent home
from Oxford with one of his mysterious bouts of fever, which with his
final examinations before him was very hard. Fortunately, the new
maid Lydia proved to be helpful in the sickroom, never minding
making up a poultice or fingering a leech. She would take up his
breakfast tray and he sat in a chair while she made his bed and
arranged his room. Then he was ready to see Dr Chambers or his
uncle Dr Benjamin Babington, who was always eager to see him.
Even his Uncle Sam looked in on a quick business trip from
Liverpool, bringing cherry jam from Bessy and a dramatic story of the
Great Britain, 'lying', as Brunel put it, 'like a useless saucepan kicking
about on the Doldrum sands', and of how their friend Captain
Claxton was trying to get her afloat. One Sunday a radiant Thomas
Addison appeared. He was going to get married and had brought
Elizabeth Hauxwell, a kind and loving widow, to luncheon to see
them all.

Eliza was impressed to see how well her stepson took his enforced
imprisonment. She was to tell Franck that she thought him
uncommonly like his father, such small things aroused his attention
and pleased him – the smell of a herb, the blackbird singing on the
chimney pots above his attic bed, the flare of gaslight in murky fog.
Bright did not interfere with his friend Dr Chambers' treatment, but
made him drink more milk and rationed his books. Though he knew

William was worrying over his examinations, he took out of his hands Dr Miller's two books – *Good Thoughts in Bad Times, Good Thoughts in Worse Times, mixt Contemplations in Better Times*, and *The Chase and Cure of A Wounded Conscience*, and gave him instead a new novel by Jane Austen and John Davy's treatise on fishing.

William was better by the summer and in the autumn when he left Balliol Bright had to find time to help him over his career. This involved writing letters and talking to John Jackson, the Rector of St James's Piccadilly, and Francis Faithfull of Bishop's Hatfield. William's future gradually took shape. In those days there were few theological colleges, so William was sent for training to Henry Mackenzie, an able and dominant churchman, at Great Yarmouth. Things went well. In less than four months he was offered a curacy in Wiltshire. Writing to his son, Bright compared all this with the ease with which young men could enter the medical profession, expressing himself amazed at the number of people needed to show William was 'worthy of the cloth and bond'. The testimonials of his pious and honest behaviour had then to be endorsed by three Lord Bishops, who had to know him. So Bright was delighted when William wrote to say that at last the banns had been read out at Divine Service and no person knew of 'any just cause or impediment' why he should not be admitted to holy orders forthwith. He was ordained on Sunday 19 September 1847, in Salisbury Cathedral.

As he knelt in the cathedral that day, Bright must have thought of Martha, and how surprised she would have been. Their son was to have been a doctor, not a curate; he was to have followed the steps of his grandfather, Dr William Babington, and not the steps of Henry Bright, the only member of the Bright family who had ever taken holy orders – and that 300 years ago. Then 'Poor Willie, like a bird out of a cage', introduced his parents to his rector, William Henry Spencer, and showed them something of his leafy parish of Stert.

Eliza wrote to William that Christmas, thanking him for his gifts and telling him how his lead had been missed in the family charades and how 'the clothes in the dressing-up box were discovered eaten by moths – this upset your father for he valued them and [they] had afforded us so much pleasure at this time . . .'

William took his first marriage service in January 1848, and by April of that year – probably due to consumption – he was dead and lovingly buried in St James's Piccadilly.

His eldest son's death affected Bright profoundly. It was as well, he told Phoebe, that he was not only busy with work but also embroiled in a long-standing row with the Royal Society.

He had been a loyal and proud Fellow for over twenty years, but like many of the younger members he was alive to the need for reform. He was disenchanted with the bickerings, professional jealousies and cliquishness of the old establishment under Dr Roget, who, though a devoted Secretary, was now old, inflexible and complacent.[1] Bright was now able to add his voice of dissent, plunging headlong into the controversial dispute centring round the Physiology Committee's award of the Royal Medal. They had decided that Thomas Beck should have the award for his work on the nerves of the uterus. Bright's indignant voice was added to those who pointed out that it was Robert Lee who had done the pioneering work. Having studied all Lee's published works and long been fascinated by his obstetrical observations and his ovular theory of menstruation, Bright felt justified in interfering. So he formed a special committee of enquiry; among the members were Robert Grant, Professor of Anatomy at London University, who had complained year after year about the irregularities shown in the awarding of the Royal Medal; Marshall Hall, whose papers had been rejected countless times by the Physiology Committee, and who had on and off charged them with favouritism, plagiarism, collusion, incompetence and distortion; and Wharton Jones, who had tried unsuccessfully to start a controversy over Roget's friend Newport, the entomologist, getting the award in 1836.

It took them some time to collect and sort out the evidence, but they were ready to face the Council of the Royal Society on 11 February 1847, having won the court battle to have the award rescinded, only for it to be rejected by the Council, it being not expedient 'to further the proceedings on such a matter'. As bit by bit the full story was revealed there was a public outcry, all being appalled at the shoddy treatment shown to Robert Lee. Sackings were demanded, and reform of the whole structure of the Royal Society. But from their position of strength, Bright and his colleagues behaved magnanimously to their adversaries, and they gave a large dinner in the great hall of Somerset House to show their appreciation to the seventy-year-old Dr Roget on his dismissal. That May, when he next consulted Bright, Lord Jeffrey was quick to congratulate him on the part he had played in the reshaping of the Royal Society; he was ever on the side of younger men, he said.

This time Lady Jeffrey consulted Bright as well. After their return to Scotland that summer, Jeffrey kept in touch by letter, telling Bright 'that there was not a man in the south whose advent gives Lady Jeffrey and me so much pleasure. She is very true and constant in her love for you'. Jeffrey also told him that 'your shabby regime and all your base restraints' were making a new man of him, and begged him to pay them a visit at Craigrook. 'If you will not come yourself will you not send your brother? That I think is not so vain a hope . . . especially as I see Ham Green advertised to be let. It gave me some sad sighs and tender musings'.

But it was not until the following May, when they paid their annual visit to London, that Bright saw them again. Jeffrey was in an unusual state of alarm lest something should occur to prevent Bright from coming to see Lady Jeffrey. The feeling of isolation 'that his wife's illness gave him was quite overwhelming', and he clung to his 'dear, dear friend', confident that Bright could help her get stronger. At last in June Bright pronounced Lady Jeffrey well enough to travel. He strongly recommended her to avoid 'damp railway cushions', to travel by sea to Leith, and to get rid of her stick with as little delay as possible, on the grounds that the more she walked the sooner 'the gout' would disappear from her knees.

That September the Brights went to Scotland for their holiday. They were to stay with the Jeffreys on their way through to the Highlands. The trip turned out in every way successful. Jeffrey was 'looking more his old self' and Lady Jeffrey's tic on her face was 'less active'; Bright's happiness on holiday was always infectious, and the Scottish hills he found especially exhilarating. The Jeffreys saw the whole family set off north, 'Dick with the same eagerness as his schoolboy sons', with a map costing £3.8s., fishing gear, sketchbooks, botany case, a selection of appropriate knives – 'to demonstrate to his children the insides of fish and frog' – and as always his medical case. In the valley of Glencoe they settled at a recommended lodging house. This part of Scotland was new to Bright and he wanted to see more of it. The year before, one of his patients – Lord Ashburnham – had lent him a shooting lodge on the Isle of Bute, but, as he wrote to Croker at the time, 'after having travelled several hundred of miles to find a bad imitation of the situation of Alverbank and a bad substitute for your elegant home our only advantage is a steamer which carries us in a few hours to the beautiful scenes of Argyllshire'. It was this particular country he wished to explore.

William Campbell and his wife treated the Brights 'with all the kindliness in the world', giving them the 'best of everything'. One day Mr Menzies, the minister of the local manse, called and took Bright off 'to see some sick farmer further down the valley'. On their return journey they came to a 'nice slated house on the left of the track'. Here, the minister said he wanted to draw up for a minute and out walked the laird of the country, Mr MacDonald. He had heard that a Dr Bright and his family were in the vicinity and he wished to see whether it was the same Bright he had known in London three years before. Almost unable to believe that it was indeed the same man, 'Mr MacDonald was eager to be of use to us . . . hearing that I liked to fish . . . immediately we had his boat, his fish and his gillie. It was a wonderful and unexpected ending to our holiday, even if the fish did escape me.' It was Bright who recounted all of this in a letter he wrote to Phoebe warning her of their intended visit to see her. First they broke their return journey at Sandheys to exchange news with Sam and Bessy, then they went south to see for themselves that Phoebe had really settled in at Brand Lodge. It was while Bright was at Welland House that he had an urgent message from Lowe demanding his presence at Stanmore. Leaving Eliza and the children to follow in a more leisurely manner, Bright hurried back to London. On arrival at Savile Row he found lying on the top of the letter basket the summons from Sir David Davies, and an apology 'for being the cause of bringing you here a day sooner than intended . . . but the non-Queen does not seem so well and I ask you urgently to see her'.

22

Private Practice
1849–1850

Queen Victoria had long been concerned by her aunt's increasing frailty and had repeatedly told her that she should call in Dr Bright. But Queen Adelaide was well content with her domestic physician Sir David Davies, and the occasional assistance of Dr Chambers. It was only when Sir David himself insisted on calling in another opinion that she eventually consented. He proposed Dr Watson, since Bright was out of town, but she refused to see him and said she would wait for Bright's return. So, one day in the first week of October 1849, Bright made his way to Bentley Priory, where Sir David and Dr Chambers both awaited him. They greeted him, he told Eliza later, with 'surprising cordiality and affection'. Talking over the case with the other two doctors, Bright learned something of the prolonged strain and sorrows that had slowly undermined the Dowager Queen's strength: when betrothed she had suffered from pleurisy; as a foreign bride she had met with prejudice and ingratitude from her greedy stepchildren; she had lost four of her own children, and then her beloved William. Now, a widow of fifty-seven, she was dying of lung cancer.

Queen Adelaide seemed to be surrounded with affection and simple comforts. The house, leased from the Marquess of Abercorn, was a somewhat ugly pile of grey sandstone, while the rooms, not so long ago filled with the famous and the fashionable, were now uncannily silent.

The grand, fan-fluted staircase was too steep for one whose strength had gone, so her apartments were two rooms to the left of the hall. There Bright found a frail-looking, petite woman in a large wooden bed which almost filled the room. She lay under a specially painted ceiling: she could neither read nor work at her favourite embroidery, and it was hoped that the intricate gold patterns, stucco squares, roses and dancing figures would draw her attention away from the discomforts of illness. On top of the bureau were crammed all the Queen's most loved personal possessions – miniatures of

DR RICHARD BRIGHT (1789–1858)
DR RICHARD BRIGHT (1789–1858)

Queen Victoria with Albert, and of her step-grandchildren, black and white drawings of favourite buck-hounds, souvenirs and mementoes of her numerous travels. On one side was a cage in which lived a pink and grey parrot. Had Bright had his way earlier, the bird would have been banished from the sick-room long before, the flung feathers and scattered cage-dust being incompatible with weak lungs. It was an old parrot of some character, he was told, and resented strangers. Whenever he examined the patient and the oil lamp was brought closer at his request, the bird protested, squalling and jumping up and down.

The Queen was attended by her personal maid, her two nieces and her sister, the Duchess of Saxe-Weimar. Miss Arnold (the nurse?) was very nervy, always fearful that the doctors would not be there when they were needed. Bright took unobtrusive charge of the sick-room. How far he was able to get in his physical examinations we will never know. Neither Sir David nor Dr Chambers had ever examined her nearer than the end of the bed, and one wonders whether either of them ever got as far as knowing, as Bright did, that she bandaged her knees to relieve the strain of standing. They were both to be accused of having failed to diagnose her illness early enough; when a medical colleague once asked Dr Chambers why he did not investigate her disorder, he replied, 'Dammit, I wasn't going to pull the Queen about.'[1] He was perhaps afraid of dismissal, for she was prim and prudish and would never have forgiven the taking of physical liberties. Whether Bright ever managed to place his stethoscope on her bare chest is questionable. Certainly he did not consider even tapping and prodding through the thickness of 'a bedcloth' reliable enough. But, realizing that he had in any case been called in too late, and perhaps out of consideration for her, he may have decided not to subject her to the indignity of a complete physical examination, or to drain the fluid off her chest. Anyway, he seems to have kept her under minute observation, taking samples of her blood and other secretions to analyse – which impressed the onlookers. He gave no hint that he felt that things had been mismanaged in the past, or that something might have been done earlier to prevent such a rapid decline, but was generous in his praise of the devotion of her attendants.

In no time, Queen Adelaide warmed to him and began to talk. Both loved the German language, water-colour painting, old houses, and children's parties; both hated travelling by sea. The whole household looked forward to his visits. He was helpful in countless small ways, measuring out the medicine himself and putting it into the silver cup which the Queen had held for the old King, his fingers being too stiff and knotted to hold it to his lips. He acted as interpreter to foreign enquirers and saw off unwanted visitors and reports. He gave much needed support to the nurses, who were frightened at the thought of a haemorrhage, and alarmed by the terrible spasms of her cough. When he was not in attendance Lord Howe was always calling him back: 'The Queen wishes you to come here this a.m., and as soon as you receive this letter. You can return immediately after you have seen her', or, 'Please come. The Queen's legs have annoyed her a good deal in the night.' And even when they were 'happy to see a wonderful degree of vitality and all think she seems stronger' he still had to go and 'relieve the anxiety she has over her continuing restlessness and strange drowsiness'.

During all those weeks of intermittent visits to Stanmore, Bright's children saw little of him. 'Papa keeps pretty well but is immensely busy going out of town and all sorts of things,' wrote Clara to her brothers at Rugby. As the Queen's condition worsened, he often had to stay the night, but he did so with some reluctance, for he had other patients quite as sick. In the morning he would be off and back to London as soon as he was able.

The Queen never asked to see the faithful Dr Chambers, which worried Bright not a little. His colleague seemed most anxious to be kept in the picture. 'It strikes me', he wrote to Bright, 'that if a bulletin came out perhaps you would agree with me, that my name as Physician-in-ordinary to the Queen Dowager might as well appear on it.' But when the bulletin was announced at her death in the early hours of the Sunday morning, 2 December 1849, it was signed with only two names – her household physician, Sir David Davies, and Bright, the consultant.

Sir David Davies seemed to cling on to Bright for the next few weeks, writing him several friendly letters: 'I am happy to say that we are very well here, with the exception of poor Miss Arnold, who is now suffering *all* that we had foretold from her arduous and harassing attendance upon the poor Queen.' 'The Duchess, to whom I communicated the major part of your note, begged me to thank you in her name and I was to say how much obliged she felt to you for *all* your kindness. The Duchess has seen most of the papers. We think the article in the *Morning Chronicle* the best written and the most faithful throughout.'

There are amongst the Bright family letters a number of instructions, proudly preserved, which were sent by the Earl Marshal, the Duke of Norfolk, to Bright, with regard to his attendance at the interment of 'Her Late Majesty, the Queen Dowager, in the Royal Chapel of St George at Windsor on Thursday December 13th at one o'clock'. But nobody tells us whether, as was so often the case, something else occurred to prevent his being present.

Bright was surprised to find himself amongst the Queen's legatees. He received a piece of furniture, a magnificent Bible with illustrations and illuminated covers and a large canteen of gold and silver plate. He was asked as well to consider whether £180 was sufficient remuneration for his 'valuable attendances', but on 21 December he was sent £200 by the executors. It came just at the time when Eliza and Bright had decided to make up their yearly accounts, as there were fees to be found for Follett at Cambridge and for Charles, who was starting at Rugby. His children now had inherited independent incomes, but additional expenses were met by Bright. Money was only valuable, he had written, when it could minister to the ultimate benefit of his children, especially when it came to education. 'I would willingly spend more money for this than for any object in the world.' He was happy to advance any reasonable amount for walking tours or special books. But he was fierce over debts, making certain that no child of his ever left a situation with money owing. 'Let me know your finances. Leave no shilling unpaid that you may start again fairly.' Although exceedingly generous, he hated to see money wasted and disliked having to buy clothes for himself. One of the few times the family saw him angry was when Franck bought a lame pony 'that kicked and stumbled and started'.

Bright's professional income rarely exceeded £4,000. In the year 1850, to his astonishment, he found he had made almost £6,000. Having once been content with less than £2,000, anything above was a surprise. Bright had warned Eliza that now he was getting older his salary would fluctuate and perhaps drop, but instead it continued to go up in proportion to his ever rising reputation – though it never in fact reached the £10,000 mark, which was what Sir Benjamin Brodie, the surgeon, made, and what Lord Macaulay told Prince Albert he thought 'that Dr Bright was earning'.[2]

Eliza reproved Bright many times over his handling of money: he would often wave aside his fee for a colleague's widow, a student, or an impoverished intellectual, while he sometimes felt too moved to send a bill when a patient had died or when he felt that he had failed in some way. People used him, Eliza said, constantly. Barely a week passed without some person appearing on the doorstep asking for a medical check-up for some reason or another. Where Bright resented the loss of time, Eliza was exasperated by the exploitation. Assurance companies and the like should be shamed into recognizing the right of medical men to be paid for their services.

Bright was always scrupulously honest and would give no blind opinions – as he made clear to Sir J. Wilde, later to become Lord Truro: 'When last I saw your groom he was in no state to go to Brighton nor was he then in a state to be a desirable attendant. The weather is very sharp . . . and if the medical man really thinks he ought not to go, I cannot give a contrary opinion without seeing the man. Pray take care of yourself.'

Bright's red carriage was often to be seen outside No. 8 Curzon Street at around this time. The Berrys, launched into high society by Horace Walpole of Strawberry Hill, had remained popular in Paris, Rome, Bath and London for over half a century. When Bright met the 'May-berries' – as Sydney Smith called them – they were in their early eighties, and their rooms still thronged with distinguished visitors. Miss Mary was the dominant character, scolding, appreciative and very alive, garnishing her conversation with vigorous oaths; she studied political economy, Malthus and Free Trade. Then there was Miss Agnes, grand and less vigorous; the sprightly Lady Charlotte Lindsay, also in her eighties, and Anne Turner, their faithful companion. The sisters, 'who had no vices and rather a large endowment of virtues', made Bright sit down between them while each engaged him in the symptoms of the other. Miss Mary, in a black wig, with rouged cheeks and a pink sash, had been struggling with imperfect health for some time, but apart from the mention of 'pulsations of the heart' and on one occasion of influenza, it is not clear what either of them suffered from. They shared with Bright a love of books, friends and gardens – Miss Mary was a passionate gardener; Bright must have enjoyed every moment of the company of those four elderly ladies.

Emily Eden was another of Bright's more colourful patients. A friend of all in society, Bright found her quite enchanting, though caustic in temperament and unable to tolerate bores. Some of her fragile, porcelain beauty was gone by the time Bright treated her, but she must have looked lovely even then. She wrote romantic novels, and though they were not as popular as those of Jane Austen, he was able to tell her that they were seized on by his daughters as soon as they were published. Nothing their father told them of Hatfield, Buckingham Palace or Bentley Priory could equal what Emily Eden had to say of the balls and carousels held at Bowood, Woburn or Boyle Farm. The roses and lilies which she cultivated in the garden of Eden Lodge, Kensington, were another source of conversation. As Bright took her pulse, she would tell him how she 'grudged leaving the sweet peas even for a day'.

She summoned Bright the day she heard that her brother, Lord Auckland, had dropped dead with apoplexy while out shooting with friends. And it was not long after when the news came from Edinburgh of the death of their mutual friend, Lord Jeffrey. The 'poor heart', which had kept 'going at a dull and shuffling pace' all that winter of 1849, suddenly ceased, on 28 January 1850. Carlyle's 'beautiful little man' was dead. No one had any particular reason to anticipate Lord Jeffrey's death and to all his countless friends the news came as a thunderclap.

Jeffrey's son-in-law, Empson, wrote to Bright telling him about his lucidity to the end; how he read from the *Economist* and the *Spectator*, alert to the 'advancing opinions on the Apocrypha, discovering subtle sophisms and laughing at the experience of it'. Dr Christison, heading his notepaper with 'Edinburgh Royal Infirmary' but forgetting the date, wrote,

It occurs to me that you may have expected to hear something of the medical history of the last days of your friend, the Great Reviewer. On the 22nd when on the Bench he was observed by Lord Mackenzie to be miserably dull and listless: but unfortunately he not only waded home through the slush of the final thawing day after our long frost, but actually took a further walk of 3 miles before dinner. He never had a chance in short of recovering. He died of pneumonia after $3\frac{1}{2}$ days of illness only.

Jeffrey's own physician Dr Miller wrote also, telling him something about the post-mortem, which 'showed a heart soft and flabby; aortic bristling with calcerous deposits; the brain small . . .' Then there came a word from Lady Jeffrey herself: 'Those who loved him and whom he loved will live in our hearts apart from others. You can scarcely have known separate from professional confidence and obligation what an affection he had for you: and what a pleasure it was to him to see you or to receive your letters.'

Sadly, J. W. Croker was now added to Bright's list of patients. He was having spells of giddiness and fainting, and slipping in and out of consciousness; it was never unpleasant, he told Bright, hovering on the borderland between two worlds, but as it occurred at awkward times could he not find something to help him avoid such situations? Croker had all the symptoms of heart-block, which Bright had so often in the past minutely described. But there was no battery-controlled pace-maker to insert then as there is today, and all Bright could do was to curtail Croker's activities and give him stimulants for his flagging heart-muscle.

To drive into the countryside was about the only relaxation Bright managed to have at this time; when he drove to Moseley to see Croker, sometimes Eliza would accompany him, and Clara and Emily too. He would drop them off at the Folletts' gate at Hampton and continue on his way. It is hard for us to picture what these places were like then, for they are now built-up areas. In Bright's day Hammersmith, Hampton, Richmond and the two Moseleys were all self-sufficient villages set in glorious countryside. Sometimes, irresistibly drawn by the glow of gypsy fires and the smell of cooking rabbit, Bright would stop the carriage for a moment, eager to learn how many words he could still remember out of the three dialects he knew.

His daughter Emily tells us that he stopped the carriage also whenever his calls took him by Hyde Park. He was quite stirred, he said himself, by the height of the edifice growing for the Great Exhibition, and he liked to watch the hydraulic press putting the great steel and glass plates into position. The expense of it all was the topic of conversation in every sick-room he entered. Bright himself had no chance to see the Exhibition when it was at Hyde Park, but saw it eventually when it was moved to Crystal Palace.

*

Throughout his life Bright had a tendency to make sudden inexplicable decisions. Once, while on holiday at Brand Lodge, they were looking at pictures of his mother's family, the Heywoods, when Eliza tells us that' he was instantly seized with a wish to see Manchester, 'so off he set 'with speed and quite alone this morning ... leaving Lowe to tell his patients'. He would make sudden appearances at Guy's, anxious to know whether his team had made any advances on his own conclusions on nephritis, or insisting that Addison should take him round the wards to see some of his more interesting cases. And very occasionally, his love for his sons and his fear of being a bad father suddenly overwhelming him, he would make lightning visits to Rugby. Charles Arnold, the housemaster, was an understanding man and had a great deal of sympathy for the Doctor, able only to involve himself in his sons' lives in this fitful and capricious manner. The visit would last perhaps no more than an hour, then he would be gone, as abruptly as he had appeared, returning to London in a much happier state of mind.

Bright was at the same time proud of his sons and also fearful, wondering whether the education at Rugby was really good; he did regret the fact that the Sciences were excluded from the curriculum. His own education had been excellent in this respect. Had any one of his sons wanted to get laboratory experience, he would have been compelled to send him across the Channel. Seventy years ago there had been geniuses like Priestley, Davy, Phillips and Woollaston, and such a journey would certainly not have been necessary.

While in the sixth form at Rugby, Follett had collected the gold medal for Classics and started the Athletic Sports Club, using his own money to give prizes for the flat race and the high jump. Franck had showed early his powers of learning, and by the time he reached the sixth form Charles Arnold was promising that he would be a success in whatever profession he adopted. Franck himself – attractive, powerful and able – was bent on an academic career; he would become one of an intellectual and influential group of friends which included people like J. H. Bridges, G. L. Goschen, Godfrey Lushington, Miles MacInnes, A. C. Clough and Jowett – all of whom were eventually to become distinguished in their chosen spheres.

We can read in the family letters of all the comings and goings of Rugbeians, as they travelled through London on their way to and from their homes in the country. Savile Row came to be well-known for its hospitality in holiday time. Should Bright happen to be at home, it gratified his sons to see with what deference their friends greeted him, while he in turn was amused by the way the boys exaggerated his international fame. Bright was always ready to examine and help any sickly boy, or to treat a bad case of acne. Sometimes the parents took advantage of his sympathy – the Marshalls were tediously fussy, forever coming to ask what was best for their boy or what they should do when there was a case of scarlatina in Arnold's house; while the Attys were always complaining to him about the Rugby drains.

Of Franck's Oxford friends it was T. W. Jex-Blake who appeared most often at Savile Row, and he was always reluctant to leave. He always seemed to be 'on his way to Hampstead' or 'on his way to Brighton' or 'off to catch the Tally-Ho for Rugby'. It seems that Eliza had to ration his visits; perhaps she mothered him too much, for we read about her fussing over his stye, filling the empty stomach he kept complaining about, finding a remedy for a toothache, and binding a sprained wrist. Clara found him 'very funny and odd in his way. He seems to have a starving malady for he is always ravenous.' Charles, aged thirteen, found him 'affected and quite unpleasant'. When Jex-Blake became a master at Rugby School, he complained to Franck, 'I shall never get on with Blake, he laughs at me which I cannot bear, not chaffing like Bradley but by asking me easy questions just to make me say something absurd.'

Jex-Blake ardently admired Franck, and wrote to him constantly when they were apart. If Franck was not at Savile Row when Jex-Blake happened to be there, he would write to tell Franck how he found his parents and family and what they were all doing. Everybody wrote to Franck; everybody depended on him. It was to him that his younger brothers and sisters addressed their letters and embroidered their ideas, his advice they sought. To him went the questions, 'Tell me what German poetry I should read'; 'Emmy finished the French book you left her to read, what now?'; 'Henry altered his essay to the way you told him.' He was also the go-between. 'Ask Papa, will you, if I may play at football this half. I hope I may as if I do I shall be, I think, in the House Twenty.' It was Franck who gave his brothers their treats, taking them to exhibitions, and introducing them to Oxford and later as a schoolmaster to Marlborough. 'I do not think I thanked you half enough for getting me down here. It was awfully jolly.' It was Franck who supported his mother when Henry broke his arm, carrying back a hoard of acute observations about the surgeon to feast upon at leisure with his father. It was Franck who filled Savile Row with wild flowers, taking infinite pains to pick his father's favourites and to pack them so that they arrived fresh. 'Our drawing-rooms have been for many days indebted to your outdoor labours in collected bluebells – the first that I ever beheld,' wrote Bright.

When Follett died on 29 March 1851, at Cambridge, Franck tried to spare his parents too much distress. He was only nineteen, but it was he who arranged the burial at Grantchester, on 3 April. And though Bright translated into Latin the epitaph chosen by Follett himself from a favourite poem, 'In Memoriam' by Tennyson, it was Franck who saw to the engraving on the tombstone. It was Franck who carried on paying Follett's prizes for the sports, and though it was Bright who suggested that all Follett's books should be sent to a close friend, it was Franck who sent the letter, despatched the books and received the letter of acknowledgement:

Trinity College, Cambridge.

I am sure you will believe that I would not unwillingly pain you by unnecessarily speaking of our great sorrow at losing him from among us, but I know it must be of some consolation to you to hear that his memory is still most dear to his friends here . . . If we lament his loss we rejoice in knowing that not one single act of his could be looked upon with any sorrow. All was open. He was most popular and this was owing not only to his peculiarly social and friendly disposition but also to the fact that all who approached him felt that they were entering into an atmosphere of purity and excellency.

Excuse me if I have been dealing in eulogies where none is necessary, but the very kind manner in which you have thought of me has emboldened me to speak how I once loved and how I lament and miss your brother.

Franck was like his father in some ways, he was always giving presents – a book, or a delicacy, or flowers – at the appropriate moment. 'I am sure you could not have sent them without having me and my predelictions in view . . . such a remembrance of the country and the season . . . but we cannot help wondering how you collected such large masses of each flower . . . I had my doubts whether the saxifrage and the milkworts were really wild and not garden specimens.' What was more they had arrived on a sad, wet day when a young girl Bright had been looking after for some time had just died with nephritis.

Henry, of all the children, was the most unpredictable, moody and excitable; he was intensely curious, always harassing people with questions. He was no scholar, but surprised everybody by doing well under the tutelage of the difficult William Highton; 'thinking well of him, [he] worked better in his form than in any other.' Much thought was given to the question of his future, for he seemed to fit nowhere. Bright's brother, Henry, took his responsibilities as head of the family and bachelor uncle very seriously – it was his custom to treat his eighteen nephews 'royally at his Chambers, it being his special pleasure to give them as much port as they could drink upon the single stipulation, never broken, that they must carry it without showing it'. He was particularly good to the two boys who bore his name, and it was he who persuaded Sam to take Bright's son Henry into his firm. 'He is greatly taken care of and noticed by our relatives, and on the whole I think we have chosen wisely for his happiness.'

Charles, the youngest of Bright's sons, was very like his father in character, though he had the delicate looks of his mother. He showed an early preference for all those things that most delighted Bright – poetry and art, geology, fishing and biology – and was later to become a fine doctor.

Bright was secretly disappointed that none of his sons had so far been attracted to medicine as a career but he had learned to put it to the back of his mind, doubtful at this stage whether even Charles would contemplate it. He had long given up telling them about the satisfaction, the wonder and the adventure of it all, he told Franck, appreciating fully that his long absences from home, the interrupted meals, and the continual demands upon him, only had the effect of hardening their minds against it.

Bright delighted in his daughters. Emily was seventeen; it was she who greeted him in the evenings, took his bag, undid the top button of his cloak and suggested a change of footwear. Clara, charming and romantic, was too young for life to provide any such opportunities. Bright held unusual opinions for those times, maintaining that his daughters should have the same educational opportunities and financial provision as his sons; so they were given books, calisthenic exercises and an allowance. They led quiet, cultured lives, taking piano, art and sewing lessons, and were presumably educated at a school.

Eliza had brought them up strictly and they were made to realize the responsibilities of a home, but even so they were lively, spirited girls. They giggled and gossiped, tidied their drawers, wrote their letters, and read their books; they looked forward eagerly to the boys' school holidays, and loved opening the gifts sent to their father. They filled the family sketchbook, carefully choosing and cutting out the countless sketches. They were interested in the Pre-Raphaelites, and after visiting Dante Gabriel Rossetti in his studio they wanted to paint 'ladies with red hair and dresses of the most beautiful blues and reds and greens finished like miniatures'. They depended largely on their cousins for company; they often saw Rita and Anna Follett at Hampton, while Laura, Caroline and Cathy Bright of Abbot's Leigh, and Sam's daughters of Sandheys, would all appear in London for some part of the Season. They enjoyed going to Kew Gardens, the theatre or Charles Dickens readings, and were encouraged by their father to go to Faraday's lectures for children at the Royal Institution, to picture galleries and to the House of Commons; they did the sights of London over and over again. They enjoyed everything; Clara was particularly observant – like her father – and it is she who wrote about the countless small incidents which occurred in the family.

All the children adored their father. They were constantly being disappointed by his non-appearance at so many of their social activities, but they were always careful never to disappoint him. As a result Franck found himself, however inconvenient it was, always going out of his way to spend some part of a holiday with him, while Emily once sacrificed a Follett ball, realizing at the last moment how much remaining behind to be with him would mean, 'so, I am not going . . . it being *his* week . . .'

23
Failing Strength
1851–1853

In the early months of 1851 Bright felt extremely languid; his sleep was broken and he suffered from nose-bleeds. He had experienced these same symptoms the previous year, and this time he did ponder over the efficiency of his heart. He decided to make a will and while on his rounds called on the family solicitor in the Inner Temple; wishing to minimize the fuss and spare Eliza's feelings, he said nothing about this to anyone. But one evening he felt too ill to talk; Eliza saw that something other than worrying cases was making him so pale and quiet, but she said little. Slowly, she managed to get him to confess that he felt ill, and persuaded him to go to bed. He got up as usual the following morning, determined to ignore the feeling of oppression in his chest, but he could barely lift up his arm to tie his cravat, and was overcome by a wave of dizziness. Lowe found him trying to feel for a chair and lower himself into it. Hearing about this, Eliza was alarmed and tried to persuade him to see one of his colleagues. But Bright let several days go by before a doctor came. By this time he had taken note of all his own symptoms and, studying the rhythm of his heart-beat, diagnosed trouble in the aortic valve.

He rested in bed until he was better, deciding then that it would be wise to convalesce for a while. Various places were suggested, among them Yorkshire and Wales, but Lancashire was the final choice. His first cousin, Sir Benjamin Heywood, sent his son to Savile Row with decisive instructions: nothing could be cooler and quieter than Blackpool; nothing would please them more than to have the Brights share the large and airy house, especially leased for the benefit of his ailing wife. Then began the intricate preparations for going north. Lowe never did anything simply and he could not be hurried as he painted coloured stripes of identification on their baggage, filled the Doctor's medicine chest and looked at the barometer. They went by train, breaking the journey at Coventry for two consultations.

The visit was a complete change. There was much at Blackpool to interest and amuse them. Essentially a sympathetic man, Sir

Benjamin Heywood had all his grandfather's cordiality of manner, all his grace, erudition and benevolence. He was an influential Fellow of the Royal Society, and a philanthropic banker: he had founded the Mechanics Institute for Working Class Men, and opened a children's home for working mothers. Eliza at first was not a little perplexed by the contrast between the majesty of the household ritual and its carelessness of appearances. Nobody listened to what anyone else was saying; members of the family ran endlessly in and out; dogs were allowed to jump on the chairs. Meanwhile Sir Benjamin was grand and imposing; he sent secretaries and servants scurrying, while intimidating visitors kept calling. He liked his status to be given due recognition.

But an overwhelming concern was lavished upon Bright. Sir Benjamin tried in every way to show how he appreciated the rare presence of his cousin, the doctor – not only because they were related to each other and shared many childhood memories, but also because he recognized what Bright had achieved for medicine, and it upset him to think of such industry going unhonoured. He felt that one whose advice was so continually being sought, who was so trusted in the important homes he visited, and whose name was so well known throughout the civilized world, should be offered a knighthood. Bright himself looked at his colleagues thus honoured with ironical tolerance. Like his friend Dr Chambers, had a knighthood come his way he would have refused it, not thinking that his pecuniary position was sufficiently secure, or his character sufficiently good.

Sir Thomas Heywood of Claremont called to express his concern for Bright's health and to salute Eliza, adding to his father's kindness by putting a carriage at their disposal. But the Brights were content to loiter on the beach, which stretched for miles from the gates of the house. Blackpool was then a little place, with houses, a hotel, a line of bathing huts and some disconsolate donkeys. Only a few people besides themselves were enjoying the sandy coast and bracing air. Daily they walked at the water's edge; sometimes they were alone, and sometimes a somersaulting Arthur Percival Heywood, aged four, joined them with his nurse. Bright talked to him and showed him shells, for he was fond of children. Walking to test his strength and stamina, he was never content with his endeavours, complaining always about his slow progress.

Meanwhile the Brights watched the whole household with amusement. The Heywoods were always ready for an argument about Whig policy or Tennyson's or Arnold's poetry or the general trend towards manual labour being superseded by machinery. Forthcoming family weddings were another topic of great interest to them. Bright was also pleased to have the opportunities convalescence gave him to catch up on reading.

But there came a moment when suddenly he could bear it no longer; he missed his work too much. He started worrying about his patients, and about his inability to earn money because of ill-health. At last Sir Benjamin Heywood reluctantly let them go. They left, showered with good wishes and gifts for the family. They went via Malvern, to spend a few days at Knoll House with Henry, his oldest brother. Here Bright continued to get on well, though Eliza privately thought he was too slow in gaining strength. She asked Phoebe at Brand Lodge to persuade him to stay longer, and although he agreed to the suggestion, he continued to fret.

One day he discovered from Eliza that she had not been seeing to the correspondence and owed many letters. Not only had she failed to pay the bills and write to patients seeking appointments, ignored the letters from both doctors and patients who were anxiously waiting to hear the date of his return, but she had even failed to contact Lowe to inform him of their expected return, nor had she warned the cook. These were things that mattered to people, and he railed against 'the extraordinary thoughtlessness and folly of a woman's mind'. He was not a man easily roused, but he disliked incompetence, indolence and procrastination. Usually his gentle nature just recoiled silently, but this time he was angry. The carriage was instantly ordered, telegraphs whirled through the air, messengers hurried ahead, boxes were hastily packed, and in an atmosphere decidedly chilly Eliza found herself, overladen with a sense of guilt, on the train to London. She had not even had a proper chance to thank Henry for his kindness. Telling Franck something about it later she wrote: 'Your Papa was white and silent on the journey. I fear I annoyed him very much. It gave me a shock to see him angry and upset . . . I did not know he could get so . . .'

August 1851 was remembered particularly by the girls for Bright, unaccountably relaxed and light-hearted, seemed actually to have time to spare. 'We see more of him than usual,' Clara told her brother in a letter, 'and he is sometimes able to go somewhere with us in the afternoons, which is very pleasant.' They went to the National Gallery: 'Papa said he did not think he had ever been before and

257

seemed much pleased with the collections.' They went to see a private view of Colonel Sibthorpe's china and other curiosities, 'not nearly so numerous as Bernal's, but almost all very pretty'. They walked in the Temple Gardens to see the fine chrysanthemums. They went shopping and bought a glass case to house the ferns which Mrs Astley had sent in gratitude for her restored health. They sought engravings to add to Bright's collection and bought a bouquet-holder for Rita Follett's birthday. They visited an obscure shop known to Bright and hidden in a cobbled Soho lane, to get a canary stuffed for Mrs Charles Arnold, which Emily was to take on her forthcoming visit to Rugby. And Bright had his photograph taken by a young man, who worked hard to get Bright's likeness; and as the photos turned out to be so good, Bright returned once again to the studio, this time accompanied by Dr Owen Rees, as 'we hoped he might arrange his position better'.

In September the family went to Argyllshire again, and only disappointment that Franck was not to be with them, as he was off to Norfolk with a reading party organized by Charles Arnold, cast a fleeting shadow over their departure. It seems that they stayed in the same place as before, for hardly had Bright had time to settle down to a meal before the Revd Menzies was at the door asking for him. This time he was conducted to the bedside of a young girl with a tumour on her leg about the size of a haggis. The Doctor measured it, probed it, asked questions, made a sketch of it, and sent a vivid description of it to Dr Addison, written with all the old thrill and pertinacity of his *Medical Cases*. Once again David MacDonald invited Bright to fish his waters; and daily, arranging his fishing flies with care, he was without luck, while Charles caught 'many a fish on his worm and hook tied to an umbrella'. On the last Sunday Mr Menzies gave a thundering sermon and, coming out of the Kirk, the Glen had never seemed to Bright more peaceful – 'the contrast of our Divine's loud expressions in the pulpit and the colours of nature was very striking'. They stood, he wrote to Franck, 'poised in an atmosphere so still, so translucent that a single sheep's cough shattered the crystal firmament'.

On the last day of the holiday Bright caught a fish at last. 'You . cannot tell me how glad we all were at Papa's catching a salmon,' Henry wrote to Franck. Bright never liked to return the same way as he had come, and this time they made a detour to the east, across the Grampians into Aberdeenshire. They added stones to a cairn on the summit of a hill overlooking Loch Erich, attended the greatest cattle-fair of the year, and visited Braemar, which was more of a town than they had imagined it would be: 'there were big houses and slate roofs and many visitors walking about in black suits and white cravats, and we were thankful to leave this refined and polished place.'

On their return to Savile Row they found 'the rooms full of flowers and all sorts of kind friends have welcomed us home . . . The Folletts, Jex-Blake, the Grotes and Mr Harford . . . then Lord Gainsborough came, who always has to see *me*.' One cannot help wondering about this peer, who lived in Arlington Street and paid so much attention to Eliza; he appears in many of the family letters and was always kind, opening his house to the Brights on festive occasions, allowing the girls to watch the fireworks from his windows, inviting them to join his various soirées; and it was he who, in place of the Doctor, escorted them to the Great Exhibition.

On 15 July (1852) Thomas Macaulay called Bright in: 'I sent for Bright. He came with a stethoscope; pronounced that the action of the heart was much deranged, and positively forbade me to think of going to Edinburgh [to visit his constituency].' Bright must have examined him warily. He knew that Macaulay, like his late friend Sydney Smith, regarded doctors as 'graduated homicides', and could not abide the modern physician with his stethoscope and persistent pertinent questions.

He had only just arrived back at Savile Row when Macaulay's manservant appeared, deeply worried about his master. Bright, returning in haste, found Macaulay in a state of collapse, the reason being that he had ignored Bright's warnings. As soon as the Doctor had left him that afternoon, he had, as an act of bravado, taken himself to Westbourne Terrace, longing to get the reassurance only his family could give.[1] His condition remained serious, and Bright went to see him often; sometimes he sat up with him at night. In spite of his dislike of doctors, Macaulay seems to have taken to Bright – perhaps he appreciated the fact that he did not meddle: being averse to heroic remedies he preferred to leave well alone.

One day Lady Trevelyan called on him at Savile Row, where she learned that her brother's condition was more serious than he had led her to believe. Bright, however, felt quite certain that Macaulay himself was aware of the state of affairs but said little about it for the sake of his friends and relations. Between them it was arranged that Macaulay should go to Clifton to recuperate. Bright alerted the

Harfords at Blaise Castle and wrote to the Miles of Leigh Court, hoping, no doubt, that they would show Macaulay their fine collection of pictures, but we do not know which of the Clifton doctors Bright chose to look after him. Possibly it was the Brights' own family doctor, John Estlin. Whoever it was, he kept Bright informed of Macaulay's unsatisfactory condition, for there are several notes telling him that he was doing too much. Bright in turn wrote to Macaulay that September, advising him to ask for the Chiltern Hundreds.

When Macaulay returned from Bristol, Bright was struck by how old he looked; he was only in his mid-fifties, but the underlying fear of death that was now always with him had robbed him of all his old boyish enthusiasms.[2] But lack of bodily strength does not necessarily exhaust the will, and Macaulay, like Bright, refused to let the mind recognize the failings of the body.

Christmas week of 1852 Eliza was telling Franck that his father was 'working harder than ever'. This was possibly due to the political situation at the time. There had been a sudden change of government, and not for over eighty-three years had such a thing occurred at Christmas time. The West End was usually deserted at this time of year, but now London was abuzz. Carriages sped from one impromptu political gathering to the next, from one unexpected party to another: the pavements were filled with people and hansom cabs blocked the streets. There were delivery delays and hampers filled with Christmas goods went astray. 'All this annoys me,' Eliza complained to Franck in a letter. 'And all the world is talking of this change of Ministry, to us it signifies nothing one way or another. If it's not Lord Aberdeen, then it's Lord John Russell, and if it's not him forming a government then it must be Lord North. But all of it hampers your poor father and complicates his programme with extra consultations.'

That winter of 1852–3 Bright had little chance to consider his own health. Writing to Franck, he told him how he was back 'in my daily labours, doing better than could possibly be expected; I hope I shall not overdo the thing. I do what I can by lying in bed for breakfast and try to get to bed before midnight though I own this evening hour is the most pleasant of the day. Our card-players are very merry but Mama has called them to order declaring that it is past 10 o'clock . . . '

In January and February he was again faced with cholera, which threatened once more to become epidemic. Again he sent off letters of advice; amongst them was one to Charles Arnold at Rugby School, and another to Franck with a packet of 'pills which will keep your bowels in good order and the medicine will act usefully against the perils of drinking the water at Oxford . . .' At the same time he gave him the reasons why he could not oblige those Balliol friends of Franck's, who were 'demanding that you should come'. 'You know the nature of my daily and almost hourly occupations and as I am almost obliged to make a holiday in the Autumn or at least we fancy I am – it is quite impossible for me to break in upon the solid months of my serious occupations by odd days of pleasure – indeed they are rather days of pain and anxiety than of pleasure to me.'

Eliza blamed his despondency and fatigue on 'one or two anxious cases which have obliged him to go out at all times', and added, 'I dare say it is increased by two large medical dinners that he gave last week.' These dinners, where senior students and young doctors met eminent and experienced surgeons and physicians from different hospitals and different areas, were always a success, but for Bright they were something of a strain. He was an anxious host, constantly fearful that something might go wrong or something not be to the liking of one of his guests. He relaxed only when the port was circulating and controversial medical subjects were launched. He preferred now to be the listener, since he found it tiring to speak to a lot of people and appreciated any opportunity to sit silent and observe; but more often than not he found himself asked to speak. Sometimes on these occasions it was even possible to settle a long-standing dispute between two doctors. All present were ready to listen and to hear both sides, it then being left to Bright, as host, to adjudicate and suggest the right solution. Again someone might come who confessed he did not know the best way to treat a particular disease he had diagnosed. Whatever happened, Bright always managed to make the evenings interesting.

None of his colleagues at this time dared show concern over his worn looks, his pallor and his swollen feet. There were strong rumours circulating that Bright had fallen victim to his own speciality, and because he was as secretive about his heart condition as he was in preserving the confidences of his own patients, the rumour persisted. It is odd to find at this particular time, when the symptoms of his aortic stenosis were troubling him so much, that he should have had many cardiac patients listed in his diary. To the care of these patients he must now have brought even more sympathy and understanding than before, for he himself must have been experiencing the same strange sensations, the same feelings of fear and insecurity, the same awareness of failing strength.

'We are being dull this season on account of your father which I am sorry for the girls' account . . .' Eliza wrote to Franck. But, as it was Emily's year for 'coming out', Bright, when he felt able, gladly risked his health for her sake. One evening he escorted her to a small and select soirée that was being given by Sir Henry Holland. 'But we had to leave on account of Father at a quarter to eleven, just when the gaiety was arriving.' However, 'Emmy, looking nice in her beige', was launched into the drawing rooms of the season by Lord Gainsborough who, at Bright's request, took her, Eliza and Henry along to the Rundells' ball. 'It was an extremely gay affair and very pleasant. I never saw so nice a house . . . Henrietta Cooper went with us and we got a little table which just held Mama and us 2 and Astley Cooper waited upon us. We had a very jolly supper, so much so that one or two gentlemen whom Mama did not know said they quite envied our comfortable party.' But the party given by the Attorney-General was apparently dull: 'the only things to look at were the goldfish in a small fountain and the banks of flowers.'

Mrs Grote, who lived next door at 12 Savile Row, made a great fuss of both Emily and Clara. This colourful and delightful London hostess, tall, stately and impressive, was anything but fashionable, wearing flamboyant silks and feathers and extraordinary turbans. George Grote was an historian of Greece, a delightful man, easy and intelligent. He must have known Bright for some time, for as far back as 1838 he had written to his brother-in-law Mr Lewis about 'the melancholy change in Emilion's health', advising him 'to call in the advice of Dr Bright. I name him as the best known to me by reputation to satisfy ourselves that the treatment being pursued is after all satisfactory.' Then Mrs Grote herself became a patient.

At Easter 1853 came the usual stream of visitors: Eliza's brother John and his family, and two German doctors. One of them was a professor and, with typical German thoroughness, rushed all the Brights to an opera, 'where the box in the stalls was most comfortable and where between the opera and the ballet your father had a sound nap'. There were post-graduates from Paris, sent by Professor Pierre Rayer, long an admirer of Bright's. Indeed, he had been the first person in France to use the term 'Maladie de Bright'. There came also Henry Arthur, Sam's eldest boy, who brought with him Nathaniel

Hawthorne. He had got to know him when, at the age of twenty, he had been sent out to America by his father to learn something about commerce. Hawthorne had been just about to leave for Liverpool as American Consul, and quite naturally Sam had now befriended him. Henry Arthur was a great favourite with the young Brights; in less than an hour, they were all sitting very much at their ease by the drawing-room fires, and becoming acquainted with the author, whose book *The Scarlet Letter* was still on Eliza's library list. Hawthorne endeared himself to them all by saying that of *all* the people he had met from England, Henry Arthur was the 'very best'.

Both Sam and Bessy followed their son to London; though they did not stay at Savile Row, 'they mean to see as much of us as possible . . . we are very sorry they are coming, as we hoped to have been quiet for a little while . . . we asked Lushington to come and spend Sunday with us and he stayed till Tuesday.' For Bright any visitors were now a trial. Even his relations upset him, since he could in no way give them his undivided attention.

The mantelshelf in Eliza's boudoir was at this time particularly full of cards – notices of meetings, private views and scientific or geological gatherings, and invitations for concerts and parties. Bright himself took little notice of these, going only to the occasional musical evening, as he found them restful. He went to the Andersons, and enjoyed hearing Albinoni and Giuglini, and he could never resist the capricious Jenny Lind, who sang often at No. 12. Some people found Mrs Grote something of a trial, but Bright found her untidy mind stimulating, and was amazed at her endless patience with young children. The Grotes were thinking of moving to Reigate: 'we shall be sorry when they go and we shall miss Mrs. Grote's piano very much,' wrote Eliza.

It was always possible for Bright to slip away unnoticed from musical affairs, but dinner parties he refused; after a long day's work he usually felt disinclined for conversation. Besides, should he be called away urgently from the table, it was embarrassing for him and most upsetting for both Eliza and his host. He did dine that Easter at the house of Sir Charles Young, but it was the first time in three years that he had dined out anywhere.

Early that May (1853), the medical world was shocked by the sudden death of Bransby Cooper. He fell in the entrance hall of the Athenaeum, a respected and popular figure at Guy's to that very last hour. Bright, as he told Addison, had always held Bransby Cooper in loving esteem – 'he, whose mind was so ardently bent upon the object which occupied it'.

Then came Bright's visit to Oxford. He and Eliza were invited to a Collathis in New College to be received by the Chancellor, and the following day Bright was to receive the DCL (Doctorate of Civil Law). He looked forward eagerly to seeing Franck, but viewed the ceremony with dread. He was not primarily a public character, remaining always a little remote from the medical scene – though there were certain meetings he attended when he could, and as a senior member of two of the most august bodies of the land he could scarcely but be involved.

On the morning of 8 June 1853 Eliza, fearful that Lydia, her maid, would bruise the flowers and stick pins into her new slipstraw bonnet, supervised the packing herself. As for Bright, he said that the narrow-legged black trousers he wore for funerals would have to do. Franck had found rooms for them and Emmy in Magpie Lane, a place conveniently near University College, and it was there he took all his friends to see Bright. Bright enjoyed the company of undergraduates, though he was struck by the strictness of the age of which his son was a representative, compared with the more leisurely, easy-going late eighteenth century when he himself had been a student. He compared, too, Jowett, Arthur Clough, Jex-Blake and Lushington with the medical students of his own day, and envied their greater confidence. He was touched, too, by the notice he received going about the town, for all he met showed him attention, which he was really at a loss to account for till he found they all boasted of being friends of Franck. Emmy was greatly amused when he told her, for she assured him that in Belgravia she had to suffer the same reflected glory on *his* account.

Franck was proud of his father, and talked about him a great deal. On hearing of Bright's illness, an associate master at Marlborough wrote to him: 'The tidings of your father's illness cannot be a matter of unconcern and from having heard you speak of him so often and so descriptively I cannot help realising in some degree what his illness is to you.' Franck's friends now found Bright's mind was still every bit as keen as theirs, and they appreciated the way he and Eliza included them in their activities, treating them to refreshments and offering them amusements as they did the sights of Oxford. In return the older couple were made a fuss of, and if ever it seemed that they were wanting in anything, that thing would be waiting for them in the hall of their lodging house.

On 9 June Bright received his Doctorate. He had not looked forward to the ceremony, Eliza told Franck. After their return home Bright himself wrote to Franck, saying that he had enjoyed his visit, particularly meeting all his (Franck's) friends.

One more day was spent with Sir Henry Acland, Professor of Medicine at Oxford, who arranged for him to see the new Ashmolean Museum and the Radcliffe Library, and in the evening wined and dined him at the High Table. Bright had had many amicable dealings with him before, and now, once again, he presented Bright with a puzzling case of renal degeneration, which he persuaded Bright to take over. In spite of professional interest Bright, for the first time ever, found himself doing so with great reluctance: there were too many names already upon his list, and his involvement with his patients seemed to devour all his strength.

In the summer of 1853 measles attacked the royal children;[3] Bright was called in as a consultant to make certain there were no complications and the right steps were being taken. Bright's reticence has robbed us of much, and from him we learn nothing of these visits. But he must have answered some of Clara's questions, and besides she kept in close touch with Lowe. She listened to his gossip and then reported it to Franck, and sometimes to Charles, who was quick to absorb anything of interest. Once she accompanied her father to Buckingham Palace, where she waited for him in the carriage. 'Today I went with Papa to the Palace. The Prince of Wales is isolated in his own suite and is already better, but he is lonely and his room is gloomy. Papa says he has no light literature, no bright things and the Bibles are large and musty. He has unbending tutors, while further down the corridor Prince Albert and his sisters have much more fun, with good-natured nurses in squeaky shoes, and treasures and discarded toys. Papa said he recognised the toy carriage and horse as the present from Queen Adelaide.'

Both Bright's own daughters caught the measles, and Henry at Rugby succumbed too, though mildly. Bright seems to have taken little notice of this, for Mrs Arnold commented, in a letter to Franck, on his parents' lack of reaction to the news.

24
Last Years
1854–1858

Britain's entry into the Crimean War in March 1854 brought new demands on Bright's time. Being an honorary member of every medical society in Europe he was battered with questions and appeals; the Medical Society of Turkey sought his aid over an epidemic of enteric fever which was devastating their people.

Amongst the many who came to Savile Row to discuss the war was Isambard Brunel. He brought with him a plan to transport troops in large numbers and wished to discuss the health hazards of a crowded steamship. Lady MacGrigor hurried round from her house in Harley Street, begging him for a list of medicaments, and for suggestions as to how to make the work of her doctor-son, who was working with Florence Nightingale at Scutari, easier and safer. Breathless and roundfaced, hardly of age, came also a Captain Poffnet, obsessed with the imbecility of the War Office. He opened out his heart to the dismayed Bright, telling how in spite of writing daily to 'the honourable board' begging for arms, his regiment was expected to embark with 410 scabbards and no bayonets to sheath in them. There must have been others, and all of them gave Bright a terrible feeling of impotence.[1]

Like everyone else Bright was upset by the absence of any direction in the Crimea, and the way military hospitals had been allowed to become charnel houses of confusion. There were many veterans of Waterloo amongst his colleagues who, like himself, were shaken by the chaos of the whole disastrous campaign before Sebastopol. What a waste of the lessons learned at Waterloo – of the importance of hygiene and inoculations; of the benefits of chloroform; of the advantages of having trained medical personnel – why had they not been utilized in the field? Though he usually looked at things so objectively, now Bright could not help but take the failure of his profession in a more personal way, and he devoted what energy he had to guiding and advising – while his brother-in-law, Dr Babington, offered to do the work of any member of the medical staff at Guy's Hospital who volunteered to go to the Crimea.

The unfolding incompetence surrounding his profession on the battlefield followed Bright wherever he went. Every person he met said they wanted to help; every patriotic daughter badgered him into speaking to her mother about her potential as a nurse; every member of the Patriot Fund showed him their knitting, the bandages, and the night-shirts they had sewn; every time he returned to his own house Eliza told him about the homemade brawn which she was sending to the troops; while every post brought letters from Charles Arnold, sorrowfully exclaiming against the strange world which could set out to kill anything so promising as a Rugby pupil, most of them of Franck's age, and on every page pouring scorn on the arrogance and obstructivism of government officials.

*

In April 1855 Franck left Oxford, having got a First in Law and History. His future was very uncertain at this time; he had applied for a German master's post at Marlborough, he had submitted his name to become a Fellow of Balliol, and he was also musing on the Church. It seems that he had inherited some of his father's diffidence and uncertainty about his own capabilities: his presence at Savile Row brightened the household greatly. After a long, tiring day it was for Bright a rare joy to establish himself with his son in front of the fire to talk and drink cocoa. But the evenings together were few; a restless Franck divided his time between mesmerism, phrenology and 'trying to communicate with the dead' – all bogus sciences prevalent at that time which Bright abhorred.

Bright seems to have demanded little from his children, and perhaps because of this they seem always to have felt able to go their own way, while remaining devoted to him. On one occasion, when there was no sign of Franck returning from Oxford, Bright wrote asking him to help with some difficult dinner parties he and Eliza felt obliged to give. Bright must have been feeling unusually harassed and depressed, for this is one of the very few instances I can find where he asks for the attention of somebody else, instead of giving it himself.

In the summer of 1855 Bright hurriedly left for Bristol to see his brother Robert, who was seriously ill. Oddly enough, Bright almost welcomed the interruption, and the opportunity to sit back in the railway carriage and 'relax as it rattled along'. At Abbot's Leigh he found Caroline sad and agitated, and was shocked by his brother's

appearance; Robert was deeply jaundiced and hiccoughing continually, and although he managed to rouse himself at the sight of his
older brother, he slipped quickly back into the torpor in which he had
lain for days. Robert talked 'as if we were nine years old again,
making gases in the laboratory at Ham Green'.

It was this delirium and 'general nervous agitation and injured
conjunctive . . . which often closes the scene of life' that so concerned
Bright. 'We had a grand consultation upon him after church today,'
Bright told Eliza that night in a letter. Both Mr Harrison and Dr
Bernard from the Bristol Infirmary were quick to agree on the
treatment.

As soon as he was satisfied that Robert was well out of danger,
Bright left, with everything in meticulous order, and 'tidily under
Cathy and Con's control'. The family always maintained that 'the
doctor' saved his brother's life, but Bright praised the good home
nursing.

Later the same month Bright returned to Abbot's Leigh,
accompanied by Emily. This time, as his brother was making good
progress, he left his daughter there with her cousins. The Revd John
Gibbs had just flung himself at the feet of the young Isabel, and in
place of illness there was now much happiness. His visits to Abbot's
Leigh seem to have taken the place of a holiday that year.

In February 1855, for some reason or another, work was by no
means overwhelming; yet Bright complained that he could not get to
the Science Exhibition at the Crystal Palace, and was beginning to
doubt whether he would ever be able to see the new Museum of
Technology. He went to see the pictures by Turner at the Royal
Society of Arts, but, as he told Franck, he was only there long enough
to be confused: 'Your Uncle Harry was there and was so anxious to
pull me from room to room to show me the best that at last I saw
none.'

That autumn (1855) there were endless demands upon Bright's
time. 'I rose at quarter to seven this morning and not one moment had
I until I got home to my solitary room at 9', he told Franck. ' . . .
Yesterday the same thing, only my dinner at nine was served with a
note desiring me to go to Hyde Park district immediately and it was
past eleven when I got home to my cocoa. All this will explain why
you hear so little from me . . .'

Bright was also forced to take some notice of his own health. Once
more he experienced that wearisome idleness and terrible malaise;

pain which, though intermittent, could scarcely be ignored; and the strange yet increasingly familiar 'thrill' in the artery of his neck. He knew exactly how to handle heart cases, and how to prevent certain situations arising, but in the conduct of his own case he was sketchy and careless. It was imperative, in Eliza's view, that he should consult one of his colleagues again, and though he refused to do this he did put himself to bed. Somehow the news was noised around Oxford, Marlborough (where Franck was now a master) and Rugby that he was ill again. Franck was in Munich, so it is from Arthur Clough's letter to him that we learn of Bright's slow recovery, while Theodore Walroud Pelham, too, was glad 'to receive improving reports of your father from your mother'. Jex-Blake, it appears, was also interested in the progress of a sermon case which Clara and Emily were embroidering for Franck. 'I am afraid you will think it too gay and probably dislike the Cross and if you do we can make a plain one.' Again, Arthur Clough informs us of Bright's progress: 'I am very glad to say that your father has been prevailed upon to leave town; our only fear is that he will hurry back to harness before he is fit for it. What do they say is the matter with him? I suppose whatever the form is the root of the matter is too much work and too little rest.'

When Bright returned from Brighton, where he had been staying for a rest, he felt much better but was distressed to find an exhausted Eliza. Easter visitors had once again drained her resources; she had barely been allowed to be alone one minute of the day. Even so 'the visits went off quite charmingly, all parties pleased'. Hardly had she recovered when, in May (1856), there was a further descent of guests. 'I am overdone by all the Bright family who for some weeks have called upon us on their way to and from Stocks . . . I see no end to the bustle.' Stocks, a large Georgian mansion in Albury in Hertfordshire, had come into the hands of Robert's eldest son Dick through his marriage to Emma Gordon Whalley. It features much in the correspondence, and Emily, Clara and Charles were frequently invited there.

By the end of the month, when she wrote her weekly letter to her children, we learn of Bright's insistence that Eliza should go away. 'I cannot get well at home and I shall try what a little Brighton air will do for me. I am to try German water and sea-warm baths . . . Clara will come with me and Emily will stay and look after your father with the help of Aunt Lizzie.'

*

For quite some time after Eliza's return, the Brights remained unsettled as to where to go for their yearly holiday. Bright was willing, he said to Franck, to go anywhere just to pick flowers and make sketches. 'As for any residences in the United Kingdom we have heard of none. If we felt ourselves able we should I doubt not go abroad. But wherever it is to be I do hope that you will make some plan to be with us and I am heartily sorry that your college adopts the Rugby instead of the Eton holiday.'

We are not told how the Brights heard of Tennyson's willingness to lease his house at Farringford on the Isle of Wight during August and September. He himself was taking his family to Wales that year. It could have been through any of Bright's innumerable connections, or through Franck's intellectual circle, all of whom were admirers of the poet and often sought his company; or perhaps Tennyson had consulted Bright about his health in June of that year, when he came to London to see a doctor about a bad toothache and neuralgia – though if that was the case then it was unbeknown to Emily, who did not describe his appearance until the following year.

The house itself put them in mind of Alverbank, Croker's seaside house, for it was similar in style and sheltered in the same way by ilex, pines and magnolias, many planted, they were told, by the poet himself. It was in a delightful position, being in sight and sound of the sea, tucked in a fold of the downs which spread west to the Needles; the large windows of the front rooms looked out to Freshwater Bay. Inside, it was comfortable, though some of the fifteen rooms were dark and some too full of pictures – put there, Eliza suggested, to cover up the stains on the walls. There were worn patches in the carpets, and in the drawing room no covers had been renewed for years. The back staircase, Tennyson's escape route from visitors, led also to a small room which served him as a Turkish bath. His absent presence was felt everywhere; in his walking sticks, his hundreds of spills, his two-gallon tobacco jar and above all his books. The tobacco Tennyson had smoked so incessantly permeated the air; the draperies, the carpets and the antimacassars were stained yellow with it.

In the evenings the family took turns to read aloud. Bright himself led them through the langours of the *Lotus Eaters* to the resolutions of *Ulysses*. Eliza chose the lyrics from the newly published *Maud*, while Franck chose *In Memoriam*. Henry read well, and Clara's and Charles's sense of the dramatic in *The Lady of Shalott* met with stifled laughter, though none of them, declared Eliza to Franck (after he had left), had William's way of acting.

When Franck departed, Bright turned to sketching. He never had sufficient breath to accompany his family to the Beacon, but he painted the Needles, the lighthouse, Portland Bay, Brooks Point, Calbourne and certain corners of the village. Watching him, Emmy said, he made it seem so easy and 'after three years of drawing lessons I feel even more incompetent'. But he was disconcerted to find that when on the beach, bending down to pick up the polypons, crabs and sea-anemones, his chest felt constricted. This irritated him, for he liked to be fit and in the midst of things. He left the rest of the family to go without him to the occasional picnic parties which were given by Rita Follett (now married). The Folletts were also staying somewhere near Freshwater, sharing a house, apparently, with the usual circle of Giffards, Pennells and Walpoles.

'I came here for the purpose of writing you a letter,' Bright wrote to Franck, 'but I found that Mama monopolizes all the correspondence. I think from what she read from your letter that she has given worse accounts of my health than I deserve. We cannot expect that each summer I should continue to rally as quickly . . . every year I get older and I am fast getting to the natural and recorded limits of life . . . I do not think that much depends on one good air or another . . . the girls are in the field drawing the house and are to come in at twelve so that we may go together into the village to finish our sketches and at three we have ordered the carriage to take us to Mrs Prettyman and then to Yarmouth when we hope to walk home all together from the ferry.

Some time in September they left Farringford. For a sick man Bright did a great deal of travelling that autumn. They all went to Abbot's Leigh – he wanted to reassure himself about his brother, still suffering from jaundice – and then on to Malvern, where they spent fourteen days. After 'seeing a patient, dining and sleeping at Gloucester we intend to go by train via Swindon to Marlborough to dine and sleep at the Alesbury Arms . . . we shall want a bedroom for ourselves and one for the girls. Mrs Moore goes with the heavy luggage from this place [Knoll Lodge] to London.'

Bright, now sixty-six, was beginning to find tender old lady-patients commiserating with him for the extreme frailty of his person. He was worn out upon the roads when he should have been resting before a comfortable fire and in the arms of his wife, one patient wrote to him. His holiday, she said, had done him little good. And though he found the work hard at first, Eliza was quick to reassure Franck that it had 'already become what it is usually like'.

In November, Tennyson appeared on the doorstep of 11 Savile Row. There is no record of his consultations with Bright. On his visits to London the poet would go from doctor to doctor; he had the reputation of being unreliable in telling his medical history, and shy about his past epilepsy, cold bath treatments and dietary cures. One of the doctors had managed to get him off both opium and alcohol, but he always remained obsessed with tobacco. Emily described Tennyson to Franck as 'swarthy, and not at all like his picture . . . and too thin . . . a most odd looking person, bowed, with thin, long black hair, beard and whiskers and a mouth brown with tobacco . . . he was most agreeable and kind . . .'

Another hard winter (1857) brought the usual outbreak of diseases of the chest, but this time 'far the greater number of cases occurring to those who have long passed the meridian of life'. His own heart condition he tried as far as possible to ignore. If he had any idea of its gravity, he makes no mention of it. He lost none of his skill as a doctor. 'The love and kindness which he is ever shedding over me and my family' moved Miss Birkenhead to present him with a theatre box so that Eliza, Emmy and Clara could see Charles Kean act in *The Corsican Brothers*.

In between seeing patients suffering with pneumonia and acute bronchitis, he went to see a Mr X with a tumour the size of an orange, to give him the support he so badly needed to face the surgeon. He went on a tedious journey to Battersea, with delays in freezing winds, paying 8d at Battersea Bridge, to see a young girl with diphtheria, whose throat he painted and scraped; he went to see a boy no older than his son Charles, with a 'brain that was turned the wrong way'. He went continually to Holly Lodge, to see Lord Macaulay, who was seldom free now from cardiac asthma and was troubled by 'a disturbing cough'. He was learning by heart the four acts of *The Merchant of Venice*, and each time he went Bright found him that much further on. He went to see J. W. Croker, before he died suddenly in the arms of his beloved emanuensis Lady Barrow. He went to Duke Street, to see Isambard Brunel, always on a Saturday, for Brunel was too preoccupied with the troubles facing him at Napier's Yard in the Isle of Dogs to take much notice of his swelling ankles and the gnawing pain in his loins. The *Great Eastern* was about to be launched, and the problem of getting that great cliff of iron off the marshes into the water was possessing the whole of his incredible mind. It was no time for Bright to tell him to rest, and it was too late to tell him that had it not been for the pace and pressure of his work, and the conditions of exposure he had so frequently experienced in the past, he would not now be in renal failure. Tragically, Brunel stood before Bright as the classical and pathological picture of the disease he had so ably described. It must have upset Bright a great deal to have to tell his old family friend that his months were numbered.

In the last two years of Bright's life, he tells us little of his illness. Eliza was continually worried, and it is from her that we hear how haggard he was beginning to look and how nothing that he wore fitted him, his clothes seeming not to belong to him. 'Your father is living entirely on fish and bread and milk and is not at all in the same comfortable state as he was before.' Yet nothing stopped him working. 'He is going again this afternoon to see General Angelinos [name almost indecipherable]. I am almost afraid it will knock him up. It is terribly cold . . . '

The cold plunged Bright into a kind of stupor. Sometimes it forced him to walk, it being too icy to sit for long in the carriage. He watched anxiously for the spring. Towards the end of March he thought of his yearly holiday, and everyone was swept up in his initial excitement. Flemions, the favourite courier, was not available this time, so another one had to be sought and booked; hotels had to be chosen and accommodation reserved; the itinerary had to be planned and then Franck was generally consulted. A letter written by Eliza to Franck that March tells us: 'We leave on August 1st to Vienna by mail through Berlin, we talk of going no further than the German towns, but I know your father will be going on towards Italy – this is all we can tell you at present and as there are months of hard work ahead before the time, you know the chances as well as I do.' He was far from well and Eliza must have longed to tell him that it was time to give up work. But his imperious will and his indomitable sense of duty made it impossible for him to do this. He rose above the symptoms of his disease – the disturbed nights of bad dreams, the morning sensation of faintness, the intermittent pain and terrible lassitude – by interesting himself in every detail of each case. He tried to curtail extraneous activities, leaving other members of the family to attend the weddings of a nephew and a niece, and refusing to go to a judicial court of the Privy Council. What exactly this case of Liddle v. Westerton was all about we do not know. We are told only by Bright himself that he did not feel equal to giving his attention to such a long and complicated trial.

One morning Bright had to go to a Buckingham Palace levée, which he managed 'without much fatigue'. He borrowed his cousin's knee-breeches and as he was little seen in society he was greeted with pleasure. Few people were invited to Savile Row, for he had no intimate friends – even his colleagues at this period knew nothing of his personal feelings. His prestige remained high, and at the Royal College of Physicians early that summer they were talking about having his portrait painted and a sculpture done. Occasionally he was called in for a consultation. He remained astonishingly faithful to some of his old parish patients, and was always there if they needed his help, while young doctors still turned to him. He never adopted the tone of a comfortable authority, as some other consultants did; he was never discouraging, and he let them discover things for themselves. Bright was proud to follow Barlow's and Johnson's progress, and amused to find that Owen Rees now had a profitable practice, going about the East End in a green brougham driven by a red-faced coachman.

There were times when he felt infinitely weary. Emmy told Franck how her father lived for the next free evening, when he would sit in the comfortable firelight (a fire specially lit for his benefit even though it was June), unable to move, in a kind of timeless glow, quite forgetting a possible journey for an urgent call, or that someone was coming to call, to consult him over their problems. When Eliza entered the drawing room he would invariably be dozing in his chair, and she was always shocked to see how, when his eyes were closed, there was no life in his face. 'Sir Henry Holland came last night, but fortunately we heard his knock, so had time to wake Papa.'[2]

It is known that Bright wrote a long letter to Eliza at this time and, so as to forget about it, put it into the secret drawer at the back of his large mahogany bureau.

By August Bright was in a fever of impatience to be out of London. Characteristically, on the eve of departure he was filled with vague forebodings, while Eliza was equally fretful, doubtful whether something might not crop up to prevent their departure, 'for,' she wrote to her sister Anna Synge, 'I remember how hopeful we were at the same time last year and what a very bad change we had to make all of a sudden'.

They were to make an early start in the morning, and Franck was in charge of the itinerary, which had been changed. Chartres and Paris were listed, otherwise their route is a puzzle.

At Dover, Bright experienced his usual fear of the sea, but as they reached Calais he regained his equanimity. But at first nothing about the trip was easy for Bright. He was deadly weary and breathless; Eliza noted his difficulty in bending down, and how his feet were too puffy for his shoes to fit comfortably. She was only dimly aware of what was physically happening, but it must have been difficult for her to watch him retreat into that heavy, silent world of the sick – though he was determined that his health should cast no more than a fleeting shadow over his family's happiness.

Once Paris was left behind they travelled south down the Loire Valley, and Franck took over his father's usual role. It must have been hard to see Bright's usual enthusiasm replaced by a forced interest, but Franck seems to have kept them all cheerful. The brothers and sisters wandered into Avignon, explored the surrounding countryside of the Rhône, or sat together talking under the trees. Dull as Bright felt himself to be, the family did manage to enliven him a little. Franck stayed with the party long enough to catch the sun on his face, then, for some reason or another, he returned to Oxford, and it was to the talkative Henry that he passed on the itinerary, along with a formidable list of books to be read – including the novels of Victor Hugo and Chateaubriand, and the poetry of Lamartine.

The void created by Franck's absence was agonizing to Bright. It is obvious, too, that Eliza missed his dependable arm: 'I feel quite ill with anxiety and fear that we are doing wrong to go on, but your father will not hear of going back the same road as we came . . . he is still weak and listless and very pale and thin, not at all in his enjoying spirits, still we pursue our way towards Nice. We think of spending a few days at Cannes, in the hope that the sea air might invigorate him a little.' Somewhere along the route to the coast they stayed a few days with a family known to some friends of theirs, for Eliza speaks of the hospitality they received and the simple kindness of their hosts. At Arles they rested again. Eliza longed for the comfort of her own bed, but 'the children are all happy and amuse themselves in various ways'. At Cannes the longed-for letter from Franck never came. It was expected daily, and Bright was cruelly disappointed. Bright made the effort to write to Franck, 'we have been over and over again most sadly disappointed at not receiving one line from you since we left Avignon – so that although we have no doubts about your safety yet we should certainly be more comfortable if we could find a line somewhere. Our only chance now will be Milan.'

They all loved Cannes. It was a small place, and they stayed in a comfortable pension, surrounded with orange trees, 'just as orchards do with us'. Here Bright got better. His sense of humour and curiosity returned, and his wish to communicate with his children. He suddenly had lots of energy and a renewed interest in biology, showing Charles things like the six-sided sac of a crayfish's heart. He liked to warm his limbs in the sun and stroll in the evening under the stars. A resident doctor and two artists sought his company, and 'I shall have pleasure in renewing my acquaintance with Brougham'. He left his cards in the afternoon, and by mid-morning of the following day Lord Brougham and he were reverting to the Edinburgh of their youth remembering the effervescent days with Horner, Dugald Stewart, Christopher North and Jeffrey.

At Nice, in the Hôtel des Etrangers, Bright picked up more strength. Here he ate partridge and drank white wine, walked in the foothills picking asphodel, and did not seek his bed as early as the rest of them. There was a band, and flower-decked tables on the new esplanade, and though Clara declared it was like an oven, stacked high with burning coal, and Eliza fretted that it might do her husband harm, Bright was enjoying himself.

Leaving the hills of scrub and wild lavender behind them, the party moved on to Genoa. Here, in what seems to have been a delightfully situated pension, selected by a Genoese colleague of Bright's, they rested. By day their rooms were shuttered against the sun, but in the evening, when the shutters were flung back, all Genoa lay before them. The scourge of fleas, the lizards sliding in and out of the stones, and the confusion of foreign smells, were temporarily forgotten for the pleasure of finding Franck's letters awaiting their arrival; they had been written in Paris, London and Marlborough, and mentioned amongst many other things was the inhospitable reception he got from the staff at Savile Row.

In Genoa several foreign residents tried to renew their acquaintance with the Brights; a M de la Rue, a Swiss banker, is one of the names frequently mentioned. Otherwise Eliza, haunted it seems by a phantom of her dead brother Webb, was keen to leave 'the crumbling old city and its memories', while Bright, rather amazingly for such a sick man, showing once again his old devotion to medicine and enjoyment of other intellectual pursuits, rather reluctantly fell in with her wishes.

Venice was beyond all Bright's expectations; he was silent with pleasure. It is sad to read only Eliza's description of the city, for with Bright's natural gift of language and his acute power of observation he would surely have given us a clear and expressive picture of the beauty he saw around him. The only note that survives of his tells how much he was out and about in 'this strange city, the like of which I have never dreamt'. Instead of the gilded sedan chairs which had conveyed them through the narrow streets of Genoa, they had now their own gondola, lent to them by Mr Wilkie, the Consul, who had once been a patient of Bright's. Every morning, they left the hotel at ten o'clock, and did not return until five. After a rest and some refreshment the party sallied forth once again. In St Mark's Square, they listened to an Austrian band; they were serenaded on the Isle of Murano. Then at last they slowly made their way back to bed – and sound sleep.

'Papa is well and enjoying everything,' wrote Emmy to Franck. And thus, still feeling carefree and happy, leaving all the responsibilities to the courier, with every day touched by a curious unreality and new interests, Bright and his family filtered their way home to London through Verona, Milan and Berne.

*

His holiday over, Bright returned to his professional duties. He visited his patients, and he attended meetings at the Fever Hospital and the Veterinary College. He went on impulse to Rugby to see Charles, now the only member of the family left in Arnold's house, and drove to Hampshire to visit his nephew (Robert's son) and his family.

But in the bitterly cold January of 1858, he felt too ill to fulfil his obligations and for several days was imprisoned in his room. For him the chief pleasure in recovering was to see the joy it gave to all around him. Both Eliza and his brother Henry then implored him to curtail his future commitments, but like most professional people of his generation it never occurred to him to stop working. Certainly, it had once been his dream to do less medicine and more geology, philosophy, painting and writing. But instead he found himself being driven on by the fascination of his profession, the family pressures on his pocket, and his lengthening list of patients. So he battled on.

All that summer Bright was driven on by those who sought his aid, not noticing his increasing weakness. He paid what must have been his last visit to Guy's, telling Franck of the great debt he felt he still owed to that great institution. He saw Brunel again. This time he found it difficult to tell him that there was further degeneration in his kidneys and that it was now affecting both his heart and his lungs. He brought Sir Benjamin Brodie in in the hope that he could convince Brunel that a warmer climate was necessary – Brodie had known Brunel as a much younger man.

Brunel was reluctant to winter in Egypt that year, and teasingly threatened to take Bright away with him. Instead, he had a 'toady of a doctor' to accompany him and his family up the Nile. Bright, when bidding farewell to Brunel, must have realized that they were unlikely to see each other again.

That autumn Bright had a further spell of breathlessness and pain, but as usual he recovered almost immediately. Oddly enough, we enter now a period in which he enjoyed unbridled high spirits, which was noted with pleasure by all. One evening at the Royal Society Bright, coming down the stairs, was stopped by a fellow member, a Quaker, who remarked, 'Thou lookest cheerful, Bright', and Bright told him that he felt it, for his health was such as he had not known for years.

A week later he was dead. 'The lamented gentleman', *The Times* told its public, 'received patients and was out in his carriage on Saturday, December 11th, after which he complained of indisposition and retired to his chamber, which he was destined never to leave again.'

All we know of his last illness is that it came unexpectedly, where before he had always rallied and slipped back into his customary routine, this time an internal haemorrhage occurred and little could be done. Nowhere is his end described, and few knew of it. There was no onslaught of enquiries as there had been in previous lapses; no special deliveries of flowers and fruit; no favourite students or friends calling. Both Lowe and Wilkinson seem to have been too upset to inform his patients, and the following Monday many of them were waiting for him to appear. Waiting longer than usual, they wondered what it was that kept him and some sent their servants round to Savile Row to ask for him. Lady MacGrigor was on the point of ordering more bottles of sherry to be delivered to Savile Row but, hearing the news in time, she altered it to flowers.

Bright to the end seems to have inspired uncritical love in all who knew him, and when the news of his death swept his circle, they were devastated.

In his will he had asked for a private funeral, so the ceremony took place with all simplicity at Kensal Rise. Later, a monument was put up to his memory in St James's, Piccadilly. Somewhere in the churchyard lay the bodies of William and little Anna; nearby too was the family pew, frequented weekly by Bright.

Wakley, once so scathing, now had only good to say of Bright; Eliza must have longed to share with him the irony of *The Lancet*'s final tribute:

The sudden and unexpected demise of Dr Bright has created a deep impression of grief and regret, such as only a sense of irretrievable loss could occasion. In him all feel that the medical profession of England has lost one of the most original, observant and philosophical minds that have ever contributed to the glory and the usefulness of the body. A man of peculiar independence of thought, of high morale, and untiring energy, he had contributed more than, perhaps, any other to form the medical opinion of his day. With the acute application of truth which with him was almost an instinct, he was foremost to perceive that the progress of medical science must now greatly depend upon the successful study of pathological changes; and by the singular devotion to pathological investigation which characterised his career, he was at once enabled to accomplish investigations which have immortalised his name, while he gave a beneficial impulse to the whole science. The life-history of Richard Bright is one of unswerving energy of purpose and increasing labour.

There were many obituary notices, and Eliza must have received hundreds of letters. Amongst Franck's correspondence there are a few written by his friends, and all of them contain the same message: 'There never was a man more to be loved when living or to be regretted when called away, than your father.' 'There can be very few, Franck,' wrote the headmaster of Rugby, 'who have left widely a feeling of real gratitude for real kindness in hundreds of hearts.' While the housemaster, Arnold, wrote a fitting end to this, Bright's story:

'In this house your father is so closely associated with many of our joys and sorrows during our whole Rugby life, that we have all felt that we have lost a most dear and kind friend, whose loss can never be replaced – but if the loss of a man, like your father, be irreparable to his friends and still more to his family, there is still fund of blessing which will be continually springing up fresh to you all from the recollection of his life: from the love and kindness which he was ever shedding over all who came in his way, and which will surely return in rich measure of blessing on those whom he has left behind.'

SACRED TO THE MEMORY OF
RICHARD BRIGHT. M.D., D.C.L.,
PHYSICIAN EXTRAORDINARY TO THE QUEEN,
FELLOW OF THE ROYAL SOCIETY AND OTHER LEARNED BODIES.
HE DEPARTED THIS LIFE ON THE 16TH DECEMBER, 1858,
IN THE SIXTY-NINTH YEAR OF HIS AGE.
HE CONTRIBUTED TO MEDICAL SCIENCE MANY DISCOVERIES
AND WORKS OF GREAT VALUE;
AND DIED WHILE IN THE FULL PRACTICE OF HIS PROFESSION.
AFTER A LIFE OF WARM AFFECTION, UNSULLIED PURITY,
AND GREAT USEFULNESS.

APPENDICES

APPENDIX I

A Birthday Ode

May 1812. To Ann Heywood (later Mrs Eliot), his cousin of 23 Bedford Place, Russell Sq.

Dear Ann,

      Accept my apology. R.B.

God who in boundless wisdom formed mankind
The image of himself, has woven in our frame
So fine a tissue exquisitely worked
By his own hand, that should we e'er compare
(Failing all other objects of our sense)
The subtle rays of light, almost unseen,
To this, on earth great nature's masterpiece,
The light would from comparison shrink back abashed.
And as the strings of the Aeolian harp
Touched by the gentlest streamlet of the summer breeze
Vibrates. So by the influence obscure
Of thought, vibrates the Mental structure . . .
Let not a poet so unskilled essay
To paint the agitation of his mind
When kindest words his infant lay approved
And, proof of approbation! sought for more.
Whether his muse were pleased, abashed, alarmed,
Or feared the subject then proposed, too bright
Should dazzle his weak eyes, and in the attempt
To soar amidst thy high perfection,
He should face, and with him, all his little merit die,
Whate'er the cause, silence was all he could.
And now mayhap thy natal day has passed unsung,
But not unheeded in the hearts of those
Whom every day has been through thee, a natal day of bliss.

APPENDIX II

From Chapter 1 of *Guy's Hospital Reports*, Vol. I, where Bright summarizes his renal discoveries:

The importance and extensive prevalence of that form of disease, which, after it has continued for some time, is attended by the peculiar changes in the structure of the kidney, now pretty generally known by the names of 'mottling', 'white degeneration', 'contraction', or 'granulation', impresses itself every year more and more deeply on my mind; and whether I turn to the wards of the hospital, or reflect on the experience of private practice, I find, on every side, such examples of its fatal progress and unrelenting ravages, as induce me to consider it amongst the most frequent, as well as the most certain causes of death in some classes of the community, while it is of common occurrence in all; and I believe I speak within bounds, when I state, that not less than five hundred die of it annually in London alone. It is, indeed an humiliating confession, that, although much attention has been directed to this disease for nearly ten years, and during that time there has probably been no period in which at least twenty cases might not have been pointed out in each of the large hospitals of the metropolis – and there is reason to believe that double that number may, at this moment, and at all times, be found in the wards of Guy's hospital – yet little or nothing has been done towards devising a method of permanent relief, when the disease has been confirmed; and no fixed plan has been laid down, as affording a tolerable certainty of cure in the more recent cases. I believe that our want of success, in what are considered the more recent attacks, is frequently owing to the fact that the disease is far more advanced than we suspect, when it first becomes the object of our attention; and I am most anxious, in the present communication, to impress upon the members of our profession the insidious nature of this malady, that they may be led to watch its first approaches, with all the solicitude which they would feel on discovering the first suspicious symptoms of phthisis or of epilepsy. There is great reason to suppose that the seeds of this disease are often sown at an early period; and that intervals of apparent health produce a false security in the patient, his friends, and his medical attendants, even where apprehension has been early excited.

The first indication of the tendency to this disease is often haematuria, of a more or less decided character; this may originate from various causes, and yet may give evidence of the same tendency: scarlatina has apparently laid the foundation for the future mischief . . . Intemperance seems its most usual source; and exposure to cold the most common cause of its development and aggravation.

APPENDIX III

Bright's description of nephritis from *Guy's Hospital Reports*, Vol. I.

The history of this disease, and its symptoms, is nearly as follows:

A child, or an adult, is affected with scarlatina, or some other acute disease; or has indulged in the intemperate use of ardent spirits for a series of months or years: he is exposed to some casual cause or habitual source of suppressed perspiration: he finds the secretion of his urine greatly increased, or he discovers that it is tinged with blood; or, without having made any such observations, he wakes in the morning with his face swollen, or his ankles puffy, or his hands oedematous. If he happens, in this condition, to fall under the case of a practitioner who suspects the nature of his disease, it is found that already his urine contains a notable quantity of albumen: his pulse is full and hard, his skin dry, he has often headache, and sometimes a sense of weight or pain across the loins. Under treatment more or less active, or sometimes without any treatment, the more obvious and distressing of these symptoms disappear; the swelling, whether casual or constant, is no longer observed; the urine ceases to evince any admixture of red particles; and, according to the degree of importance which has been attached to these symptoms, they are gradually lost sight of, or are absolutely forgotten. Nevertheless, from time to time the countenance becomes bloated; the skin is dry; headaches occur with unusual frequency; or the calls to micturition disturb the night's repose. After a time, the healthy colour of the countenance fades; a sense of weakness or pain in the loins increases; headaches, often accompanied by vomiting, add greatly to the general want of comfort; and a sense of lassitude, of weariness, and of depression, gradually steals over the bodily and mental frame. Again, the assistance of medicine is sought. If the nature of the disease is suspected, the urine is carefully tested; and found, in almost every trial, to contain albumen, while the quantity of urea is gradually diminishing. If, in the attempt to give relief to the oppression of the system, blood is drawn, it is often buffed, or the serum is milky and opaque; and nice analysis will frequently detect a great deficiency of albumen, and sometimes manifest indications of the presence of urea. If the disease is not suspected, the liver, the stomach, or the brain divide the case of the practitioner, sometimes drawing him away entirely from the more important seat of disease. The swelling increases and decreases; the mind grows cheerful, or is sad; the secretions of the kidney or the skin are augmented or diminished, sometimes in alternate ratio, sometimes without apparent relation. Again, the patient is restored to tolerable health; again he enters on his active duties; or he is, perhaps, less fortunate; – the swelling increases, the urine becomes scanty, the powers of life seem to yield, the lungs become oedematous, and in a state of asphyxia or coma, he sinks into the grave; or a sudden effusion of serum into the glottis closes the passages of the air, and brings on a more sudden dissolution. Should he, however, have resumed the avocations of life, he is usually subject to constant recurrence of his symptoms; or again, almost dismissing the recollection of his ailment, he is suddenly seized with an acute attack of pericarditis, or with a still more acute attack of peritonitis, which, without any renewed warning, deprives him, in eight and forty hours, of his life. Should he escape this danger likewise, other perils await him; his headaches have been observed to become more frequent; his stomach more deranged; his vision indistinct; his hearing depraved; he is suddenly seized with a convulsive fit, and becomes blind. He struggles through the attack; but again and again it returns; and before a day or a week has elapsed, worn out by convulsions, or overwhelmed by comas, the painful history of his disease is closed.

Of the appearance presented after death, enough will be said in another part of the present communication: but one question may be asked in this place – Do we always find such lesion of the kidney as to bear us out in the belief, that the peculiar condition of the urine, to which I have already referred, shews that the disease, call it what we may, is connected necessarily and essentially with the derangement of that organ? After ten years' attentive – though, perhaps, I must not say completely impartial observation – I am ready to answer this question in the affirmative; and yet I confess that I have occasionally met with anomalies which have been somewhat difficult to explain . . .

There has not yet, perhaps, been sufficient time, since this disease of the kidneys first attracted attention, to say to what extent life may be prolonged while the body is under its influence; but I believe with care, its fatal effects may be kept at bay, and a hazardous life may be protected for many years. Should that care be neglected, the chance of life will be greatly diminished.

The cases which I now offer will be found to bear upon many points in the history I have just sketched out; and amongst others, will tend to illustrate the subject of the probable duration of the disease, and some of the more insidious attacks which attend the fatal termination.

Case.	Kidney.	Pleura.	Lung.	Pericardium.	Heart.	Cavity of Abdomen.	Peritoneum.
18. James Jones, æt. 45, *died of cerebral irritation*	soft, large, mottled slightly	adhesion	healthy	....	large, flaccid	effusion of clear serum, with transparent membranes	opaque, and old adhesions
19. Man of Colour, æt. 55, *died of effusion of blood on brain*	hard, small, contracted, scabrous	adhesion	hardened by old pneumonia, bronchi dilated	....	great hypertrophy of left ventricle	effusion of clear yellow serum	....
20. Jas. Kennedy, æt. 63, *died of softening of brain*	slightly granulated	....	....	....	mitral valve ossified	....	....
21. John Ruggles, æt. 46, *died of bronchitis, with œdema*	slightly granulated	old adhesions	partial hepatiza- tion, bronchitis	....	large, right ventricle thick	....	....
22. Thos. Tweed, æt. 52, *died with symptoms of cerebral congestion*	soft, extensive white deposit	old adhesions	gorged, and partially hepatized, bronchitis	....	large and flaccid	....	....
23. Margaret Field, æt. 40, *died with anasarca comatose*	hard, rough, lobulated	adhesions	bronchitis, & lobular pneumonia	effusion of serum	firm, large	abundant effusion of serum	....
24. Jane George, æt. 36, *died with anasarca*	hard, granulated, mottled	strong adhesions	....	general cellular adhesion	great hyper- trophy of right side, disease of all the valves, particularly the tricuspid	effusion	opaque, and thickened
25. —— Jessy, *died apoplectic*	hard, granulated	....	healthy, with slight hepatization	....	large valves healthy	....	....
26. —— ——, *died apoplect*	hard, pale, granulated	general adhesion	healthy	....	left side rather too firm	....	....
27. —— ——, æt. 73, *died comatose*	hard, granulated	inflamed	emphysema, partial inflammation	....	left side firm, mitral valve and tricuspid diseased	....	....
28. John Baldrey, æt. 61, *died apoplectic*	hard, granulated	slight adhesions	emphysema, apex indurated	healthy	large, particularly left ventricle	....	....
29. Robt. Wardess, æt. 50, *died apoplectic*	soft, white	inflamed	œdema, and emphysema	....	coronary vessels ossified	....	....
30. Wm. Saunders, æt. 47, *died apoplectic*	hard, small, contracted	inflamed	compressed	fibrin, and viscid serum	hypertrophy of left ventricle	....	....
31. Martha Russell, æt. 40, *died of hydrothorax*	hard, small, granulated	great effusion	healthy	....	hypertrophy of left ventricle, disease of mitral valve	....	....
32. M—— L——, æt. 40, *died epileptic*	hard, granulated, contracted	....	....	....	....	....	adhesions
33. S. Barnet, æt. 28, *died epileptic*	hard, scabrous	....	....	....	....	....	....

Liver.	Intestines.	Stomach.	Spleen.	Pancreas.	Aorta.	Brain.	Uterus.	Bile.
granulated	contracted	mucous membrane granulated and scabrous	very large and firm	....	healthy	arachnoid opaque.		
slightly granulated	....	....	small	....	dilated, atheromatous deposit	great effusion of blood on surface, and marks of old similar disease.		
hard, granulated	....	....	small, rather hard	....	....	softened externally, vessels diseased.		
gorged with blood	congested	....	....	....	....	vascular and mottled.		
....	....	....	....	....	few opaque spots	brain marbled with congestion, serum beneath the arachnoid, vessels atheromatous		
somewhat fatty	large intestines, ulcerated throughout	....	healthy	healthy	....	....	some cysts in the ovaries	mucus with bile.
hard, and full of blood	mucous membrane œdematous	thick and granular	....		....	much serum beneath arachnoid	enlarged.	
slightly granulated	healthy	slightly contracted	external cartilaginous deposit	healthy	atheromatous	serous effusion, disease of plexus choroides		calculi and little bile.
gorged with blood	....	distended with flatus	....	....	....	serous effusion in arachnoid, disease of choroid plexus.		
healthy	contracted	healthy	small and contracted	obstructed	....	serous effusion.		
healthy	healthy	mucous membrane thick and corrugated	cartilaginous deposit externally	healthy	diseased throughout	apoplectic clot, vessels diseased.		
....	....	....	....	....	extensive ossification	apoplectic clot, serous effusion, vessels diseased.		
granulated	....	mucous membrane hard and rough	....	....	....	diseased vessels, old apoplectic clots.		
healthy	....	....	....	....	....	apoplectic clot, vessels diseased.		
....	....	....	....	....	....	calvaria thick and solid.		
healthy	soft	soft	hard	....	....	calvaria thick and solid.		

NOTES

I have endeavoured to have as few notes as possible. Unless otherwise stated the main sources of information for this book are:

A Papers on the history of the Houses of Anthony Gibbs and Son. Family letters.
B The Bright collection of documents and letters.
Guy's Hospital Reports.
Bright's own writings.

There are many books on the history of medicine and most contain short accounts of Bright and his works. The ones listed have been obtained from the bibliography of Richard Bright which is to be found in the special edition of *Guy's Hospital Reports* in commemoration of the centenary of his death: Vol. 107, No 4, 1958.

Follett papers and letters discovered were few and the more informative are the property of Miss Susan Follett, Ashleworth, Gloucestershire.

*

A (i) John Gibbs, *The History of Anthony and Dorothea Gibbs and their Contemporary Relatives* (St Catherine's Press, London, 1922).
　(ii) Various diaries and letters to be found in the Guildhall of London archives.
B (i) Colwall collection of family letters and manuscripts. Original with Mrs M. Lloyd, Barton Court, Colwall. Now on microfilm in the Bristol Archives, City Hall.
　(ii) Norfolk collection of family letters. Most of these are written by Eliza Follett, the wife of Richard Bright. Others are by his children and their friends. Property of Major Athill, Holt, Norfolk.
　(iii) Australian collection of family manuscripts and letters. Property of David and Charles Bright. This remarkable collection of family papers must be mentioned since they comprise an unusual and extraordinarily valuable source of material for historians. The documents of the Bright activities in Jamaica go back to 1700. Records of the commercial and legal activities of the Brights and their partners in the Caribbean, in Philadelphia and in South Carolina are to be found here, as well as all the genealogical data which Richard Bright of Ham Green amassed when fighting the legal suits brought to court by the Meylers.

There are documents dealing with Richard Bright's friendship with Joseph Priestley, the Garnetts of Paris and New Jersey, the Revd Randolph and the Vaughan family of Jamaica, London and Paris; and of all the travels of Samuel Bright when working for the Gibbs of Liverpool. As most of the journals written by Richard Bright and Lowbridge are also preserved, there is a day-by-day record not only of what they were doing but of what was going on in the country and in commerce between 1808 and 1840. Each bundle is a vignette of history.

This huge collection is now at Melbourne University, and is being slowly sifted through and documented. Robert Kark M.D., Professor of Renal Medicine, St Luke's Hospital, Chicago, was instrumental in all this.

CHAPTER I

1 Alexander Pope, letter to Martha Blount, quoted in W. Hunt's book on Bristol (1887).

2 Many members of the family were mayors and sheriffs of Bristol. H. A. Bright, in a letter to the editor of *The Herald and Genealogist*, London; J. Pinel, 'The Brights of Colwall', see Burke's *Genealogical and Heraldic History of the Landed Gentry*, 1952; C. H. Cave, *A History of Banking in Bristol 1750–1899* (1899).

3 H. A. Bright, 'A Historical Sketch of Warrington Academy', *Transactions of the Historical Society of Lancashire and Cheshire*, 1888; J. Fulton, 'The Warrington Academy 1757–1786', *Bulletin of the Institute of Historical Medicine*, Vol. I, Johns Hopkins University, 1933.

4 He had two gifted sons, Arthur and Charles, and his daughter Letitia was later to become Mrs Barbauld. They formed lasting friendships with Richard Bright and his family. Charles went to Guy's.

5 H. A. Bright, *op. cit.*

6 W. Buckland, obituary of Richard Bright of Ham Green, *Proceedings of the Geological Society of London*, 1841, 3. Holographic draft amongst family papers.

7 Obituary, 18 March 1827, *Bristol Mercury*.

8 Blagden Letters, Library of the Royal Society, London. Letters between Richard Bright (Snr) and Benjamin Vaughan on the development of the docks in Bristol. Richard Bright's plan for improvement of the docks can be seen in the archives of the Bristol Museum.

9 Still in perfect condition and in the possession of Mrs M. Lloyd, Barton Court, Colwall.

10 Bright, in a letter of recollection to his son William, 1840.

CHAPTER 2

1 Revd. Charles Southey (ed.), *Life and Correspondence of Robert Southey*, 6 vols (London 1849–50).

2 Letter from Henry Bright to his mother.

3 Southey, *op. cit.*

4 *Ibid.*

5 John Cam Hobhouse (then Lord Broughton), *Recollections of a Long Life*, Vol. I, 1786–1816.

6 Taken at random from the Brights' business letters.

7 Unpublished letters from S. T. Coleridge to the Revd J. P. Estlin, communicated by H. A. Bright to the Philobiblon Society in 1884.

8 Information given by Dr Buckland, the geologist, to the Geological Society in 1858.

9 A chapter by Arrowsmith on 'The History of Merchant Venturers of the City of Bristol' in J. Latimer, *The Annals of Bristol*, 3 vols (Bristol, reprinted 1970).

10 J. Sowerby, *British Mineralogy*, Vol. I (London, 1806).

CHAPTER 3

1 H. Martineau, *Autobiography* (1877).
R. L. Carpenter, *Memoir of Lant Carpenter* (1842); J. Manton, *Children of the Streets. Life of Mary Carpenter* (Heinemann, 1976).

2 This story has been passed down by word of mouth through successive Brights.

3 Carpenter, *op. cit.*

4 'Young Holland is come into the country to practice with his father for two years. He aims at being a London physician, and if information and good sense could ensure success, he would have a fair chance of rising in that line to great eminence: but I think ignorance and plenty of small talk and flattery are more likely to succeed.' Letter in M. J. Stanley, *Early Married Life of Maria, Lady Stanley*, Vol. II (Longman, 1899).

CHAPTER 4

1 Sir Henry Holland, *Recollections of the Past Life* (New York, 1872).

2 W. Watson, *The History of the Speculative Society 1764–1904* (1905). Henry, Benjamin and Bright were all members. The older brothers were contemporaries of Jeffrey, Brougham, Cockburn and Horner.

3 Dr Christison, *Life of Sir Robert Christison*, ed. by his sons (1885).

CHAPTER 5

1 Professor R. M. Kark, Professor of Renal Medicine, St Luke's Hospital, Chicago, tells me that Henry Holland also wrote an account of their ascent in The Diary of Henry Holland (p. 129, Vol. i, 1810), which is in the museum at Reykjavik.

2 According to Ebenezar Henderson, a missionary, who followed Bright to Iceland. He was a patient of Bright's. Apparently Thomas Macaulay read 'Henderson's book on Iceland at breakfast: a favourite breakfast book with me. Why?'

3 Nos. 33754, 33755, 33756.

CHAPTER 6

1 W. S. Thayer, in *British Medical Journal*, 1927.

2 Bright, *Medical Cases*, Vol. I.

3 Lord Sheffield, letter to B. Way, 1806. Discussed by Lady Stanley in *The Early Married Life of Maria, Lady Stanley*, Vol. II (Longman, 1899). Lord Sheffield was also a Governor of the Fever Hospital.

4 Bright, paper on gangrene read to the Royal Medical Society of Edinburgh in 1813.

5 H. C. Cameron, *Mr Guy's Hospital* (Longman, 1958).

6 *Ibid.*

7 Letter from Dr Laird to Richard Bright.

8 R. M. Kark, 'The Life, Work and Geological Collections of R. Bright, M.D.', *Archives of Natural History*, 1981.

9 Stanley, *op. cit.*

CHAPTER 8

1 Bright, *Travels from Vienna*, from which most of the material for this chapter is taken.

2 Lord Russell Brock, *Life of Sir Astley Cooper* (1952).

CHAPTER 9

1 Letter from Bright to Dr Laird, 3 January 1816.

2 W. Munk, *The Roll of the Royal College of Physicians*(1878), under Thomas Bateman, 1778–1821.

3 Letter from Eliza to Bright, May 1822. In the same letter she asks, 'What went wrong with his love affair?'

4 Sir Henry Holland, *Recollections of a Past Life* (New York, 1872).

5 The usual amount taken in venesection was 18 oz. Bright rarely took more than 4–6 oz; Prichard was known to take 20 oz. In a letter dated 15 June 1855 offering condolences to Prichard's nephew, J. R. Estlin, on Prichard's death, Bright wrote that 'he with your father certainly saved my life 40 years ago'.

6 There is a very long account of the case in the *Bristol Journal*.

7 Pierre François Olive Rayer (1793–1867), renal physician and dermatologist. *Traité des Maladies des Reins* (Baillière, 1837).

8 Hunter-Bright correspondence on books of antiquity, BM 25676 A17.

9 Cosmo Innes (1798–1874), Scottish antiquarian of Deeside, admitted to Scottish bar in 1822; author.

10 How true this was is questionable, however, and it remains a mystery how this appointment came about. For it seems that Richard Bright wrote sixty letters to influential persons and Governors of Guy's Hospital supporting his son's application. Professor R. M. Kark, St Luke's Medical Centre, Chicago.

CHAPTER 10

1 Sir Benjamin Brodie, *Personal Memoir* (1952).

2 Bright, *Medical Cases*, Vol. I.

CHAPTER 11

1 S. S. Sprigge, *Life and Times of Thomas Wakley* (1897).
2 *Ibid.*
3 H. C. Cameron, *Mr Guy's Hospital* (Longman, 1958).
4 Owen Rees in a letter to Eliza written years later.
5 A description of conditions in hospitals at this time in Abel-Smith, *The Hospitals.*
6 Cameron, *op. cit.*
7 Bright, *Medical Cases*, Vol. II.
8 *Ibid.*, Vol. I.
9 *Ibid.*
10 Bright, *Elements of the Practice of Medicine.*
11 Bright, *Medical Cases*, Vol. I.
12 Eliza in a letter to Webb.
13 Bright, Introduction to *Medical Cases*, Vol. I.
14 *Ibid.*

CHAPTER 12

1 Bright's personal obituary eulogy to William Babington, 1833; and in his book *Travels from Vienna.* He witnessed at Leva the funeral of a postmaster's wife.
2 Aunt Phoebe Heywood, in a letter found in the possession of Sir Oliver Heywood, Bart.

CHAPTER 13

1 Dr Laird in a letter to Eliza.
2 Bright, 'Introductory Address . . . on the Practice of Medicine'.

CHAPTER 14

1 Sir Benjamin Brodie, *Personal Memoir* (1952).

CHAPTER 15

1 The sixth British Association Meeting was held in Bristol in 1836. Following a 'philosophical excursion to Portishead', we learn from Mr Hilhouse's nephew Barclay Fox that '110 sages' on the return journey down the Avon, 'landed at Ham Green, the beautiful residence of R. Bright, Esq. His sons were waiting on the shore and escorted us to their house. We found the old gentleman lying on a sofa, having broken his thigh, but he received us with the utmost politeness and hospitality. They showed us into another room most sumptuously provided with fruit and pastry and we readjourned to the other for tea and talk.'

CHAPTER 16

1 W. Munk, *The Roll of the Royal College of Physicians* (1878), under R. Bright.
2 Sir W. Hale-White, 'Richard Bright and his discovery of the disease bearing his name', *Guy's Hospital Reports*, 1921, 71.
3 H. C. Cameron, *Mr Guy's Hospital* (Longman, 1958).
4 Lord Russell Brock, *Life of Sir Astley Cooper* (1952).

CHAPTER 18

1 James Gray, *History of the Royal Medical Society of Edinburgh 1737–1937*, (Edinburgh U. P., 1952).
2 In his history of Crawley, F. W. Pledge says that Henry kept no company and lived with his servant in two or three rooms. A misogynist, 'he would go out of his way rather than meet a woman, and never passed along the village street. His nephew Professor Franck Bright, Master of University College, Oxford, says that "he was a very polished and refined old gentleman and a keen geologist." Always dressed with extreme shabbiness, he was arrested in his own garden as a suspicious character by a zealous member of the then newly established police force.'

CHAPTER 19

1 H. C. Cameron, *Mr Guy's Hospital* (Longman, 1958).
2 Bright's preface to an article by Barlow and Rees on albuminous urine in *Guy's Hospital Reports*, 1843.

CHAPTER 21

1 D. M. Emblem, in *Peter Mark Roget* (Longman, 1970), gives a good account of the whole affair.
2 Letter from William Empsom to Bright.

CHAPTER 22

1 Mrs Hardy, *Biography of Thomas Hardy*, Vol. I. (1929).
2 The discussion between them was centred round the reason why no eminent London physicians became Regius Professors of Medicine in University towns. With a salary of £2,000 it was no wonder. It was for this reason, Prince Albert maintained, that neither Oxford nor Cambridge made good medical schools. Sir George Trevelyan, *Life and Letters of Thomas Macaulay* (Longman, 1876).

CHAPTER 23

1 Sir George Trevelyan, *Life and Letters of Thomas Macaulay* (Longman, 1876).
2 *Ibid.*

3 The Prince of Wales developed measles on 23 June 1853, Prince Albert in July. Information from Jane Langton, Registrar of the Windsor Archives.

CHAPTER 24

1 This letter of Captain Poffnet's was found amongst the collection in Norfolk. There was one, too, from his nephew, Robert Onesipherus, who was at the Crimea and described the lack of material.

2 Henry Holland outlived Bright by fifteen years, dying in 1873. He revisited Iceland at the age of eighty-three.

RICHARD BRIGHT, MD, FRCP, FRS
– A BIBLIOGRAPHY

Separate Works

Disputatio Medica Inaugarlis de Erysipitate Contagiosa (Edinburgh, 1813).

Mackenzie, Sir George, *Travels in the Island of Iceland* (Edinburgh, 1811). Bright contributed sketches, a short account of the climb on Snaëfell Jokul, and the chapters on plants and animals.

Travels from Vienna through Lower Hungary; with some remarks on the state of Vienna during the Congress in the year 1814 (Edinburgh, 1818).

Outlines of a course of lectures on the Practice of Medicine delivered in the Medical School of Guy's, published as was the custom then to outline a course of lectures (1827).

Reports of Medical Cases selected with a view of illustrating the Symptoms and Cure of Diseases with a reference to Morbid Anatomy, 2 vols (London, 1827–31).

'Introductory Address delivered at the commencement of a course of lectures on the practice of Medicine' (London, 1833). Published at the request of his pupils.

An account of a remarkable misplacement of the stomach (London, 1836).

Elements of the Practice of Medicine (with Thomas Addison) (Longman, 1839).

Clinical memoirs on abdominal tumours and intumescence (New Sydenham Society, 1861).

Articles in Periodical Publications

'On the strata in the neighbourhood of Bristol', *Transactions of the Geological Society* 1817, 4.

'On the hills of Badacson, Siliget, etc. in Hungary', *Transactions of the Geological Society*, 1821, 5.

'A case of traumatic tetanus', *Lancet*, 1825–6, 9.

'A singular case', (on syringomyelia), *Lancet*, 1825–6, 9.

'The Contagious nature of erysipelas', *Lancet*, 1825–6, 9.

'Guy's Hospital Anniversary Dinner', *Lancet*, 1826–7, 10.

'Proceedings of Societies. Guy's Physical Society', *London Medical Gazette*, 1829–30, 5.

'Character of the late Dr Babington', *London Medical Gazette*, 1833, 12.

'Goulstonian Lectures on the functions of the abdominal viscera with observations on the diagnostic marks of the diseases to which the viscera are subject', *London Medical Gazette*, 1833, 12.

'Cases and observations connected with diseases of the pancreas and duodenum', *Medico-Chirurgical Transactions*, 1833, 18; *Lancet*, 1832–3; *London Medical Gazette*, 1833.

'Cases and observations illustrative of diagnosis when adhesions have taken place in the peritoneum, with remarks upon some other morbid changes of that membrane', *Medico-Chirurgical Transactions*, 1835, 19; *London Medical Gazette*, 1834–5 ('A good and possibly the first description of chronic proliferative peritonitis'. Hale-White).

'Observations on the treatment of fever', *Guy's Hospital Reports*, 1836, 1; *London Medical Gazette*, 1835–6.

'Cases illustrative of the effects produced when the arteries of the brain are diseased selected chiefly with a view to diagnosis in such affections', *Guy's Hospital Reports*, 1836, 1.

'Permanent contraction of all extremities with numberless cartilaginous deposits in the arachnoid of the spinal marrow', *Guy's Hospital Reports*, 1836, 1.

'Cases of fatal epilepsy from local disease of the brain', *Guy's Hospital Reports*, 1836, 1.

'Case of tetanus in which quinine and stimulants were administered very extensively with success', *Guy's Hospital Reports*, 1836, 1.

'Cases and observations illustrative of renal disease accompanied with the secretion of albuminous urine', *Guy's Hospital Reports*, 1836, 1; *London Medical Gazette*, 1835–6, 18.

'Tabular view of the morbid appearance in 100 cases connected with albuminous urine, with observations', *Guy's Hospital Reports*, *1836, 1*.

'Observations on jaundice, more particularly on that form of the disease which accompanies the diffused inflammation of the substance of the liver', *Guy's Hospital Reports*, 1836. (The original description of acute yellow atrophy of the liver).

'Observations on the situation and structure of malignant disease of the liver', *Guy's Hospital Reports*, 1836, 1.

'Retrospective address to the Medico-Chirurgical Society', *Lancet*, 1837–8.

'Cases and observations illustrative of diagnosis when tumours are situated at the base of the brain', *Guy's Hospital Reports*, 1837, 2.

'Observations on abdominal tumours and intumescence; illustrated
(1) by some cases of acephalocyst hydatids;
(2) illustrated by cases of ovarian disease;
(3) illustrated by cases of diseases of the spleen;
(4) illustrated by cases of renal disease', *Guy's Hospital Reports*, 1837, 2, 3 and 4.

'Cases of spasmodic disease accompanying affections of the pericardium', *Medico-Chirurgical Transactions*, 1839, 22; *London Medical Gazette*, 1838–9.

'Internal congretion of phosphate of lime', *London Medical Gazette*, 1839–40.

'Cases and observations illustrative of renal disease accompanied with the secretion of albuminous urine', *Guy's Hospital Reports*, 1840, 5.

'Observations on abdominal tumours and intumescence; illustrated by cases of diseased liver', *Guy's Hospital Reports*, 1860, 5.

'Letter concerning the pathology of the kidney', *London Medical Gazette*, 1841–2, 29.

'Account of the observations made under the superintendance of Dr Bright on patients whose urine was albuminous', *Guy's Hospital Reports*, 1843.

'On Gangrene', *Guy's Hospital Reports*, 1928, 78. (This is a reprint of his paper read to the Royal Medical Society of Edinburgh in 1813.)

Articles Written on Bright

Author unknown, *London Medical Gazette*, 1837, 10. 496.

—, 'Right of students', *Lancet*, 1837–8, i.

—, 'Medical portraits; the lecturers at Guy's and St. Thomas's Hospital', *Medical Times*, 1840, ii.

—, 'Pencillings of eminent medical men. Dr Bright', *Medical Times*, 1843–4, 9.

—, 'Dr Richard Bright. Honorary degrees at Oxford', *Lancet*, 1853, i.

—, Obituary notice, *Edinburgh Medical Journal*, 1858, 4.

—, Obituary notice, *Lancet*, 1858, ii.

—, Obituary notice, *Medical Times and Gazette*, 1858, 17.

—, 'Heroes of medicine, Richard Bright', *Practitioner*, 1901, 67.

—, 'Studies in biography No. 1. Richard Bright', *Intercolonial Medical Journal*, 1905, 10.

—, 'Some great men of Guy's', *Practitioner*, 1906, 76.

—, '100 years ago. Richard Bright on September 13th, 1813', *British Medical Journal*, 1913, ii.

—, *Clinical Medicine and Surgery*, 1929, 36.

—, Colorado Medicine, 1931, 28.

—, *New England Journal of Medicine*, 1936, 214.

Barkley, A. H., *Kentucky Medical Journal*, 1926, 24.

Barlow, G. H., 'Eulogium on Dr Bright', *Lancet*, 1843–4, i.

—, 'Introduction to the New Sydenham Society's reprint of his papers on Abdominal Tumours'.

Beilin, A., 'Richard Bright, 1789–1858; distinguished pioneer, physician and investigator', *Hygeia*, 1837, 15.

Burdick, A. S., Biographical notice. *Medical Standard*, 1903, 26.

Cave, H. A., 'Contributions to the history of narcolepsy (case described by Richard Bright in 1836)', *Archives of Neurology and Psychiatry*, 1937, 38.

Chance, B., 'An ophthalmologist's appreciation', *Annals of Medical History*, 1927, 9.

—, 'Richard Bright, traveller and artist. With illustrations', *Bulletin of the History of Medicine*, 1940, 8.

Christian, H. A., 'Kidney disease as described by Richard Bright in the light of knowledge of a century later', *Annals of Medical History*, 1927, 9.

Eason, Sir H. L., 'The situation of the clinical wards at Guy's Hospital in the time of Richard Bright', *Guy's Hospital Reports*, 1927, 77.

Garrison, F. H., 'Richard Bright's travels in Lower Hungary, a physician's holiday', *Johns Hopkins Hospital Bulletin*, 1912, 23.(A very good article on Bright's travels with many quotations from his work and several illustrations.)

—, The same, *Guy's Hospital Gazette*, 1912, 26. (A brief abstract of the above.)

Hacker, W. L., *Albany Medical Annals*, 1908, 29.

Hale-White, Sir W., 'Richard Bright and his discovery of the disease bearing his name', *Guy's Hospital Reports*, 1921, 71.

—, 'Bright's observations other than those on renal disease', *Guy's Hospital Reports*, 1921, 71. (Both these two papers are admirable studies of Bright's work and teaching.)

—, 'Bright's contributions to medicine', *Guy's Hospital Gazette*, 1921, 35. (This article covers much the same ground as the previous two.)

—, 'The Centenary of the discovery of Bright's Disease', *Lancet*, 1925, ii.

—, 'Richard Bright and his work', *London, Guy's Hospital Reports*, 1927.

Kark, R. M., in *American Journal of Medicine*, 1958.

GENERAL BIBLIOGRAPHY

Aikin, A. L. B., *The Works of Anne Letitia Barbauld with Memoir* (Longman, 1825).

Barrett, *The History of Antiquities of Bristol* (1789).
Bettany, G. T., *Eminent Doctors: Their Lives and their Work* (London, 1885).
Brock, Russell Lord, *The Life of Sir Astley Cooper* (1952).
Brodie, Sir Benjamin, *Personal Memoir* (1952).
Bristol and its environs (London, Bristol Executive Committee of the British Association, 1875).

Cameron, H. C., *Mr Guy's Hospital 1726–1948* (Longman, 1958).
Carpenter, R. L., *Memoir of Lant Carpenter* (1842).
Cave, C. H., *A History of Banking in Bristol 1750–1899* (1899).
Comrie, D., *History of Scottish Medicine to 1860* (1932).
Cooper, Bransby, FRCS, *The Life and Work of Sir Astley Cooper*, 2 vols (1883).
Croker, W. C., *Correspondence and Diaries* (Murray, 1884).

Davy, John, *Memoirs of the Life of Sir Humphry Davy, Bart.* (London, 1849).

Eden, The Hon. Emily, *The Eden Letters.*
Emblem, D. M., *Peter Mark Roget* (Longman, 1970).

Gibbs, Anthony J., *History of Anthony and Dorothea Gibbs & of the Early Years of Gibbs, Bright and Sons* (Catherine Press, 1922).
Gray, James, *History of the Royal Medical Society of Edinburgh 1737–1937* (Edinburgh U.P., 1952).
Guthrie, Douglas, *A History of Medicine* (Nelson, 1945).
Hobhouse, J. Cam, (Lord Broughton) *Recollections of a Long Life*, Vol. I, 1786–1816 (1896).
Hodgkin Family Papers, The Friends House Library, Euston Rd.
Holland, Elizabeth Lady, *Journal*, Vol. 2 (London, 1908).
Holland Letters (of Knutsford), Cheshire County Record office.
Holland, Sir Henry, *Recollections of a Past Life* (New York, 1872).
Holmes, T., *Masters of Medicine. Sir Benjamin Brodie* (1952).
Hope Simpson, J., *Rugby since Arnold* (London, 1942).
Hopkirk, M., *Queen Adelaide* (Murray, 1946).

Kark, R. M., and D. T. Moore, 'The Life, Work and Geological Collections of R. Bright, M.D.', *Archives of Natural History* (1981).

Latimer, J., *The Annals of Bristol*, 3 vols (Georges, Bristol, reprinted 1970).
Lewis, T. (Ed.), *Extracts of the Journals and Correspondence of Miss Berry, from the year 1788–1852* (Longman, 1885).

MacCormac, H., 'At the Public Dispensary', *British Journal of Dermatology and Syphilology*, 45, 1933.
Manton, J., 'Children of the Streets. Life of Mary Carpenter' (Heinemann 1976).
Minchinton, W. E., *The Trade of Bristol in the Eighteenth Century*, Vol. 20 (Bristol Records Society Pubs, 1957).
Munk, W., *The Roll of the Royal College of Physicians* (1878).

Noble, Lady Celia Brunel, *The Brunels, Father and Son* (London, 1938).

Pettigrew, T. J., *Medical Portrait Gallery: Biographical Portraits of the Most Celebrated Physicians, Surgeons etc who have contributed to the Advancement of Medical Science* (1840).
Pledge, F. W., *Crawley* (1907).

Rolt, L. T. C., *Isambard Kingdom Brunel* (Longman, 1957).
Rutt, J. T., *Life and Correspondence of Joseph Priestley* (1832).

Southey, Charles (Ed.), *Life and Correspondence of Robert Southey*, 6 vols (London, 1849–50).
Speculative Society of Edinburgh, History of (Constable, 1968).
Sprigge, S. S., *Life and Times of Thomas Wakley* (1897).
Stanley of Alderley, M. J., *Early Married Life of Maria, Lady Stanley*, Vol II (Longman, 1899).
Stimson, D., *Scientists and Amateurs: A History of the Royal Society* (New York, 1948).

Thompson, J., *Report on Observations after Waterloo* (Edinburgh U. P., 1820).
Todd, M., *The Life of Sophia Jex-Blake* (1919).
Trevelyan, Sir George, *The Life and Letters of Thomas Macaulay* (Longman, 1876).
Turton, T., *Dissenting Academies in Education* (1900).

Wilks and Bettany, *Biographical History of Guy's Hospital* (1885).
Woodward, H. B., *The History of the Geological Society of London* (1907).

INDEX